Collins

GCSE Maths
2 tier-higher
for Edexcel A
YEAR 10

BRIAN SPEED

KEITH GORDON

KEVIN EVANS

William Collins' dream of knowledge for all began with the publication of his first book in 1819. A self-educated mill worker, he not only enriched millions of lives, but also founded a flourishing publishing house. Today, staying true to this spirit, Collins books are packed with inspiration, innovation and a practical expertise. They place you at the centre of a world of possibility and give you exactly what you need to explore it.

Collins. Do more.

Published by Collins
An imprint of HarperCollins*Publishers*
77–85 Fulham Palace Road
Hammersmith
London
W6 8JB

Browse the complete Collins catalogue at
www.collinseducation.com

© HarperCollins*Publishers* Limited 2006

10 9 8 7 6 5 4 3 2
ISBN-13 978-0-00-725683-9
ISBN-10 0-00-725683-3

British Library Cataloguing in Publication Data. A Catalogue record for this publication is available from the British Library

Commissioned by Marie Taylor, Vicky Butt and Michael Cotter

Project managed by Penny Fowler

Edited by Marian Bond and Paul Sterner

Answer checker: Amanda Whyte

Internal design by JPD

Cover design by JPD

Cover illustration by Andy Parker, JPD

Page make-up and indexing by Gray Publishing

Page make-up of Really Useful Maths! spreads by EMC Design

Illustrations by Gray Publishing, EMC Design, Peters and Zabransky, Peter Cornwell, Bob Lea (Artists Partners), Martin Sanders (Beehive Illustration) and Laszlo Veres (Beehive Illustration)

Production by Natasha Buckland

Printed and bound in Hong Kong by Printing Express Ltd.

Acknowledgements

With special thanks to Lynn and Greg Byrd

The Publishers gratefully acknowledge the following for permission to reproduce copyright material. Whilst every effort has been made to trace the copyright holders, in cases where this has been unsuccessful or if any have inadvertently been overlooked, the Publishers will be pleased to make the necessary arrangements at the first opportunity.

Edexcel material reproduced with permission of Edexcel Limited. Edexcel Ltd accepts no responsibility whatsoever for the accuracy or method of working in the answers given.

Grade bar photos © 2006 JupiterImages Corporation

© 2006 JupiterImages Corporation, p1, p23, p61, p83, p111, p149, p171, p209, p300, p315, p333

© Mr Woolman, p42

© Dave Roberts / Istock, p191

© Agence Images / Alamy, p279

CONTENTS

Welcome to Collins GCSE Maths, the easiest way to learn and succeed in Mathematics. This textbook uses a stimulating approach that really appeals to students. Here are some of the key features of the textbook, to explain why.

Each chapter of the textbook begins with an **Overview**. The Overview lists the Sections you will encounter in the chapter, the key ideas you will learn, and shows how these ideas relate to, and build upon, each other. The Overview also highlights what you should already know, and if you're not sure, there is a short Quick Check activity to test yourself and recap.

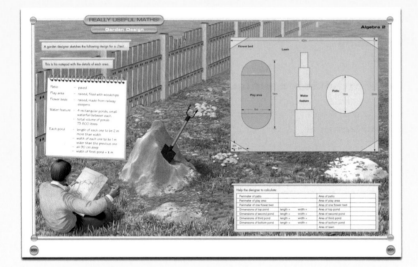

Maths can be useful to us every day of our lives, so look out for these **Really Useful Maths!** pages. These double pa spreads use big, bright illustrations to depict real-life situations, and present short series of real-world problems for you to practice your latest mathematic skills on.

Each **Section** begins first by explaining what mathematical ideas you are aiming to learn, and then lists the key words you will meet and use. The ideas are clearly explained, and this is followed by several examples showing how they can be applied to real problems. Then it's your turn to work through the exercises and improve your skills. Notice the different coloured panels along the outside of the exercise pages. These show the equivalent exam grade of the questions you are working on, so you can always tell how well you are doing.

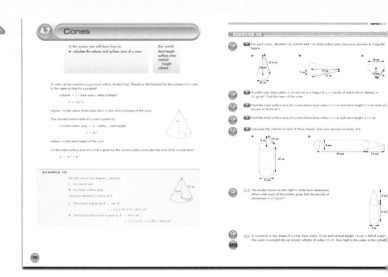

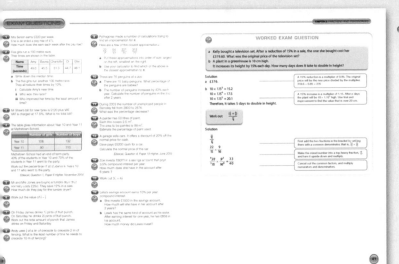

Every chapter in this textbook contains lots of **Exam Questions**. These provide ideal preparation for your examinations. Each exam question section also concludes with a fully worked example. Compare this with your own work, and pay special attention to the examiner's comments, which will ensure you understand how to score maximum marks.

Throughout the textbook you will find **Activities** – highlighted in the green panels – designed to challenge your thinking and improve your understanding.

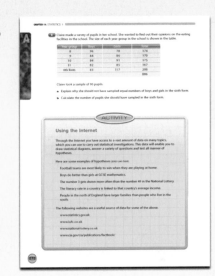

Review the **Grade Yourself** pages at the very end of the chapter. This will show what exam grade you are currently working at. Doublecheck **What you should now know** to confirm that you have the knowledge you need to progress.

Working through these sections in the right way should mean you achieve your very best in GCSE Maths. Remember though, if you get stuck, answers to all the questions are at the back of the book (except the exam question answers which your teacher has).

We do hope you enjoy using Collins GCSE Maths, and wish you every good luck in your studies!

Brian Speed, Keith Gordon, Kevin Evans

ICONS

 You may use your calculator for this question

 You should not use your calculator for this question

 Indicates a Using and Applying Mathematics question

 Indicates a Proof question

Number

1 Solving real problems

2 Division by decimals

3 Estimation

4 Multiples, factors and prime numbers

5 Prime factors, LCM and HCF

6 Negative numbers

This chapter will show you ...

- how to calculate with integers and decimals
- how to round off numbers to a given number of significant figures
- how to find prime factors, least common multiples (LCM) and highest common factors (HCF)

What you should already know

- How to add, subtract, multiply and divide with integers
- What multiples, factors, square numbers and prime numbers are
- The BODMAS rule and how to substitute values into simple algebraic expressions

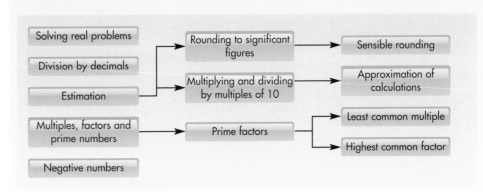

Solving real problems

Division by decimals

Estimation → Rounding to significant figures → Sensible rounding

Multiplying and dividing by multiples of 10 → Approximation of calculations

Multiples, factors and prime numbers → Prime factors → Least common multiple

Negative numbers → Highest common factor

Quick check

1 Work out the following.

   a 23×167 **b** $984 \div 24$ **c** $(16 + 9)^2$

2 Write down the following.

   a a multiple of 7   **b** a prime number between 10 and 20

   c a square number under 80   **d** the factors of 9

3 Work out the following.

   a $2 + 3 \times 5$ **b** $(2 + 3) \times 5$ **c** $2 + 3^2 - 6$

1.1 Solving real problems

This section will give you practice in using arithmetic to:

● solve more complex problems

Key words

long division

long
   multiplication

strategy

In your GCSE examination, you will be given *real* problems that you have to *read carefully, think about* and then plan a **strategy** without using a calculator. These will involve arithmetical skills such as **long multiplication** and **long division**. There are several ways to do these, so make sure you are familiar with and confident with at least one of them. The box method for long multiplication is shown in the first example and the standard column method for long division is shown in the second example. In this type of problem it is important to show your working as you will get marks for correct methods.

EXAMPLE 1

A supermarket receives a delivery of 235 cases of tins of beans. Each case contains 24 tins.

a How many tins of beans does the supermarket receive altogether?

b 5% of the tins were damaged. These were thrown away. The supermarket knows that it sells, on average, 250 tins of beans a day. How many days will the delivery of beans last before a new consignment is needed?

a The problem is a long multiplication 235×24.

The box method is shown.

×	200	30	5
20	4000	600	100
4	800	120	20

$$
\begin{array}{r}
4000 \\
600 \\
100 \\
+ \quad 800 \\
120 \\
20 \\
\hline
5640 \\
\end{array}
$$

So the answer is 5640 tins.

b 10% of 5640 is 564, so 5% is $564 \div 2 = 282$

This leaves $5640 - 282 = 5358$ tins to be sold.

There are 21 lots of 250 in 5358 (you should know that $4 \times 250 = 1000$), so the beans will last for 21 days before another delivery is needed.

EXAMPLE 2

A party of 613 children and 59 adults are going on a day out to a theme park.

a How many coaches, each holding 53 people, will be needed?

b One adult gets into the theme park free for every 15 children. How many adults will have to pay to get in?

a We read the problem and realise that we have to do a division sum: the number of seats on a coach into the number of people. This is $(613 + 59) \div 53 = 672 \div 53$

$$\begin{array}{r} 1\,2 \\ 53\,\overline{\smash{\big)}\,672} \\ \underline{530} \\ 142 \\ \underline{106} \\ 36 \end{array}$$

The answer is 12 remainder 36. So, there will be 12 full coaches and one coach with 36 people on. So, they would have to book 13 coaches.

b This is also a division, $613 \div 15$. This can be done quite easily if you know the 15 times table as $4 \times 15 = 60$, so $40 \times 15 = 600$. This leaves a remainder of 13. So 40 adults get in free and $59 - 40 = 19$ adults will have to pay.

EXERCISE 1A

1 There are 48 cans of soup in a crate. A supermarket had a delivery of 125 crates of soup.

a How many cans of soup were received?

b The supermarket is having a promotion on soup. If you buy five cans you get one free. Each can costs 39p. How much will it cost to get 32 cans of soup?

2 Greystones Primary School has 12 classes, each of which has 24 pupils.

a How many pupils are there at Greystones Primary School?

b The pupil–teacher ratio is 18 to 1. That means there is one teacher for every 18 pupils. How many teachers are at the school?

3 Barnsley Football Club is organising travel for an away game. 1300 adults and 500 juniors want to go. Each coach holds 48 people and costs £320 to hire. Tickets to the match are £18 for adults and £10 for juniors.

a How many coaches will be needed?

b The club is charging adults £26 and juniors £14 for travel and a ticket. How much profit does the club make out of the trip?

4 First-class letters cost 30p to post. Second-class letters cost 21p to post. How much will it cost to send 75 first-class and 220 second-class letters?

5 Kirsty collects small models of animals. Each one costs 45p. She saves enough to buy 23 models but when she goes to the shop she finds that the price has gone up to 55p. How many can she buy now?

6 Eunice wanted to save up for a mountain bike that costs £250. She baby-sits each week for 6 hours for £2.75 an hour, and does a Saturday job that pays £27.50. She saves three-quarters of her weekly earnings. How many weeks will it take her to save enough to buy the bike?

7 The magazine *Teen Dance* comes out every month. In a newsagent the magazine costs £2.45. The annual (yearly) subscription for the magazine is £21. How much cheaper is each magazine bought on subscription?

8 Paula buys a music centre. She pays a deposit of 10% of the cash price and then 36 monthly payments of £12.50. In total she pays £495. How much was the cash price of the music centre?

1.2 Division by decimals

This section will show you how to:
● divide by decimals by changing the problem so you divide by an integer

Key words
decimal places
decimal point
integer

It is advisable to change the problem so that you divide by an **integer** rather than a decimal. This is done by multiplying both numbers by 10 or 100, etc. This will depend on the number of **decimal places** after the **decimal point**.

EXAMPLE 3

Evaluate the following.   **a** 42 ÷ 0.2   **b** 19.8 ÷ 0.55

a The calculation is 42 ÷ 0.2 which can be rewritten as 420 ÷ 2 . In this case both values have been multiplied by 10 to make the divisor into a whole number. This is then a straightforward division to which the answer is 210.

Another way to view this is as a fraction problem.

$$\frac{42}{0.2} = \frac{42}{0.2} \times \frac{10}{10} = \frac{420}{2} = \frac{210}{1} = 210$$

b 19.8 ÷ 0.55 = 198 ÷ 5.5 = 1980 ÷ 55

This then becomes a long division problem.

This has been solved by the method of repeated subtraction.

$$
\begin{array}{rl}
1980 & \\
- \quad 1100 & 20 \times 55 \\
\hline
880 & \\
- \quad 440 & 8 \times 55 \\
\hline
440 & \\
- \quad 440 & 8 \times 55 \\
\hline
0 & 36 \times 55
\end{array}
$$

EXERCISE 1B

1 Evaluate each of these.

   a 3.6 ÷ 0.2   **b** 56 ÷ 0.4   **c** 0.42 ÷ 0.3   **d** 8.4 ÷ 0.7   **e** 4.26 ÷ 0.2

   f 3.45 ÷ 0.5   **g** 83.7 ÷ 0.03   **h** 0.968 ÷ 0.08   **i** 7.56 ÷ 0.4

2 Evaluate each of these.

   a 67.2 ÷ 0.24   **b** 6.36 ÷ 0.53   **c** 0.936 ÷ 5.2   **d** 162 ÷ 0.36   **e** 2.17 ÷ 3.5

   f 98.8 ÷ 0.26   **g** 0.468 ÷ 1.8   **h** 132 ÷ 0.55   **i** 0.984 ÷ 0.082

3 A pile of paper is 6 cm high. Each sheet is 0.008 cm thick. How many sheets are in the pile of paper?

4 Doris buys a big bag of safety pins. The bag weighs 180 grams. Each safety pin weighs 0.6 grams. How many safety pins are in the bag?

1.3 Estimation

This section will show you how to:
● use estimation to find approximate answers to numerical calculations

Key words

approximate
estimation
significant
    figures

Rounding off to significant figures

We often use significant figures when we want to **approximate** a number with quite a few digits in it.

Look at this table which shows some numbers rounded to one, two and three **significant figures** (sf).

One sf	8	50	200	90 000	0.00007	0.003	0.4
Two sf	67	4.8	0.76	45 000	730	0.0067	0.40
Three sf	312	65.9	40.3	0.0761	7.05	0.00301	0.400

The steps taken to round off a number to a particular number of significant figures are very similar to those used for rounding to so many decimal places.

● From the left, count the digits. If you are rounding to 2 sf, count 2 digits, for 3 sf count 3 digits, and so on. When the original number is less than 1.0, start counting from the first non-zero digit.

● Look at the *next* digit to the right. When the next digit is less than 5, leave the digit you counted to the same. However if the next digit is equal to or greater than 5, add 1 to the digit you counted to.

● Ignore all the other digits, but put in enough zeros to keep the number the right size (value).

For example, look at the following table which shows some numbers rounded off to one, two and three significant figures, respectively.

Number	Rounded to 1 sf	Rounded to 2 sf	Rounded to 3 sf
45 281	50 000	45 000	45 300
568.54	600	570	569
7.3782	7	7.4	7.38
8054	8000	8100	8050
99.8721	100	100	99.9
0.7002	0.7	0.70	0.700

EXERCISE 1C

1 Round off each of the following numbers to 1 significant figure.

a 46 313	**b** 57 123	**c** 30 569	**d** 94 558	**e** 85 299
f 0.5388	**g** 0.2823	**h** 0.005 84	**i** 0.047 85	**j** 0.000 876
k 9.9	**l** 89.5	**m** 90.78	**n** 199	**o** 999.99

2 Round off each of the following numbers to 2 significant figures.

a 56 147	**b** 26 813	**c** 79 611	**d** 30 578	**e** 14 009
f 1.689	**g** 4.0854	**h** 2.658	**i** 8.0089	**j** 41.564
k 0.8006	**l** 0.458	**m** 0.0658	**n** 0.9996	**o** 0.009 82

3 Round off each of the following to the number of significant figures (sf) indicated.

a 57 402 (1 sf)	**b** 5288 (2 sf)	**c** 89.67 (3 sf)
d 105.6 (2 sf)	**e** 8.69 (1 sf)	**f** 1.087 (2 sf)
g 0.261 (1 sf)	**h** 0.732 (1 sf)	**i** 0.42 (1 sf)
j 0.758 (1 sf)	**k** 0.185 (1 sf)	**l** 0.682 (1 sf)

4 What are the least and the greatest number of sweets that can be found in these jars?

a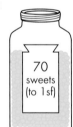

70 sweets (to 1 sf)

b

100 sweets (to 1 sf)

c

1000 sweets (to 1 sf)

5 What are the least and the greatest number of people that can be found in these towns?

Elsecar   population 800 (to 1 significant figure)

Hoyland   population 1200 (to 2 significant figures)

Barnsley   population 165 000 (to 3 significant figures)

Multiplying and dividing by multiples of 10

Questions often use multiplying together multiples of 10, 100, and so on. This method is used in estimation. You should have the skill to do this mentally so that you can check that your answers to calculations are about right. (Approximation of calculations is covered on pages 7–8.)

Use a calculator to work out the following.

a $200 \times 300 =$	**b** $100 \times 40 =$	**c** $2000 \times 0.3 =$
d $0.2 \times 50 =$	**e** $0.2 \times 0.5 =$	**f** $0.3 \times 0.04 =$

Can you see a way of doing these without using a calculator or pencil and paper? Basically, the digits are multiplied together and then the number of zeros or the position of the decimal point is worked out by combining the zeros or decimal places on the original calculation.

Dividing is almost as simple. Try doing the following on your calculator.

a $400 \div 20 =$ | **b** $200 \div 50 =$ | **c** $1000 \div 0.2 =$

d $300 \div 0.3 =$ | **e** $250 \div 0.05 =$ | **f** $30\,000 \div 0.6 =$

Once again, there is an easy way of doing these "in your head". Look at these examples.

$300 \times 4000 = 1\,200\,000$ | $5000 \div 200 = 25$ | $20 \times 0.5 = 10$

$0.6 \times 5000 = 3000$ | $400 \div 0.02 = 20\,000$ | $800 \div 0.2 = 4000$

Can you see a connection between the digits, the number of zeros and the position of the decimal point, and the way in which these calculations are worked out?

EXERCISE 1D

1 Without using a calculator, write down the answers to these.

a 200×300 | **b** 30×4000 | **c** 50×200

d 0.3×50 | **e** 200×0.7 | **f** 200×0.5

g 0.1×2000 | **h** 0.2×0.14 | **i** 0.3×0.3

j $(20)^2$ | **k** $(20)^3$ | **l** $(0.4)^2$

m 0.3×150 | **n** 0.4×0.2 | **o** 0.5×0.5

p $20 \times 40 \times 5000$ | **q** $20 \times 20 \times 900$

2 Without using a calculator, write down the answers to these.

a $2000 \div 400$ | **b** $3000 \div 60$ | **c** $5000 \div 200$

d $300 \div 0.5$ | **e** $2100 \div 0.7$ | **f** $2000 \div 0.4$

g $3000 \div 1.5$ | **h** $400 \div 0.2$ | **i** $2000 \times 40 \div 200$

j $200 \times 20 \div 0.5$ | **k** $200 \times 6000 \div 0.3$ | **l** $20 \times 80 \times 60 \div 0.03$

Approximation of calculations

How do we approximate the value of a calculation? What do we actually do when we try to approximate an answer to a problem?

For example, what is the approximate answer to 35.1×6.58?

To approximate the answer in this and many other similar cases, we simply round off each number to 1 significant figure, then work out the calculation. So in this case, the approximation is

$35.1 \times 6.58 \approx 40 \times 7 = 280$

Sometimes, especially when dividing, we round off a number to something more useful at 2 significant figures instead of at 1 significant figure. For example,

$57.3 \div 6.87$

Since 6.87 rounds off to 7, then round off 57.3 to 56 because 7 divides exactly into 56. Hence,

$57.3 \div 6.87 \approx 56 \div 7 = 8$

A quick approximation is always a great help in any calculation since it often stops you writing down a silly answer.

If you are using a calculator, whenever you see a calculation with a numerator and denominator *always* put brackets around the top and the bottom. This is to remind you that the numerator and denominator must be worked out separately before they are divided into each other. You can work out the numerator and denominator separately but most calculators will work out the answer straight away if brackets are used. You are expected to use a calculator *efficiently*, so doing the calculation in stages is not efficient.

EXAMPLE 4

a Find approximate answers to   **i** $\dfrac{213 \times 69}{42}$ **ii** $\dfrac{78 \times 397}{0.38}$

b Use your calculator to find the correct answer. Round off to 3 significant figures.

a   **i**   Round each value to 1 significant figure. $\dfrac{200 \times 70}{40}$

        Work out the numerator. $= \dfrac{14\,000}{40}$

        Divide by the denominator. $= 350$

  ii   Round each value to 1 significant figure. $\dfrac{80 \times 400}{0.4}$

        Work out the numerator. $= \dfrac{32\,000}{0.4} = \dfrac{320\,000}{4}$

        Divide by the denominator. $= 80\,000$

b   Use a calculator to check your approximate answers.

   i $\dfrac{213 \times 69}{42} = \dfrac{(213 \times 69)}{(42)}$

       So type in

       (2 1 3 × 6 9) ÷ (4 2) =

       The display should say 349.9285714 which rounds off to 350. This agrees exactly with the estimate.

       Note that we do not have to put brackets around the 42 but it is a good habit to get into.

   ii $\dfrac{78 \times 397}{0.38} = \dfrac{(78 \times 397)}{(0.38)}$

       So type in

       (7 8 × 3 9 7) ÷ (0 • 3 8) =

       The display should say 81489.47368 which rounds off to 81 500. This agrees with the estimate.

EXERCISE 1E

 1 Find approximate answers to the following.

    a 5435×7.31 **b** 5280×3.211 **c** $63.24 \times 3.514 \times 4.2$

    d $354 \div 79.8$ **e** $5974 \div 5.29$ **f** $208 \div 0.378$

 2 Work out the answers to question **1** using a calculator. Round off your answers to 3 significant figures and compare them with the estimates you made.

 3 By rounding off, find an approximate answer to these.

    a $\dfrac{573 \times 783}{107}$ **b** $\dfrac{783 - 572}{24}$ **c** $\dfrac{352 + 657}{999}$

    d $\dfrac{78.3 - 22.6}{2.69}$ **e** $\dfrac{3.82 \times 7.95}{9.9}$ **f** $\dfrac{11.78 \times 61.8}{39.4}$

 4 Work out the answers to question **3** using a calculator. Round off your answers to 3 significant figures and compare them with the estimates you made.

 5 Find the approximate monthly pay of the following people whose annual salary is given.

    a Paul £35 200   **b** Michael £25 600   **c** Jennifer £18 125   **d** Ross £8420

 6 Find the approximate annual pay of the following people whose earnings are shown.

    a Kevin £270 a week   **b** Malcolm £1528 a month   **c** David £347 a week

 7 A farmer bought 2713 kg of seed at a cost of £7.34 per kg. Find the approximate total cost of this seed.

 8 A greengrocer sells a box of 450 oranges for £37. Approximately how much did each orange sell for?

 9 It took me 6 hours 40 minutes to drive from Sheffield to Bude, a distance of 295 miles. My car uses petrol at the rate of about 32 miles per gallon. The petrol cost £3.51 per gallon.

    a Approximately how many miles did I do each hour?

    b Approximately how many gallons of petrol did I use in going from Sheffield to Bude?

    c What was the approximate cost of all the petrol I used in the journey to Bude and back again?

 10 By rounding off, find an approximate answer to these.

    a $\dfrac{462 \times 79}{0.42}$ **b** $\dfrac{583 - 213}{0.21}$ **c** $\dfrac{252 + 551}{0.78}$ **d** $\dfrac{296 \times 32}{0.325}$

    e $\dfrac{297 + 712}{0.578 - 0.321}$ **f** $\dfrac{893 \times 87}{0.698 \times 0.47}$ **g** $\dfrac{38.3 + 27.5}{0.776}$ **h** $\dfrac{29.7 + 12.6}{0.26}$

    i $\dfrac{4.93 \times 3.81}{0.38 \times 0.51}$ **j** $\dfrac{12.31 \times 16.9}{0.394 \times 0.216}$

11 Work out the answers to question **10** using a calculator. Round off your answers to 3 significant figures and compare them with the estimates you made.

12 A sheet of paper is 0.012 cm thick. Approximately how many sheets will there be in a pile of paper that is 6.35 cm deep?

13 Use your calculator to work out the following. In each case:

  i write down the full calculator display of the answer

  ii round your answer to three significant figures.

a $\dfrac{12.3 + 64.9}{6.9 - 4.1}$ **b** $\dfrac{13.8 \times 23.9}{3.2 \times 6.1}$ **c** $\dfrac{48.2 + 58.9}{3.62 \times 0.042}$

Sensible rounding

In the GCSE you will be required to round off answers to problems to a suitable degree of accuracy. Normally three significant figures is acceptable for answers. However, a big problem is caused by rounding off during calculations. When working out values, always work to either the calculator display or at least four significant figures.

Generally, you can use common sense. For example, you would not give the length of a pencil as 14.574 cm; you would round off to something like 14.6 cm. If you were asked how many tins of paint you need to buy to do a particular job, then you would give a whole number answer and not something such as 5.91 tins.

It is hard to make rules about this, as there is much disagreement even among the experts as to how you ought to do it. But, generally, when you are in any doubt as to how many significant figures to use for the final answer to a problem, round off to no more than one extra significant figure to the number used in the original data. (This particular type of rounding is used throughout this book.)

In a question where you are asked to give an answer to a sensible or appropriate degree of accuracy then use the following rule. Give the answer to the same accuracy as the numbers in the question. So, for example, if the numbers in the question are given to 2 significant figures give your answer to 2 significant figures, but remember, unless working out an approximation, do all the working to at least 4 significant figures or use the calculator display.

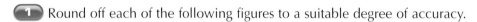
EXERCISE 1F

1 Round off each of the following figures to a suitable degree of accuracy.

  a I am 1.7359 metres tall.

  b It took me 5 minutes 44.83 seconds to mend the television.

  c My kitten weighs 237.97 grams.

  d The correct temperature at which to drink Earl Grey tea is 82.739 °C.

  e There were 34 827 people at the test match yesterday.

  f The distance from Wath to Sheffield is 15.528 miles.

  g The area of the floor is 13.673 m².

2 Rewrite the following article, rounding off all the numbers to a suitable degree of accuracy if they need to be.

It was a hot day, the temperature was 81.699 °F and still rising. I had now walked 5.3289 km in just over 113.98 minutes. But I didn't care since I knew that the 43 275 people watching the race were cheering me on. I won by clipping 6.2 seconds off the record time. This was the 67th time it had happened since records first began in 1788. Well, next year I will only have 15 practice walks beforehand as I strive to beat the record by at least another 4.9 seconds.

3 About how many test tubes each holding 24 cm^3 of water can be filled from a 1 litre flask?

4 If I walk at an average speed of 70 metres per minute, approximately how long will it take me to walk a distance of 3 km?

5 About how many stamps at 21p each can I buy for £12?

6 I travelled a distance of 450 miles in 6.4 hours. What was my approximate average speed?

7 At Manchester United, it takes 160 minutes for 43 500 fans to get into the ground. On average, about how many fans are let into the ground every minute?

8 A 5p coin weighs 4.2 grams. Approximately how much will one million pounds worth of 5p pieces weigh?

1.4 Multiples, factors and prime numbers

This section will remind you about:
- multiples and factors
- prime numbers
- square numbers and triangular numbers
- square roots

Key words
factor
multiple
prime number
square number
triangular number

You should remember the following.

Multiples: Any number in the times table. For example, the multiples of 7 are 7, 14, 21, 28, 35, etc.

Factors: Any number that divides exactly into another number. For example, factors of 24 are 1, 2, 3, 4, 6, 8, 12, 24.

Prime numbers: Any number that only has two factors, 1 and itself. For example, 11, 17, 37 are prime numbers.

Square numbers: A number that comes from multiplying a number by itself. For example, 1, 4, 9, 16, 25, 36 … are square numbers.

Triangular numbers: Numbers that can make triangle patterns, For example, 1, 3, 6, 10, 15, 21, 28 … are triangular numbers.

Square roots: The square root of a given number is a number which, when multiplied by itself, produces the given number. For example, the square root of 9 is 3, since $3 \times 3 = 9$.

A square root is represented by the symbol $\sqrt{}$. For example, $\sqrt{16} = 4$.

Because $-4 \times -4 = 16$, there are always two square roots of every positive number.

So $\sqrt{16} = +4$ or -4. This can be written as $\sqrt{16} = \pm 4$, which is read as plus or minus four.

Cube roots: The cube root of a number is the number that when multiplied by itself three times gives the number. For example, the cube root of 27 is 3 and the cube root of -8 is -2.

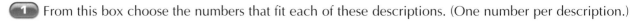

EXERCISE 1G

1 From this box choose the numbers that fit each of these descriptions. (One number per description.)

12   21
    8   15
13
      17
9   18
    10
          6
14   16

   a A multiple of 3 and a multiple of 4.

   b A square number and an odd number.

   c A factor of 24 and a factor of 18.

   d A prime number and a factor of 39.

   e An odd factor of 30 and a multiple of 3.

   f A number with four factors and a multiple of 2 and 7.

   g A number with five factors exactly.

   h A triangular number and a factor of 20.

   i An even number and a factor of 36 and a multiple of 9.

   j A prime number that is one more than a square number.

   k If you write the factors of this number out in order they make a number pattern in which each number is twice the one before.

   l An odd triangular number that is a multiple of 7.

2 If hot-dog sausages are sold in packs of 10 and hot-dog buns are sold in packs of 8, how many of each do you have to buy to have complete hot dogs with no wasted sausages or buns?

3 Rover barks every 8 seconds and Spot barks every 12 seconds. If they both bark together, how many seconds will it be before they both bark together again?

4 A bell chimes every 6 seconds. Another bell chimes every 5 seconds. If they both chime together, how many seconds will it be before they both chime together again.

5 Copy these sums and write out the *next four* lines.

$$1 = 1$$
$$1 + 3 = 4$$
$$1 + 3 + 5 = 9$$
$$1 + 3 + 5 + 7 = 16$$

6 Write down the negative square root of each of these.

    a 4   **b** 25   **c** 49   **d** 1   **e** 81

    f 121   **g** 144   **h** 400   **i** 900   **j** 169

7 Write down the cube root of each of these.

    a 1   **b** 27   **c** 64   **d** 8   **e** 1000

    f −8   **g** −1   **h** 8000   **i** 64 000   **j** −64

8 The triangular numbers are 1, 3, 6, 10, 15, 21 …

    a Continue the sequence until the triangular number is greater than 100.

    b Add up consecutive pairs of triangular numbers starting with 1 + 3 = 4, 3 + 6 = 9, etc. What do you notice?

9   **a** $36^3 = 46\,656$. Work out $1^3, 4^3, 9^3, 16^3, 25^3$.

    b $\sqrt{46656} = 216$. Use a calculator to find the square roots of the numbers you worked out in part **a**.

    c $216 = 36 \times 6$. Can you find a similar connection between the answer to part b and the numbers cubed in part **a**?

    d What type of numbers are 1, 4, 9, 16, 25, 36?

10 Write down the values of these

    a $\sqrt{0.04}$ **b** $\sqrt{0.25}$ **c** $\sqrt{0.36}$ **d** $\sqrt{0.81}$

    e $\sqrt{1.44}$ **f** $\sqrt{0.64}$ **g** $\sqrt{1.21}$ **h** $\sqrt{2.25}$

11 Estimate the answers to these.

    a $\dfrac{13.7 + 21.9}{\sqrt{0.239}}$ **b** $\dfrac{29.6 \times 11.9}{\sqrt{0.038}}$ **c** $\dfrac{87.5 - 32.6}{\sqrt{0.8} - \sqrt{0.38}}$

This section will show you how to:
- write a number as a product of its prime factors
- find the least common multiple (LCM) and highest common factor (HCF) of two numbers

Key words
highest common
    factor (HCF)
least common
    multiple (LCM)
prime factor

Start with a number – say 110 – and find two numbers which, when multiplied together, give that number, for example, 2×55. Are they both prime? No. So take 55 and repeat the operation, to get 5×11. Are these prime? Yes. So:

$$110 = 2 \times 5 \times 11$$

These are the **prime factors** of 110.

This method is not very logical and needs good tables skills. There are, however, two methods that you can use to make sure you do not miss any of the prime factors.

The next two examples show you how to use the first of these methods.

EXAMPLE 5

Find the prime factors of 24.

Divide 24 by any prime number that goes into it. (2 is an obvious choice.)

Divide the answer (12) by a prime number. Repeat this process until you have a prime number as the answer.

```
2 | 24
2 | 12
2 |  6
      3
```

So the prime factors of 24 are $2 \times 2 \times 2 \times 3$.

A quicker and neater way to write this answer is to use index notation, expressing the answer in powers. (Powers are dealt with in Chapter 10.)

In index notation, the prime factors of 24 are $2^3 \times 3$.

EXAMPLE 6

Find the prime factors of 96.

```
2 | 96
2 | 48
2 | 24
2 | 12
2 |  6
      3
```

So, the prime factors of 96 are $2 \times 2 \times 2 \times 2 \times 2 \times 3 = 2^5 \times 3$.

The second method is called prime factor trees. You start by splitting the number into a multiplication sum. Then you split this, and carry on splitting until you get to prime numbers.

EXAMPLE 7

Find the prime factors of 76.

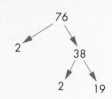

We stop splitting the factors here because 2, 2 and 19 are all prime numbers.

So, the prime factors of 76 are $2 \times 2 \times 19 = 2^2 \times 19$.

EXAMPLE 8

Find the prime factors of 420.

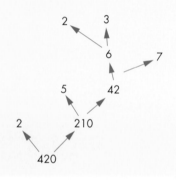

The process can be done upside down to make an upright tree.

So, the prime factors of 420 are

$$2 \times 5 \times 2 \times 3 \times 7 = 2^2 \times 3 \times 5 \times 7.$$

EXERCISE 1H

1 Copy and complete these prime factor trees.

a

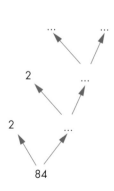

b

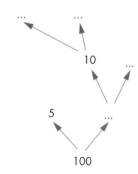

c

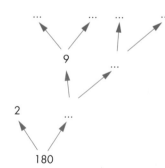

d

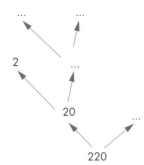

e

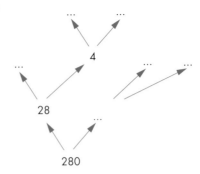

f

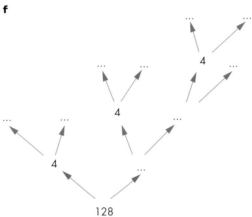

g

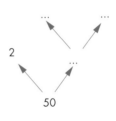

2 Using index notation, for example,

$$100 = 2 \times 2 \times 5 \times 5 = 2^2 \times 5^2$$

and $540 = 2 \times 2 \times 3 \times 3 \times 3 \times 5 = 2^2 \times 3^3 \times 5$

rewrite the answers to question **1** parts **a** to **g**.

3 Write the numbers from 1 to 50 in prime factors. Use index notation. For example,

$1 = 1$ $2 = 2$ $3 = 3$ $4 = 2^2$ $5 = 5$ $6 = 2 \times 3$ ...

4 **a** What is special about the prime factors of 2, 4, 8, 16, 32, ...?

b What are the next two terms in this sequence?

c What are the next three terms in the sequence 3, 9, 27, ...?

d Continue the sequence 4, 16, 64, ..., for three more terms.

e Write all the above sequences in index notation. For example, the first sequence is

$$2, 2^2, 2^3, 2^4, 2^5, 2^6, 2^7, ...$$

Least common multiple

The **least** (or lowest) **common multiple** (usually called the **LCM**) of two numbers is the smallest number that belongs in both times tables.

For example the LCM of 3 and 5 is 15, the LCM of 2 and 7 is 14 and the LCM of 6 and 9 is 18.

There are two ways of working out the LCM.

EXAMPLE 9

Find the LCM of 18 and 24.

Write out the 18 times table: 18, 36, 54, (72), 90, 108, ...

Write out the 24 times table: 24, 48, (72), 96, 120, ...

You can see that 72 is the smallest (least) number in both (common) tables (multiples).

EXAMPLE 10

Find the LCM of 42 and 63.

Write 42 in prime factor form. $42 = 2 \times 3 \times 7$

Write 63 in prime factor form. $63 = 3^2 \times 7$

Write down the smallest number in prime factor form that includes all the prime factors of 42 and of 63.

You need $2 \times 3^2 \times 7$ (this includes $2 \times 3 \times 7$ and $3^2 \times 7$).

Then work it out.

$2 \times 3^2 \times 7 = 2 \times 9 \times 7 = 18 \times 7 = 126$

The LCM of 42 and 63 is 126.

Highest common factor

The **highest common factor** (usually called the **HCF**) of two numbers is the biggest number that divides exactly into both of them.

For example the HCF of 24 and 18 is 6, the HCF of 45 and 36 is 9 and the HCF of 15 and 22 is 1.

There are two ways of working out the HCF.

EXAMPLE 11

Find the HCF of 28 and 16.

Write out the factors of 28.   1, 2, (4), 7, 14, 28

Write out the factors of 16.   1, 2, (4), 8, 16

You can see that 4 is the biggest (highest) number in both (common) lists (factors).

EXAMPLE 12

Find the HCF of 48 and 120.

Write 48 in prime factor form. $48 = 2^4 \times 3$

Write 120 in prime factor form. $120 = 2^3 \times 3 \times 5$

Write down the biggest number in prime factor form that is in the prime factors of 48 and 120.

You need $2^3 \times 3$ (this is in both $2^4 \times 3$ and $2^3 \times 3 \times 5$).

Then work it out.

$2^3 \times 3 = 8 \times 3 = 24$

The HCF of 48 and 120 is 24.

EXERCISE 1I

1 Find the LCM of each of these pairs of numbers.

   a 4 and 5   **b** 7 and 8   **c** 2 and 3   **d** 4 and 7

   e 2 and 5   **f** 3 and 5   **g** 3 and 8   **h** 5 and 6

2 What connection is there between the LCM and the pairs of numbers in question **1**?

3 Find the LCM of each of these pairs of numbers.

   a 4 and 8   **b** 6 and 9   **c** 4 and 6   **d** 10 and 15

4 Does the same connection you found in question **2** still work for the numbers in question **3**? If not, can you explain why?

5 Find the LCM of each of these pairs of numbers.

   a 24 and 56   **b** 21 and 35   **c** 12 and 28   **d** 28 and 42

   e 12 and 48   **f** 18 and 27   **g** 15 and 25   **h** 16 and 36

6 Find the HCF of each of these pairs of numbers.

   a 24 and 56   **b** 21 and 35   **c** 12 and 28   **d** 28 and 42

   e 12 and 48   **f** 18 and 27   **g** 15 and 25   **h** 16 and 36

   i 42 and 27   **j** 48 and 64   **k** 25 and 35   **l** 36 and 54

7 In prime factor form $1250 = 2 \times 5^4$ and $525 = 3 \times 5^2 \times 7$.

   a Which of these are common multiples of 1250 and 525?

      i $2 \times 3 \times 5^3 \times 7$ **ii** $2^3 \times 3 \times 5^4 \times 7^2$ **iii** $2 \times 3 \times 5^4 \times 7$ **iv** $2 \times 3 \times 5 \times 7$

   b Which of these are common factors of 1250 and 525?

      i 2×3 **ii** 2×5 **iii** 5^2 **iv** $2 \times 3 \times 5 \times 7$

Negative numbers

This section will show you how to:
- multiply and divide with positive and negative numbers

Key words
positive
negative

Multiplying and dividing with negative numbers

The rules for multiplying and dividing with negative numbers are very easy.

- When the signs of the numbers are the *same*, the answer is **positive**.

- When the signs of the numbers are *different*, the answer is **negative**.

Here are some examples.

$2 \times 4 = 8$ $12 \div -3 = -4$

$-2 \times -3 = 6$ $-12 \div -3 = 4$

Negative numbers on a calculator

You can enter a negative number into your calculator and check the result.

Enter –5 by pressing the keys **5** and **+/–** . (You may need to press **+/–** or **–** followed by **5**, depending on the type of calculator that you have.) You will see the calculator shows –5.

Now try these two calculations.

$-8 - 7 \rightarrow$ **8** **+/–** **–** **7** **=** –15

$6 - -3 \rightarrow$ **6** **–** **–** **3** **=** 9

EXERCISE 1J

1 Write down the answers to the following.

a -3×5	**b** -2×7	**c** -4×6	**d** -2×-3	**e** -7×-2
f $-12 \div -6$	**g** $-16 \div 8$	**h** $24 \div -3$	**i** $16 \div -4$	**j** $-6 \div -2$
k 4×-6	**l** 5×-2	**m** 6×-3	**n** -2×-8	**o** -9×-4

2 Write down the answers to the following.

a $-3 + -6$	**b** -2×-8	**c** $2 + -5$	**d** 8×-4	**e** $-36 \div -2$
f -3×-6	**g** $-3 - -9$	**h** $48 \div -12$	**i** -5×-4	**j** $7 - -9$
k $-40 \div -5$	**l** $-40 + -8$	**m** $4 - -9$	**n** $5 - 18$	**o** $72 \div -9$

D

3 What number do you multiply –3 by to get the following?

    a 6   **b** –90   **c** –45   **d** 81   **e** 21

4 Evaluate the following.

    a $-6 + (4 - 7)$ **b** $-3 - (-9 - -3)$ **c** $8 + (2 - 9)$

5 Evaluate the following.

    a $4 \times (-8 \div -2)$ **b** $-8 - (3 \times -2)$ **c** $-1 \times (8 - -4)$

6 Write down six different division sums that give the answer –4.

Hierarchy of operations

You will remember BODMAS (Brackets, Order, Division, Multiplication, Addition, Subtraction) which tells you the order in which to do mathematical operations in complex calculations. Many errors are made in GCSE due to negative signs and doing calculations in the wrong order. For example -6^2 could be taken as $(-6)^2 = +36$ or $-(6^2) = -36$. It should be the second of these as the power (order) would come before the minus sign.

EXERCISE 1K

1 Work out each of these. Remember to work out the bracket first.

    a $-2 \times (-3 + 5) =$ **b** $6 \div (-2 + 1) =$ **c** $(5 - 7) \times -2 =$

    d $-5 \times (-7 - 2) =$ **e** $-3 \times (-4 \div 2) =$ **f** $-3 \times (-4 + 2) =$

2 Work out each of these.

    a $-6 \times -6 + 2 =$ **b** $-6 \times (-6 + 2) =$ **c** $-6 \div 6 - 2 =$

    d $12 \div (-4 + 2) =$ **e** $12 \div -4 + 2 =$ **f** $2 \times (-3 + 4) =$

    g $-(5)^2 =$ **h** $(-5)^2 =$ **i** $(-1 + 3)^2 - 4 =$

    j $-(1 + 3)^2 - 4 =$ **k** $-1 + 3^2 - 4 =$ **l** $-1 + (3 - 4)^2 =$

3 Copy each of these and then put in brackets where necessary to make each one true.

    a $3 \times -4 + 1 = -11$ **b** $-6 \div -2 + 1 = 6$ **c** $-6 \div -2 + 1 = 4$

    d $4 + -4 \div 4 = 3$ **e** $4 + -4 \div 4 = 0$ **f** $16 - -4 \div 2 = 10$

4 $a = -2$, $b = 3$, $c = -5$.

Work out the values of the following.

    a $(a + c)^2$ **b** $-(a + b)^2$ **c** $(a + b)c$ **d** $a^2 + b^2 - c^2$

1 Frank earns £12 per hour. He works for 40 hours per week. He saves $\frac{1}{5}$ of his earnings each week.
How many weeks will it take him to save £500?

 2 A floor measures 4.75 metres by 3.5 metres. It is to be covered with square carpet tiles of side 25 centimetres. Tiles are sold in boxes of 16. How many boxes are needed?

 3 As the product of prime factors $60 = 2^2 \times 3 \times 5$
 a What number is represented by $2 \times 3^2 \times 5$?
 b Find the lowest common multiple (LCM) of 60 and 48?
 c Find the highest common factor (HCF) of 60 and 78?

 4 **a** Express the following numbers as products of their prime factors.
 i 60   **ii** 96.
 b Find the highest common factor of 60 and 96.
 c Work out the lowest common multiple of 60 and 96.
Edexcel, Question 2, Paper 6 Higher, June 2003

 5 Use your calculator to work out the value of
$$\frac{6.27 \times 4.52}{4.81 + 9.63}$$
 a Write down all the figures on your calculator display.
 b Write your answer to part **a** to an appropriate degree of accuracy.
Edexcel, Question 4, Paper 19 Higher, June 2004

 6 Use approximations to estimate the value of
$$\frac{212 \times 7.88}{0.365}$$

 7 Mary set up her Christmas tree with two sets of twinkling lights.
Set A would twinkle every 3 seconds.
Set B would twinkle every 4 seconds.
How many times in a minute will both sets be twinkling at the same time?

 8 **a** You are given that $8x^3 = 1000$.
 Find the value of x.
 b Write 150 as the product of its prime factors.

 9 **a** p and q are prime numbers such that $pq^3 = 250$
 Find the values of p and q.
 b Find the highest common factor of 250 and 80.

 10 The number 40 can be written as $2^m \times n$, where m and n are prime numbers. Find the value of m and the value of n.
Edexcel, Question 11, Paper 5 Higher, June 2005

 WORKED EXAM QUESTION

Estimate the result of the calculation
$$\frac{195.71 - 53.62}{\sqrt{0.0375}}$$
Show the estimates you make.

Solution

$$\frac{200 - 50}{\sqrt{0.04}}$$
 First round off each number to 1 significant figure.

$$\frac{150}{0.2}$$
 Work out the numerator and do the square root in the denominator

$$\frac{150}{0.2} = \frac{1500}{2} = 750$$
 Change the problem so it becomes division by an integer

SUMMARY

GRADE YOURSELF

D Able to recognise and work out multiples, factors and primes

D Able to multiply and divide with negative numbers

D Able to estimate the values of calculations involving positive numbers bigger than one

D Able to round numbers to a given number of significant figures

C Able to estimate the values of calculations involving positive numbers between zero and one

C Able to write a number as the product of its prime factors

C Able to work out the LCM and HCF of pairs of numbers

C Able to use a calculator efficiently and know how to give answers to an appropriate degree of accuracy

B Able to work out the square roots of some decimal numbers

B Able to estimate answers involving the square roots of decimals

What you should know now

- How to solve complex real-life problems without a calculator

- How to divide by decimals of up to two decimal places

- How to estimate the values of calculations including those with decimal numbers, and use a calculator efficiently

- How to write a number in prime factor form and find LCMs and HCFs

- How to find the square roots of some decimal numbers

1 One quantity as a fraction of another

2 Adding and subtracting fractions

3 Multiplying fractions

4 Dividing by a fraction

5 Percentage increase and decrease

6 Expressing one quantity as a percentage of another

7 Compound interest and repeated percentage change

8 Finding the original quantity (reverse percentage)

This chapter will show you ...

- how to apply the four rules (addition, subtraction, multiplication and division) to fractions
- how to calculate the final value after a percentage increase or decrease
- how to calculate compound interest
- how to calculate the original value after a percentage increase or decrease

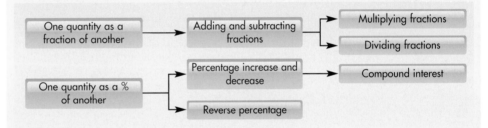

What you should already know

- How to cancel down fractions to their simplest form
- How to find equivalent fractions, decimals and percentages
- How to add and subtract fractions with the same denominator
- How to work out simple percentages, such as 10%, of quantities
- How to convert a mixed number to a top-heavy fraction and vice versa

Quick check

1 Cancel down the following fractions to their simplest form.

   a $\frac{8}{20}$ **b** $\frac{12}{32}$ **c** $\frac{15}{35}$

2 Complete this table of equivalences.

Fraction	Percentage	Decimal
$\frac{3}{4}$		
	40%	
		0.55

3 What is 10% of

   a £230   **b** £46.00   **c** £2.30

One quantity as a fraction of another

This section will show you how to:
● find one quantity as a fraction of another

Key words
cancel
fraction

An amount often needs to be given as a **fraction** of another amount.

EXAMPLE 1

Write £5 as a fraction of £20.

As a fraction this is written $\frac{5}{20}$. This **cancels** down to $\frac{1}{4}$.

EXERCISE 2A

1 Write the first quantity as a fraction of the second.

 a 2 cm, 6 cm **b** 4 kg, 20 kg

 c £8, £20 **d** 5 hours, 24 hours

 e 12 days, 30 days **f** 50p, £3

 g 4 days, 2 weeks **h** 40 minutes, 2 hours

2 In a form of 30 pupils, 18 are boys. What fraction of the form consists of boys?

3 During March, it rained on 12 days. For what fraction of the month did it rain?

4 Linda wins £120 in a competition. She keeps some to spend and puts £50 into her bank account. What fraction of her winnings does she keep to spend?

5 Frank gets a pay rise from £120 a week to £135 a weak. What fraction of his original pay was his pay rise?

6 When she was born Alice had a mass of 3 kg. After a month she had a mass of 4 kg 250 g. What fraction of her original mass had she increased by?

7 After the breeding season a bat colony increased in size from 90 bats to 108 bats. What fraction had the size of the colony increased by?

8 After dieting Bart went from 80 kg to 68 kg. What fraction did his weight decrease by?

2.2 Adding and subtracting fractions

This section will show you how to:
- add and subtract fractions with different denominators

Key words
denominator
equivalent fraction
lowest common denominator

Fractions can only be added or subtracted after we have changed them to **equivalent fractions**, both having the same **denominator**.

EXAMPLE 2

Work out $\frac{5}{6} - \frac{3}{4}$

The **lowest common denominator** of 4 and 6 is 12.

The problem becomes $\frac{5}{6} - \frac{3}{4} = \frac{5}{6} \times \frac{2}{2} - \frac{3}{4} \times \frac{3}{3} = \frac{10}{12} - \frac{9}{12} = \frac{1}{12}$

EXAMPLE 3

Work out   **a** $2\frac{1}{3} + 3\frac{5}{7}$ **b** $3\frac{1}{4} - 1\frac{3}{5}$

The best way to deal with addition and subtraction of mixed numbers is to deal with the whole numbers and the fractions separately.

a $2\frac{1}{3} + 3\frac{5}{7} = 2 + 3 + \frac{1}{3} + \frac{5}{7} = 5 + \frac{7}{21} + \frac{15}{21} = 5 + \frac{22}{21} = 5 + 1\frac{1}{21} = 6\frac{1}{21}$

b $3\frac{1}{4} - 1\frac{3}{5} = 3 - 1 + \frac{1}{4} - \frac{3}{5} = 2 + \frac{5}{20} - \frac{12}{20} = 2 - \frac{7}{20} = 1\frac{13}{20}$

EXERCISE 2B

1 Evaluate the following.

   a $\frac{1}{3} + \frac{1}{5}$ **b** $\frac{1}{3} + \frac{1}{4}$ **c** $\frac{1}{5} + \frac{1}{10}$ **d** $\frac{2}{3} + \frac{1}{4}$

   e $\frac{1}{5} - \frac{1}{10}$ **f** $\frac{7}{8} - \frac{3}{4}$ **g** $\frac{5}{6} - \frac{3}{4}$ **h** $\frac{5}{6} - \frac{1}{2}$

2 Evaluate the following.

   a $\frac{1}{3} + \frac{4}{9}$ **b** $\frac{1}{4} + \frac{3}{8}$ **c** $\frac{7}{8} - \frac{1}{2}$ **d** $\frac{3}{5} - \frac{8}{15}$

   e $1\frac{7}{18} + 2\frac{3}{10}$ **f** $3\frac{1}{3} + 1\frac{9}{20}$ **g** $1\frac{1}{8} - \frac{5}{9}$ **h** $1\frac{3}{16} - \frac{7}{12}$

   i $\frac{5}{6} + \frac{7}{16} + \frac{5}{8}$ **j** $\frac{7}{10} + \frac{3}{8} + \frac{5}{6}$ **k** $1\frac{1}{3} + \frac{7}{10} - \frac{4}{15}$ **l** $\frac{5}{14} + 1\frac{3}{7} - \frac{5}{12}$

D

3 In a class of children, three-quarters are Chinese, one-fifth are Malay and the rest are Indian. What fraction of the class are Indian?

4 In a class election, half of the pupils voted for Aminah, one-third voted for Janet and the rest voted for Peter. What fraction of the class voted for Peter?

5 A one-litre flask filled with milk is used to fill two glasses, one of capacity half a litre, and the other of capacity one-sixth of a litre. What fraction of a litre will remain in the flask?

6 Because of illness, $\frac{2}{5}$ of a school was absent one day. If the school had 650 pupils on the register, how many were absent that day?

7 Which is the biggest: half of 96, one-third of 141, two-fifths of 120, or three-quarters of 68?

8 To increase sales, a shop reduced the price of a car stereo radio by $\frac{2}{5}$. If the original price was £85, what was the new price?

9 At a burger-eating competition, Lionel ate 34 burgers in 20 minutes while Brian ate 26 burgers in 20 minutes. How long after the start of the competition would they have consumed a total of 30 burgers between them?

2.3 Multiplying fractions

This section will show you how to:
● multiply fractions

Key words
cancel
denominator
numerator

There are four steps to multiplying fractions.

Step 1: make any mixed numbers into top-heavy fractions.

Step 2: cancel out any common multiples on the top and bottom.

Step 3: multiply together the **numerators** to get the new numerator, and multiply the **denominators** to get the new denominator.

Step 4: if the fraction is top-heavy, make it into a mixed number.

EXAMPLE 4

Work out   **a** $\frac{4}{9} \times \frac{3}{10}$ **b** $2\frac{2}{5} \times 1\frac{7}{8}$

a 4 and 10 are both multiples of 2, and 3 and 9 are both multiples of 3. Cancel out the common multiples before multiplying.

$$\frac{{}^2\cancel{4}}{{}_3\cancel{9}} \times \frac{\cancel{3}^1}{\cancel{10}_5} = \frac{2}{15}$$

b Make the mixed numbers into top heavy fractions, then cancel if possible. Change the answer back to a mixed number.

$$2\frac{2}{5} \times 1\frac{7}{8} \qquad \frac{{}^3\cancel{12}}{{}_1\cancel{5}} \times \frac{\cancel{15}^3}{\cancel{8}_2} = \frac{9}{2} = 4\frac{1}{2}$$

EXERCISE 2C

1 Evaluate the following, leaving your answers in their simplest form.

a $\frac{1}{2} \times \frac{1}{3}$ **b** $\frac{1}{4} \times \frac{2}{5}$ **c** $\frac{3}{4} \times \frac{1}{2}$ **d** $\frac{3}{7} \times \frac{1}{2}$

e $\frac{14}{15} \times \frac{3}{8}$ **f** $\frac{8}{9} \times \frac{6}{15}$ **g** $\frac{6}{7} \times \frac{21}{30}$ **h** $\frac{9}{14} \times \frac{35}{36}$

2 Evaluate the following, leaving your answers as mixed numbers where possible.

a $1\frac{1}{4} \times \frac{1}{3}$ **b** $1\frac{2}{3} \times 1\frac{1}{4}$ **c** $2\frac{1}{2} \times 2\frac{1}{2}$ **d** $1\frac{3}{4} \times 1\frac{2}{3}$

e $3\frac{1}{4} \times 1\frac{1}{5}$ **f** $1\frac{1}{4} \times 2\frac{2}{3}$ **g** $2\frac{1}{2} \times 5$ **h** $4 \times 7\frac{1}{2}$

3 A merchant buys 28 crates, each containing three-quarters of a tonne of waste metal. What is the total weight of this order?

4 A greedy girl eats one-quarter of a cake, and then half of what is left. How much cake is left uneaten?

5 Kathleen spent three-eighths of her income on rent, and two-fifths of what was left on food. What fraction of her income was left after buying her food?

6 Which is larger, $\frac{3}{4}$ of $2\frac{1}{2}$ or $\frac{2}{5}$ of $6\frac{1}{2}$?

7 After James spent $\frac{2}{5}$ of his pocket money on magazines, and $\frac{1}{4}$ of his pocket money at a football match, he had £1.75 left. How much pocket money did he have in the beginning?

8 If £5.20 is two-thirds of three-quarters of a sum of money, what is the total amount of money?

Dividing by a fraction

This section will show you how to:
- divide by fractions

Key word
reciprocal

To divide by a fraction, we turn the fraction upside down (finding its **reciprocal**), and then multiply.

EXAMPLE 5

Work out   **a** $\frac{5}{6} \div \frac{3}{4}$ **b** $2\frac{1}{2} \div 3\frac{1}{3}$

a   Rewrite as $\frac{5}{6} \times \frac{4}{3}$.

$$\frac{5}{6} \div \frac{3}{4} = \frac{5}{{}_{3}\cancel{6}} \times \frac{\cancel{4}^{2}}{3} = \frac{10}{9} = 1\frac{1}{9}$$

b   First make the mixed numbers into top heavy fractions.

$$2\frac{1}{2} \div 3\frac{1}{3} = \frac{5}{2} \div \frac{10}{3} = \frac{\cancel{5}^{1}}{2} \times \frac{3}{\cancel{10}_{2}} = \frac{3}{4}$$

EXERCISE 2D

D

1   Evaluate the following, leaving your answers as mixed numbers where possible.

   a $\frac{1}{4} \div \frac{1}{3}$ **b** $\frac{2}{5} \div \frac{2}{7}$ **c** $\frac{4}{5} \div \frac{3}{4}$ **d** $\frac{3}{7} \div \frac{2}{5}$ **e** $5 \div 1\frac{1}{4}$

   f $6 \div 1\frac{1}{2}$ **g** $7\frac{1}{2} \div 1\frac{1}{2}$ **h** $3 \div 1\frac{3}{4}$ **i** $1\frac{5}{12} \div 3\frac{3}{16}$ **j** $3\frac{3}{5} \div 2\frac{1}{4}$

2   For a party, Zahar made twelve and a half litres of lemonade. His glasses could each hold five-sixteenths of a litre. How many of the glasses could he fill from the twelve and a half litres of lemonade?

3   How many strips of ribbon, each three and a half centimetres long, can I cut from a roll of ribbon that is fifty-two and a half centimetres long?

4   Joe's stride is three-quarters of a metre long. How many strides does he take to walk along a bus twelve metres long?

C

5   Evaluate the following, leaving your answers as mixed numbers wherever possible.

   a $2\frac{2}{9} \times 2\frac{1}{10} \times \frac{16}{35}$ **b** $3\frac{1}{5} \times 2\frac{1}{2} \times 4\frac{3}{4}$ **c** $1\frac{1}{4} \times 1\frac{2}{7} \times 1\frac{1}{6}$ **d** $\frac{18}{25} \times \frac{15}{16} \div 2\frac{2}{5}$

   e $(\frac{2}{5} \times \frac{2}{5}) \times (\frac{5}{6} \times \frac{5}{6}) \times (\frac{3}{4} \times \frac{3}{4})$ **f** $(\frac{4}{5} \times \frac{4}{5}) \div (1\frac{1}{4} \times 1\frac{1}{4})$

2.5 Percentage increase and decrease

This section will show you how to:
- calculate percentage increases and decreases

Key words
multiplier
percentage decrease
percentage increase

Increase

There are two methods for **increasing** by a **percentage**.

Method 1
Find the increase and add it to the original amount.

EXAMPLE 6

Increase £6 by 5%.

Find 5% of £6: $\frac{5}{100} \times 600\text{p} = 30\text{p}$. 5% of £6 = £0.30.

Add the £0.30 to the original amount: £6 + £0.30 = £6.30.

Method 2
Using a **multiplier**. An increase of 6% is equivalent to the original 100% plus the extra 6%. This is a total of 106% ($\frac{106}{100}$) and is equivalent to the multiplier 1.06.

EXAMPLE 7

Increase £6.80 by 5%.

A 5% increase is a multiplier of 1.05.

So £6.80 increased by 5% is £6.80 × 1.05 = £7.14

EXERCISE 2E

1 What multiplier is equivalent to a percentage increase of each of the following?

　　a 10%　　　　**b** 3%　　　　**c** 20%　　　　**d** 7%　　　　**e** 12%

2 Increase each of the following by the given percentage. (Use any method you like.)

　　a £60 by 4%　　　**b** 12 kg by 8%　　　**c** 450 g by 5%　　　**d** 545 m by 10%

　　e £34 by 12%　　　**f** £75 by 20%　　　**g** 340 kg by 15%　　　**h** 670 cm by 23%

　　i 130 g by 95%　　　**j** £82 by 75%　　　**k** 640 m by 15%　　　**l** £28 by 8%

3 In 2000 the population of Melchester was 1 565 000. By 2005 that had increased by 8%. What was the population of Melchester in 2005?

4 A small firm made the same pay increase for all its employees: 5%.

　　a Calculate the new pay of each employee listed below. Each of their salaries before the increase is given.

　　　Bob, caretaker, £16 500　　　　Jean, supervisor, £19 500
　　　Anne, tea lady, £17 300　　　　Brian, manager, £25 300

　　b Is the actual pay increase the same for each worker?

5 An advertisement for a breakfast cereal states that a special offer packet contains 15% more cereal for the same price than a normal 500 g packet. How much breakfast cereal is in a special offer packet?

6 At a school disco there are always about 20% more girls than boys. If at one disco there were 50 boys, how many girls were there?

7 VAT is a tax that the government adds to the price of most goods in shops. At the moment, it is 17.5% on all electrical equipment.

Calculate the price of the following electrical equipment after VAT of 17.5% has been added.

Equipment	Pre-VAT price
TV set	£245
Microwave oven	£72
CD player	£115
Personal stereo	£29.50

8 A hi-fi system was priced at £420 at the start of 2004. At the start of 2005, it was 12% more expensive. At the start of 2006, it was 15% more expensive than the price at the start of 2005. What is the price of the hi-fi at the start of 2006?

9 A quick way to work out VAT is to divide the pre-VAT price by 6. For example, the VAT on an item costing £120 is approximately £120 ÷ 6 = £20. Show that this approximate method gives the VAT correct to within £5 for pre-VAT prices up to £600.

Decrease

There are two methods for **decreasing** by a **percentage**.

Method 1
Find the decrease and take it away from the original amount.

EXAMPLE 8

Decrease £8 by 4%.

Find 4% of £8: $\dfrac{4}{100} \times 800p = 32p$. 4% of £8 = £0.32.

Take the £0.32 away from the original amount: £8 − £0.32 = £7.68.

Method 2
Using a multiplier. A 7% decrease is 7% less than the original 100%, so it represents 100% − 7% = 93% of the original. This is a multiplier of 0.93.

EXAMPLE 9

Decrease £8.60 by 5%.

A decrease of 5% is a multiplier of 0.95.

So £8.60 decreased by 5% is £8.60 × 0.95 = £8.17

EXERCISE 2F

1 What multiplier is equivalent to a percentage decrease of each of the following?

a 8%   b 15%   c 25%   d 9%   e 12%

2 Decrease each of the following by the given percentage. (Use any method you like.)

a £10 by 6%   b 25 kg by 8%   c 236 g by 10%

d 350 m by 3%   e £5 by 2%   f 45 m by 12%

g 860 m by 15%   h 96 g by 13%   i 480 cm by 25%

3 A car valued at £6500 last year is now worth 15% less. What is its value now?

4 A large factory employed 640 people. It had to streamline its workforce and lose 30% of the workers. How big is the workforce now?

5 On the last day of the Christmas term, a school expects to have an absence rate of 6%. If the school population is 750 pupils, how many pupils will the school expect to see on the last day of the Christmas term?

6 Since the start of the National Lottery a particular charity called Young Ones said it has seen a 45% decrease in the money raised from its scratch cards. If before the Lottery the charity had an annual income of £34 500 from its scratch cards, how much does it collect now?

7 Most speedometers in cars have an error of about 5% from the true reading. When my speedometer says I am driving at 70 mph,

   a what is the slowest speed I could be doing,

   b what is the fastest speed I could be doing?

8 You are a member of a club which allows you to claim a 12% discount off any marked price in shops. What will you pay in total for the following goods?

   Sweatshirt   £19

   Tracksuit   £26

9 I read an advertisement in my local newspaper last week which stated: "By lagging your roof and hot water system you will use 18% less fuel." Since I was using an average of 640 units of gas a year, I thought I would lag my roof and my hot water system. How much gas would I expect to use now?

10 A computer system was priced at £1000 at the start of 2004. At the start of 2005, it was 10% cheaper. At the start of 2006, it was 15% cheaper than the price at the start of 2005. What is the price of the computer system at the start of 2006?

11 Show that a 10% decrease followed by a 10% increase is equivalent to a 1% decrease overall.

> **HINTS AND TIPS**
>
> Choose an amount to start with.

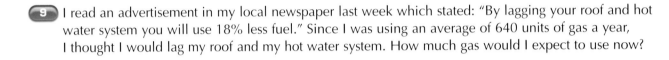

2.6 Expressing one quantity as a percentage of another

This section will show you how to:
● express one quantity as a percentage of another

Key words
percentage gain
percentage loss

Method 1
We express one quantity as a percentage of another by setting up the first quantity as a fraction of the second, making sure that the *units of each are the same*. Then, we convert that fraction to a percentage by simply multiplying it by 100%.

EXAMPLE 10

Express £6 as a percentage of £40.

Set up the fraction and multiply it by 100%. This gives:

$$\frac{6}{40} \times 100\% = 15\%$$

EXAMPLE 11

Express 75 cm as a percentage of 2.5 m.

First, change 2.5 m to 250 cm to get a common unit.

Hence, the problem becomes 75 cm as a percentage of 250 cm.

Set up the fraction and multiply it by 100%. This gives

$$\frac{75}{250} \times 100\% = 30\%$$

We can use this method to calculate **percentage gain** or **loss** in a financial transaction.

EXAMPLE 12

Bert buys a car for £1500 and sells it for £1800. What is Bert's percentage gain?

Bert's gain is £300, so his percentage gain is

$$\frac{300}{1500} \times 100\% = 20\%$$

Notice how the percentage gain is found by

$$\frac{\text{difference}}{\text{original}} \times 100\%$$

Method 2
This method uses a multiplier. Divide the increase by the original quantity and change the resulting decimal to a percentage.

EXAMPLE 13

Express 5 as a percentage of 40.

$$5 \div 40 = 0.125$$

$$0.125 = 12.5\%.$$

EXERCISE 2G

1 Express each of the following as a percentage. Give suitably rounded off figures where necessary.

    a £5 of £20   **b** £4 of £6.60

    c 241 kg of 520 kg   **d** 3 hours of 1 day

    e 25 minutes of 1 hour   **f** 12 m of 20 m

    g 125 g of 600 g   **h** 12 minutes of 2 hours

    i 1 week of a year   **j** 1 month of 1 year

    k 25 cm of 55 cm   **l** 105 g of 1 kg

2 John went to school with his pocket money of £2.50. He spent 80p at the tuck shop. What percentage of his pocket money had he spent?

3 In Greece, there are 3 654 000 acres of agricultural land. Olives are grown on 237 000 acres of this land. What percentage of agricultural land is used for olives?

4 During the wet year of 1981, it rained in Manchester on 123 days of the year. What percentage of days were wet?

5 Find, to one decimal place, the percentage profit on the following.

Item	Retail price (selling price)	Wholesale price (price the shop paid)
a CD player	£89.50	£60
b TV set	£345.50	£210
c Computer	£829.50	£750

6 Before Anton started to diet, he weighed 95 kg. He now weighs 78 kg. What percentage of his original weight has he lost?

7 In 2004 the Melchester County Council raised £14 870 000 in council tax. In 2005 it raised £15 970 000 in council tax. What was the percentage increase?

8 When Blackburn Rovers won the championship in 1995, they lost only four of their 42 league games. What percentage of games did they not lose?

9 In the year 1900 the value of Britain's imports were as follows.

British Commonwealth	£109 530 000
USA	£138 790 000
France	£53 620 000
Other countries	£221 140 000

    a What percentage of the total imports came from each source?

    b Add up the answers to part **a**. Explain your answer.

This section will show you how to:
- calculate compound interest
- solve problems involving repeated percentage change

Key words
annual rate
multiplier
principal

Compound interest is calculated where the interest earned at the end of the first year is added to the **principal** (original amount), and the new total amount then earns further interest at the same **annual rate** in the following year. (Compound interest is usually used to calculate the interest on savings accounts.) This pattern is repeated year after year while the money is in the account. Therefore, the amount in the account grows bigger by the year, as does the actual amount of interest. The best way to calculate the total interest is to use a **multiplier**.

EXAMPLE 14

A bank pays 6% compound interest per year on all amounts in a savings account. What is the final amount that Elizabeth will have in her account if she has kept £400 in her bank for three years?

The amount in the bank increases by 6% each year, so the multiplier is 1.06, and

after 1 year she will have £400 × 1.06 = £424

after 2 years she will have £424 × 1.06 = £449.44

after 3 years she will have £449.44 × 1.06 = £476.41 (rounded)

If you calculate the differences, you can see that the actual increase gets bigger and bigger.

From this example, you can see that you could have used £400 × $(1.06)^3$ to find the amount after 3 years. That is, you could have used the following formula for calculating the total amount due at any time:

total amount = P × multiplier raised to the power $n = P \times (1 + x)^n$

where P is the original amount invested, x is the rate of interest expressed as a decimal, and n is the number of years for which the money is invested.

So, in Example 14, P = £400, x = 0.06, and n = 3,

and the total amount = £400 × $(1.06)^3$

Using your calculator

You may have noticed that you can do the above calculation on your calculator without having to write down all the intermediate steps.

To add on the 6% each time just means multiplying by 1.06 each time. That is, you can do the calculation as

Or

Or

You need to find the method with which you are comfortable and which you understand.

The idea of compound interest does not only concern money. It can be about, for example, the growth in population, increases in salaries, or increases in body weight or height. Also the idea can involve regular reduction by a fixed percentage: for example, car depreciation, population losses and even water losses. Work through the next exercise and you will see the extent to which compound interest ideas are used.

EXERCISE 2H

1 A baby octopus increases its body weight by 5% each day for the first month of its life. In a safe ocean zoo, a baby octopus was born weighing 10 kg.

    a What was its weight after

        i 1 day?   **ii** 2 days?   **iii** 4 days?   **iv** 1 week?

    b After how many days will the octopus first weigh over 15 kg?

2 A certain type of conifer hedging increases in height by 17% each year for the first 20 years. When I bought some of this hedging, it was all about 50 cm tall. How long will it take to grow 3 m tall?

3 The manager of a small family business offered his staff an annual pay increase of 4% for every year they stayed with the firm.

    a Gareth started work at the business on a salary of £12 200. What salary will he be on after 4 years?

    b Julie started work at the business on a salary of £9350. How many years will it be until she is earning a salary of over £20 000?

4 Scientists have been studying the shores of Scotland and estimate that due to pollution the seal population of those shores will decline at the rate of 15% each year. In 2006 they counted around 3000 seals on those shores.

  a If nothing is done about pollution, how many seals will they expect to be there in

   i 2007?   **ii** 2008?   **iii** 2011?

  b How long will it take for the seal population to be less than 1000?

5 I am told that if I buy a new car its value will depreciate at the rate of 20% each year. I buy a car in 2006 priced at £8500. What would be the value of the car in

  a 2007?   **b** 2008?   **c** 2010?

6 At the peak of the drought during the summer of 1995, a reservoir in Derbyshire was losing water at the rate of 8% each day. On 1 August this reservoir held 2.1 million litres of water.

  a At this rate of losing water, how much would have been in the reservoir on the following days?

   i 2 August   **ii** 4 August   **iii** 8 August

  b The danger point is when the water drops below 1 million litres. When would this have been if things had continued as they were?

7 The population of a small country, Yebon, was only 46 000 in 1990, but it steadily increased by about 13% each year during the 1990s.

  a Calculate the population in

   i 1991   **ii** 1995   **iii** 1999.

  b If the population keeps growing at this rate, when will it be half a million?

8 How long will it take to accumulate one million pounds in the following situations?

  a An investment of £100 000 at a rate of 12% compound interest.

  b An investment of £50 000 at a rate of 16% compound interest.

 9 An oak tree is 60 cm tall. It grows at a rate of 8% per year. A conifer is 50 cm tall. It grows at a rate of 15% per year. How many years does it take before the conifer is taller than the oak?

 10 A tree increases in height by 18% per year. When it is 1 year old, it is 8 cm tall. How long will it take the tree to grow to 10 m?

 11 Show that a 10% increase followed by a 10% increase is equivalent to a 21% increase overall.

Finding the original quantity (reverse percentage)

This section will show you how to:
- calculate the original amount after you know the result of a percentage increase or decrease

Key words
multiplier
original
    amount
unitary
    method

There are situations when we know a certain percentage and wish to get back to the **original amount**. There are two methods.

Method 1
The first method is the **unitary method**.

EXAMPLE 15

The 70 men who went on strike represented only 20% of the workforce. How large was the workforce?

Since 20% represents 70 people, then

   1% will represent 70 ÷ 20 people [don't work it out]

so 100% will represent (70 ÷ 20) × 100 = 350

Hence the workforce is 350.

Method 2
Using a **multipler**.

EXAMPLE 16

The price of a refrigerator is decreased by 12% in a sale. The new price is £220. What was the original price before the reduction?

A decrease of 12% is a multiplier of 0.88.

Simply divide the new price by the multiplier to get the original price. 220 ÷ 0.88 = 250

So the original price was £250.

EXERCISE 21

1 Find what 100% represents in these situations.

    a 40% represents 320 g

    b 14% represents 35 m

    c 45% represents 27 cm

    d 4% represents £123

    e 2.5% represents £5

    f 8.5% represents £34

2 On a gruelling army training session, only 28 youngsters survived the whole day. This represented 35% of the original group. How large was the original group?

3 VAT is a government tax added to goods and services. With VAT at 17.5%, what is the pre-VAT price of the following priced goods?

T shirt	£9.87	Tights	£1.41
Shorts	£6.11	Sweater	£12.62
Trainers	£29.14	Boots	£38.07

4 Howard spends £200 a month on food. This represents 24% of his monthly take-home pay. How much is his monthly take-home pay?

5 Tina's weekly pay is increased by 5% to £315. What was Tina's pay before the increase?

6 The number of workers in a factory fell by 5% to 228. How many workers were there originally?

7 In a sale a TV is reduced to a price of £325.50. This is a 7% reduction on the original price. What was the original price?

8 If 38% of plastic bottles in a production line are blue and the remaining 7750 plastic bottles are brown, how many plastic bottles are blue?

9 I received £3.85 back from the tax office, which represented the 17.5% VAT on a piece of equipment. How much did I pay for this equipment in the first place?

10 A man's salary was increased by 5% in one year and reduced by 5% in the next year. Is his final salary greater or less than the original one and by how many per cent?

11 A quick way of estimating the pre-VAT price of an item with VAT added is to divide by 6 and then multiply by 5. For example, if an item is £360 including VAT, it is approximately $(360 \div 6) \times 5 = £300$ before VAT. Show that this gives an estimate to within £5 of the pre-VAT price for items costing up to £280.

1 Mrs Senior earns £320 per week.
She is awarded a pay rise of 4%.
How much does she earn each week after the pay rise?

2 Five girls run a 100 metre race.
Their times are shown in the table.

Name	Amy	Bavna	Charlotte	Di	Ellie
Time (seconds)	49.0	45.5	51.3	44.7	48.1

a Write down the median time.

b The five girls run another 100 metre race.
They all reduce their times by 10%.

   i Calculate Amy's new time.

   ii Who won this race?

   iii Who improved her time by the least amount of time?

3 Mr Shaw's bill for new tyres is £120 plus VAT.
VAT is charged at 17.5%. What is his total bill?

4 The table gives information about Year 10 and Year 11 at Mathstown School.

	Number of girls	Number of boys
Year 10	108	132
Year 11	90	110

Mathstown School had an end of term party.
40% of the students in Year 10 and 70% of the students in Year 11 went to the party.

Work out the percentage of all students in Years 10 and 11 who went to the party.

Edexcel, Question 1, Paper 6 Higher, November 2004

5 Mr and Mrs Jones are buying a tumble dryer that normally costs £250. They save 12% in a sale.
How much do they pay for the tumble dryer?

6 Work out the value of $\frac{3}{5} - \frac{3}{8}$

7 On Friday James drinks $1\frac{3}{4}$ pints of fruit punch.
On Saturday he drinks $2\frac{1}{3}$ pints of fruit punch.
Work out the total amount of punch that James drinks on Friday and Saturday.

8 Andy uses $\frac{3}{8}$ of a tin of creosote to creosote 2 m of fencing. What is the *least* number of tins he needs to creosote 10 m of fencing?

9 Pythagoras made a number of calculations trying to find an approximation for π.

Here are a few of the closest approximations

$$\frac{22}{7} \quad \frac{54}{17} \quad \frac{221}{71} \quad \frac{312}{77}$$

a Put these approximations into order of size, largest on the left, smallest on the right.

b Use your calculator to find which of the above is the closest approximation to π.

10 These are 75 penguins at a zoo.

a There are 15 baby penguins. What percentage of the penguins are babies?

b The number of penguins increases by 40% each year. Calculate the number of penguins in the zoo after 2 years.

11 During 2003 the number of unemployed people in Barnsley fell from 2800 to 2576.
What was the percentage decrease?

12 A painter has 50 litres of paint.
Each litre covers 2.5 m².
The area to be painted is 98 m².
Estimate the percentage of paint used.

13 A garage sells cars. It offers a discount of 20% off the normal price for cash.

Dave pays £5200 cash for a car.

Calculate the normal price of the car.

Edexcel, Question 4, Paper 19 Higher, June 2003

14 Zoe invests £6000 in a savings account that pays 3.5% compound interest per year.
How much does she have in the account after 6 years ?

15 Work out $3\frac{3}{4} \div 4\frac{1}{2}$

16 Leila's savings account earns 10% per year compound interest.

a She invests £1500 in the savings account.
How much will she have in her account after 2 years?

b Lewis has the same kind of account as his sister.
After earning interest for one year, he has £858 in his account.
How much money did Lewis invest?

WORKED EXAM QUESTION

a   Kelly bought a television set. After a reduction of 15% in a sale, the one she bought cost her
£319.60. What was the original price of the television set?

b   A plant in a greenhouse is 10 cm high.
It increases its height by 15% each day. How many days does it take to double in height?

Solution

a   £376.

> A 15% reduction is a multiplier of 0.85. The original price will be the new price divided by the multiplier.
> $319.6 \div 0.85 = 376$

b $10 \times 1.15^3 = 15.2$
$10 \times 1.15^4 = 17.5$
$10 \times 1.15^5 = 20.1$

> A 15% increase is a multiplier of 1.15. After n days the plant will be 10×1.15^n high. Use trial and improvement to find the value that is over 20 cm.

Therefore, it takes 5 days to double in height.

Work out $\dfrac{\left(\frac{2}{3} + \frac{4}{5}\right)}{1\frac{7}{9}}$

Solution

$\dfrac{\frac{22}{15}}{1\frac{7}{9}}$

> First add the two fractions in the bracket by writing them with a common denominator, that is, $\frac{10}{15} + \frac{12}{15}$

$\dfrac{22}{15} \times \dfrac{9}{16}$

> Make the mixed number into a top heavy fraction, $\frac{16}{9}$, and turn it upside down and multiply.

$\dfrac{^{11}\cancel{22}}{^{5}\cancel{15}} \times \dfrac{\cancel{9}^{3}}{\cancel{16}^{8}} = \dfrac{33}{40}$

> Cancel out the common factors, and multiply numerators and denominators.

Mrs Woolman is a sheep farmer in Wales. When she sends her lambs to market, she keeps a record of how many lambs she sends, and the total live weight of these lambs in kilograms.

Once they have been processed, she receives an information sheet showing the total weight of the meat from the lambs in kilograms, and the total price she has been paid for this meat.

For every week that she sends lambs to the market, she calculates the mean live weight of the lambs (to the nearest kilogram).

Copy the table below and complete the *Mean live weight in kg* column for her.

Mrs Woolman is happy with the condition of her lambs if the weight of the meat as a percentage of the live weight is over 42%.

Complete the *Meat as a % of live weight* column in your table. Indicate with a tick or a cross if she is happy with the condition of those lambs. Give percentages to one decimal place.

After Mrs Woolman has been paid for the meat, she calculates the price she is paid per kilogram of meat.

Compete the final column, *Price paid per kg of meat* in your table. Give each price to the nearest penny.

Date	Number of lambs	Total live weight in kg	Mean live weight in kg	Total weight of meat in kg	Meat as % of live weight	Total price paid for meat	Price paid per kg of meat
1st April	13	468	36	211	45.1% ✓	£812.56	£3.85
15th April	8	290		134		£451.91	
22nd April	18	672		312		£1105.31	
29th April	11	398		179		£625.04	
6th May	18	657		291		£907.89	
20th May	8	309		130		£386.15	
3rd June	10	416		171		£480.46	
17th June	4	174		72		£196.54	

At the end of the season Mrs Woolman analyses the information she has calculated.

Fill in the spaces in her notebook for her.

The mean weight per lamb has increased from _____kg to _____kg. This is an increase of _____%. However the price per kg of lamb has fallen from £_____ to £_____, a decrease of _____%.

The only two weeks when the condition of the lambs fell below 42% were _____ and _____.

Mrs Woolman finds a line graph in a farming magazine showing the average lamb prices in England and Wales from April through to June.

Copy this graph, and complete the line showing the price per kilogram that Mrs Woolman had for her lambs.

Comment on these line graphs.

Average lamb prices, April to July

SUMMARY

GRADE YOURSELF

D Able to add, subtract, multiply and divide fractions

D Able to calculate percentage increases and decreases

C Able to calculate with mixed numbers

C Able to work out compound interest problems

B Able to do reverse percentage problems

A Able to solve complex problems involving percentage increases and decreases

What you should know now

- How to calculate with fractions
- How to do percentage problems

Ratios and proportion

1 Ratio

2 Speed, time and distance

3 Direct proportion problems

4 Best buys

5 Density

This chapter will show you ...

- what a ratio is
- how to divide an amount into a given ratio
- how to solve problems involving direct proportion
- how to compare prices of products
- how to calculate speed
- how to calculate density

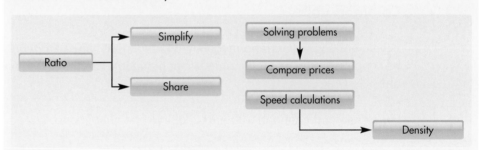

What you should already know

- Times tables up to 10×10
- How to cancel fractions
- How to find a fraction of a quantity
- How to multiply and divide, with and without a calculator

Quick check

1 Cancel down the following fractions.

a $\frac{6}{10}$ **b** $\frac{4}{20}$ **c** $\frac{4}{12}$ **d** $\frac{32}{50}$ **e** $\frac{36}{90}$ **f** $\frac{18}{24}$ **g** $\frac{16}{48}$

2 Find the following quantities.

a $\frac{2}{5}$ of £30   **b** $\frac{3}{8}$ of £88   **c** $\frac{7}{10}$ of 250 litres   **d** $\frac{5}{8}$ of 24 kg

e $\frac{2}{3}$ of 60 m   **f** $\frac{5}{6}$ of £42   **g** $\frac{9}{20}$ of 300 g   **h** $\frac{3}{10}$ of 3.5 litres

This section will show you how to:
- simplify a ratio
- express a ratio as a fraction
- divide amounts into given ratios
- complete calculations from a given ratio and partial information

A **ratio** is a way of comparing the sizes of two or more quantities.

A ratio can be expressed in a number of ways. For example, Joy is 5 years old and James is 20 years old. The ratio of their ages is Joy's age : James's age which is 5 : 20.

This simplifies to 1 : 4 (dividing both sides by 5).

A ratio can be expressed in words but it is usual to use a colon (:).

Joy's age : James's age   or   5 : 20   or   1 : 4

Common units

When working with a ratio involving different units, *always change them* to a **common unit**. A ratio can be simplified only when the units of each quantity are the *same*, because the ratio itself doesn't have any units.

For example, the ratio of 125 g to 2 kg must be changed to 125 g to 2000 g, so that we can simplify it to

	125 : 2000
Divide both sides by 25	5 : 80
Divide both sides by 5	1 : 16

Ratios as fractions

A ratio in its simplest form can be expressed as portions by changing the whole numbers in the ratio into **fractions** with the same denominator (bottom number).

EXAMPLE 1

A garden is divided into lawn and shrubs in the ratio 3 : 2.

What fraction of the garden is covered by **a** lawn, **b** shrubs?

The denominator (bottom number) of the fraction comes from *adding the numbers in the ratio* (that is, 2 + 3 = 5).

a The lawn covers $\frac{3}{5}$ of the garden.

b The shrubs cover $\frac{2}{5}$ of the garden.

EXERCISE 3A

1. A length of wood is cut into two pieces in the ratio 3 : 7. What fraction of the original length is the longer piece?

2. Jack and Thomas find a bag of marbles which they divide between them in the ratio of their ages. Jack is 10 years old and Thomas is 15. What fraction of the marbles did Jack get?

3. Dave and Sue share a pizza in the ratio of 2 : 3. They eat it all.

    a What fraction of the pizza did Dave eat?

    b What fraction of the pizza did Sue eat?

4. A camp site allocates space to caravans and tents in the ratio 7 : 3. What fraction of the total space is given to:

    a the caravans?   b the tents?

5. One morning a farmer notices that her hens, Gertrude, Gladys and Henrietta, have laid eggs in the ratio 2 : 3 : 4.

    a What fraction of the eggs did Gertrude lay?

    b What fraction of the eggs did Gladys lay?

    c How many more eggs did Henrietta lay than Gertrude?

6. The recipe for a pudding is 125 g of sugar, 150 g of flour, 100 g of margarine and 175 g of fruit. What fraction of the pudding is each ingredient?

Dividing amounts into given ratios

To divide an amount into portions according to a given ratio, you first change the whole numbers in the ratio into fractions with the same common denominator. Then you multiply the amount by each fraction.

EXAMPLE 2

Divide £40 between Peter and Hitan in the ratio 2 : 3.

Changing the ratio to fractions gives:

$$\text{Peter's share} = \frac{2}{(2+3)} = \frac{2}{5}$$

$$\text{Hitan's share} = \frac{3}{(2+3)} = \frac{3}{5}$$

So, Peter receives £40 $\times \frac{2}{5}$ = £16 and Hitan receives £40 $\times \frac{3}{5}$ = £24.

EXAMPLE 3

Divide 63 cm in the ratio 3 : 4.

An alternative method that avoids fractions is to add the parts: 3 + 4 = 7.

Divide the original amount by the total: 63 ÷ 7 = 9.

Then multiply each portion of the original ratio by the answer: 3 × 9 = 27, 4 × 9 = 36.

So 63 cm in the ratio 3 : 4 is 27 cm : 36 cm.

Note that whichever method you use, you should always check that the final values add up to the original amount: £16 + £24 = £40 and 27 cm + 36 cm = 63 cm.

EXERCISE 3B

1 Divide the following amounts in the given ratios.

   a 400 g in the ratio 2 : 3   **b** 280 kg in the ratio 2 : 5

   c 500 in the ratio 3 : 7   **d** 1 km in the ratio 19 : 1

   e 5 hours in the ratio 7 : 5   **f** £100 in the ratio 2 : 3 : 5

   g £240 in the ratio 3 : 5 : 12   **h** 600 g in the ratio 1 : 5 : 6

2 The ratio of female to male members of Banner Cross Church is about 5 : 3. The total number of members of the church is 256.

   a How many members are female?

   b What percentage of members are male?

3 A supermarket tries to have in stock branded goods and its own goods in the ratio 2 : 5. It stocks 350 kg of breakfast cereal.

   a What percentage of the cereal stock is branded?

   b How much of the cereal stock is its own?

4 The Illinois Department of Health reported that, for the years 1981 to 1992, when it tested a total of 357 horses for rabies, the ratio of horses with rabies to those without was 1 : 16.

   a How many of these horses had rabies?

   b What percentage of the horses did not have rabies?

5 Being overweight increases the chances of an adult suffering from heart disease. The formulae below show a way to test whether an adult has an increased risk.

   W and *H* refer to waist and hip measurements.
   For women, increased risk when $W/H > 0.8$
   For men, increased risk when $W/H > 1.0$

Find whether the following people have an increased risk of heart disease or not.

Miss Mott: waist 26 inches, hips: 35 inches

Mrs Wright: waist 32 inches, hips: 37 inches

Mr Brennan: waist 32 inches, hips: 34 inches

Ms Smith: waist 31 inches, hips: 40 inches

Mr Kaye: waist 34 inches, hips: 33 inches

 6 Rewrite the following scales as ratios, as simply as possible.

a 1 cm to 4 km   **b** 4 cm to 5 km   **c** 2 cm to 5 km

d 4 cm to 1 km   **e** 5 cm to 1 km   **f** 2.5 cm to 1 km

 7 A map has a scale of 1 cm to 10 km.

a Rewrite the scale as a ratio in its simplest form.

b How long is a lake that is 4.7 cm on the map?

c How long will an 8 km road be on the map?

 8 A map has a scale of 2 cm to 5 km.

a Rewrite the scale as a ratio in its simplest form.

b How long is a path that measures 0.8 cm on the map?

c How long should a 12 km road be on the map?

 9 You can simplify a ratio by changing it into the form $1 : n$.

For example, $5 : 7$ can be rewritten as $\frac{5}{5} : \frac{7}{5} = 1 : 1.4$

Rewrite each of the following in the form $1 : n$.

a $5 : 8$ **b** $4 : 13$ **c** $8 : 9$

d $25 : 36$ **e** $5 : 27$ **f** $12 : 18$

g 5 hours : 1 day   **h** 4 hours : 1 week   **i** £4 : £5

Calculating a ratio when only part of the information is known

EXAMPLE 4

Two business partners, John and Ben, divided their total profit in the ratio $3 : 5$. John received £2100. How much did Ben get?

John's £2100 was $\frac{3}{8}$ of the total profit. (Check you know why.)

So, $\frac{1}{8}$ of the total profit = £2100 ÷ 3 = £700

Therefore, Ben's share, which was $\frac{5}{8}$ of the total, amounted to £700 × 5 = £3500.

EXERCISE 3C

1 Derek, aged 15, and Ricki, aged 10, shared, in the same ratio as their ages, all the conkers they found in the woods. Derek had 48 conkers.

   a Simplify the ratio of their ages.

   b How many conkers did Ricki have?

   c How many conkers did they find altogether?

2 Two types of crisps, plain and salt'n vinegar, were bought for a school party in the ratio 5 : 3. They bought 60 packets of salt'n vinegar crisps.

   a How many packets of plain crisps did they buy?

   b How many packets of crisps did they buy altogether?

3 A blend of tea is made by mixing Lapsang with Assam in the ratio 3 : 5. I have a lot of Assam tea but only 600 g of Lapsang. How much Assam do I need to make the blend with all the Lapsang?

4 The ratio of male to female spectators at ice hockey games is 4 : 5. At the Steelers' last match, 4500 men and boys watched the match. What was the total attendance at the game?

5 "Proper tea" is made by putting milk and tea together in the ratio 2 : 9. How much "proper tea" can be made by using 1 litre of milk?

6 A "good" children's book is supposed to have pictures and text in the ratio 17 : 8. In a book I have just looked at, the pictures occupy 23 pages.

   a Approximately how many pages of text should this book have to be deemed a "good" children's book?

   b What percentage of a "good" children's book will be text?

7 Three business partners, Kevin, John and Margaret, put money into a venture in the ratio 3 : 4 : 5. They shared any profits in the same ratio. Last year, Margaret made £3400 out of the profits. How much did Kevin and John make last year?

8 Gwen is making a drink from lemonade, orange and ginger in the ratio 40 : 9 : 1. If Gwen has only 4.5 litres of orange, how much of the other two ingredients does she need to make the drink?

9 When I harvested my apples I found some had been eaten by wasps, some were just rotten and some were good ones. These were in the ratio 6 : 5 : 25. Eighteen of my apples had been eaten by wasps.

   a What percentage of my apples were just rotten?

   b How many good apples did I get?

In this section you will learn how to:
- recognise the relationship between speed, distance and time
- calculate average speed from distance and time
- calculate distance travelled from the speed and the time
- calculate the time taken on a journey from the speed and the distance

Key words

distance
speed
time

The relationship between **speed**, **time** and **distance** can be expressed in three ways:

$$Speed = \frac{Distance}{Time} \qquad Distance = Speed \times Time \qquad Time = \frac{Distance}{Speed}$$

When we refer to speed, we usually mean *average* speed, as it is unusual to maintain one exact speed for the whole of a journey.

The relationships between distance D, time T and speed S can be recalled using this diagram.

$$D = S \times T \qquad S = \frac{D}{T} \qquad T = \frac{D}{S}$$

EXAMPLE 5

Paula drove a distance of 270 miles in 5 hours. What was her average speed?

$$\text{Paula's average speed} = \frac{\text{distance she drove}}{\text{time she took}} = \frac{270 \text{ miles}}{5 \text{ hours}} = 54 \text{ miles/h}$$

EXAMPLE 6

Edith drove from Sheffield to Peebles for $3\frac{1}{2}$ hours at an average speed of 60 miles/h. How far is it from Sheffield to Peebles?

$$Distance = Speed \times Time$$

So, distance from Sheffield to Peebles is given by

$$60 \text{ miles/h} \times 3.5 \text{ h} = 210 \text{ miles}$$

Note: We changed the time to a decimal number and used 3.5, **not** 3.30!

EXAMPLE 7

Sean is going to drive from Newcastle upon Tyne to Nottingham, a distance of 190 miles. He estimates that he will drive at an average speed of 50 miles/h. How long will it take him?

$$\text{Sean's time} = \frac{\text{distance he covers}}{\text{his average speed}} = \frac{190 \text{ miles}}{50 \text{ miles/h}} = 3.8 \text{ hours}$$

Change the 0.8 hour to minutes by multiplying by 60, to give 48 minutes.

So, the time for Sean's journey will be 3 hours 48 minutes.
(A sensible rounding off would give 4 hours or 3 hours 50 minutes.)

Remember: When you calculate a time and get a decimal answer, as in Example 7, *do not mistake* the decimal part for minutes. You must either:

- leave the time as a decimal number and give the unit as hours, or

- change the decimal part to minutes by multiplying it by 60 (1 hour = 60 minutes) and give the answer in hours and minutes.

EXERCISE 3D

1 A cyclist travels a distance of 90 miles in 5 hours. What is her average speed?

2 I drive to Bude in Cornwall from Sheffield in about 6 hours. The distance from Sheffield to Bude is 315 miles. What is my average speed?

3 The distance from Leeds to London is 210 miles. The train travels at an average speed of 90 mph. If I catch the 9:30 am train in London, at what time would you expect me to get to Leeds?

4 Complete the following table.

	Distance travelled	Time taken	Average speed
a	150 miles	2 hours	
b	260 miles		40 mph
c		5 hours	35 mph
d		3 hours	80 km/h
e	544 km	8 hours 30 minutes	
f		3 hours 15 minutes	100 km/h
g	215 km		50 km/h

> **HINTS AND TIPS**
>
> Remember to convert time to a decimal if you are using a calculator. For example, 8 hours 30 minutes is 8.5 hours.

5 A train travels at 50 km/h for 2 hours, then slows down to do the last 30 minutes of its journey at 40 km/h.

a What is the total distance of this journey?

b What is the average speed of the train over the whole journey?

6 Jane runs and walks to work each day. She runs the first 2 miles at a speed of 8 mph and then walks the next mile at a steady 4 mph.

    a How long does it take Jane to get to work?

    b What is her average speed?

7 Colin drives home from his son's house in 2 hours 15 minutes. He says that he drives home at an average speed of 44 mph.

    a Change the 2 hours 15 minutes to decimal time.

    b How far is it from Colin's home to his son's house?

8 The distance between Paris and Le Mans is 200 km. The express train between Paris and Le Mans travels at an average speed of 160 km/h.

    a Calculate the time taken for the journey from Paris to Le Mans, giving your answer in decimal hour notation.

    b Change your answer to part **a** to hours and minutes.

9 The distance between Sheffield and Land's End is 420 miles.

    a What is the average speed of a journey from Sheffield to Land's End if it takes 8 hours 45 minutes?

    b If I covered the distance at an average speed of 63 mph, how long would it take me?

10 Change the following speeds to metres per second.

    a 36 km/h   **b** 12 km/h   **c** 60 km/h

    d 150 km/h   **e** 75 km/h

> **HINTS AND TIPS**
>
> Remember there are 3600 seconds in an hour and 1000 metres in a kilometre.

11 Change the following speeds to kilometres per hour.

    a 25 m/s   **b** 12 m/s   **c** 4 m/s

    d 30 m/s   **e** 0.5 m/s

12 A train travels at an average speed of 18 m/s.

    a Express its average speed in km/h.

    b Find the approximate time taken to travel 500 m.

    c The train set off at 7:30 on a 40 km journey. At approximately what time will it arrive?

> **HINTS AND TIPS**
>
> To convert a decimal of an hour to minutes just multiply by 60.

Direct proportion problems

This section will show you how to:
- recognise a direct proportion problem
- solve a problem involving direct proportion

Key words

direct
  proportion
unitary
  method

Suppose you buy 12 items which each cost the *same*. The total amount you spend is 12 times the cost of one item.

That is, the total cost is said to be in **direct proportion** to the number of items bought. The cost of a single item (the unit cost) is the constant factor that links the two quantities.

Direct proportion is concerned not only with costs. Any two related quantities can be in direct proportion to each other.

Finding the single unit value first is the best way to solve all problems involving direct proportion.

This method is called the **unitary method**, because it involves referring to a single *unit* value.

Remember: Before solving a direct proportion problem, think carefully about it to make sure that you know how to find the required single unit value.

EXAMPLE 8

If eight pens cost £2.64, what is the cost of five pens?

First, we need to find the cost of one pen. This is £2.64 ÷ 8 = £0.33.

So, the cost of five pens is £0.33 × 5 = £1.65.

EXAMPLE 9

Eight loaves of bread will make packed lunches for 18 people. How many packed lunches can be made from 20 loaves?

First, we need to find how many lunches *one* loaf will make.

One loaf will make 18 ÷ 8 = 2.25 lunches.

So, 20 loaves will make 2.25 × 20 = 45 lunches.

EXERCISE 3E

1 If 30 matches weigh 45 g, what would 40 matches weigh?

2 Five bars of chocolate cost £2.90. Find the cost of 9 bars.

3 Eight men can chop down 18 trees in a day. How many trees can 20 men chop down in a day?

4 Seventy maths textbooks cost £875.

    a How much will 25 maths textbooks cost?

    b How many maths textbooks can you buy for £100?

5 A lorry uses 80 litres of diesel fuel on a trip of 280 miles.

    a How much would be used on a trip of 196 miles?

    b How far would the lorry get on a full tank of 100 litres?

6 During the winter, I find that 200 kg of coal keeps my open fire burning for 12 weeks.

    a If I want an open fire all through the winter (18 weeks), how much coal will I need to get?

    b Last year I bought 150 kg of coal. For how many weeks did I have an open fire?

7 It takes a photocopier 16 seconds to produce 12 copies. How long will it take to produce 30 copies?

3.4 Best buys

This section will show you how to:	Key word
• find the cost per unit weight • find the weight per unit cost • find which product is the cheaper	best buy

When you wander around a supermarket and see all the different prices for the many different-sized packets, it is rarely obvious which are the **best buys**. However, with a calculator you can easily compare value for money by finding either:

    the cost per unit weight   *or*   the weight per unit cost

To find:

• *cost per unit weight*, divide *cost by weight*

• *weight per unit cost*, divide *weight by cost.*

The next two examples show you how to do this.

EXAMPLE 10

A 300 g tin of cocoa costs £1.20.

First change £1.20 to 120p. Then divide, using a calculator, to get:

cost per unit weight   120p ÷ 300 g = 0.4p per gram

weight per unit cost   300 g ÷ 120p = 2.5 g per penny

EXAMPLE 11

There are two different-sized packets of Whito soap powder at a supermarket. The medium size contains 800 g and costs £1.60 and the large size contains 2.5 kg and costs £4.75. Which is the better buy?

Find the weight per unit cost for both packets.

Medium: 800 g ÷ 160p = 5 g per penny

Large: 2500 g ÷ 475p = 5.26 g per penny

From these we see that there is more weight per penny with the large size, which means that the large size is the better buy.

EXERCISE 3F

1 Compare the following pairs of product and state which is the better buy, and why.

a Coffee: a medium jar which is 140 g for £1.10 or a large jar which is 300 g for £2.18

b Beans: a 125 g tin at 16p or a 600 g tin at 59p

c Flour: a 3 kg bag at 75p or a 5 kg bag at £1.20

d Toothpaste: a large tube which is 110 ml for £1.79 or a medium tube which is 75 ml for £1.15

e Frosties: a large box which is 750 g for £1.64 or a medium box which is 500 g for £1.10

f Rice Krispies: a medium box which is 440 g for £1.64 or a large box which is 600 g for £2.13

g Hair shampoo: a bottle containing 400 ml for £1.15 or a bottle containing 550 ml for £1.60

2 Julie wants to respray her car with yellow paint. In the local automart, she sees the following tins:

small tin: 350 ml at a cost of £1.79
medium tin: 500 ml at a cost of £2.40
large tin: 1.5 litres at a cost of £6.70

a Which tin is offered at the cheapest cost per litre?

b What is the cost per litre of paint in the small tin?

3 Tisco's sells bottled water in three sizes.

a Work out the cost per litre of the 'handy' size.

b Which bottle is the best value for money?

Handy size 40 cl
£0.38

Family size 2 l
£0.98

Giant size 5 l
£2.50

4 Two drivers are comparing the petrol consumption of their cars.

Ahmed says, 'I get 320 miles on a tank of 45 litres.'

Bashir says, 'I get 230 miles on a tank of 32 litres.'

Whose car is the more economical?

5 Mary and Jane are arguing about which of them is better at mathematics.

Mary scored 49 out of 80 on a test.

Jane scored 60 out of 100 on a test of the same standard.

Who is better at mathematics?

6 Paula and Kelly are comparing their running times.

Paula completed a 10-mile run in 65 minutes.

Kelly completed a 10-kilometre run in 40 minutes.

Given that 8 kilometres are equal to 5 miles, which girl has the greater average speed?

3.5 Density

This section will show you how to:	Key words
• solve problems involving density	density
	mass
	volume

Density is the mass of a substance per unit volume, usually expressed in grams per cm^3. The relationship between the three quantities is

$$Density = \frac{Mass}{Volume}$$

This is often remembered with a triangle similar to that for distance, speed and time.

$Mass \quad = Density \times Volume$

$Density = Mass \div Volume$

$Volume = Mass \div Density$

Note: Density is defined in terms of mass, which is commonly referred to as weight, although, strictly speaking, there is a difference between them. (You may already have learnt about this in science.) In this book, the two terms are assumed to have the same meaning.

EXAMPLE 12

A piece of metal weighing 30 g has a volume of 4 cm^3. What is the density of the metal?

$$\text{Density} = \frac{\text{Mass}}{\text{Volume}} = \frac{30\ g}{4\ cm^3} = 7.5\ g/cm^3$$

EXAMPLE 13

What is the weight of a piece of rock which has a volume of 34 cm^3 and a density of 2.25 g/cm^3?

$$\text{Weight} = \text{Volume} \times \text{Density} = 34\ cm^3 \times 2.25\ g/cm^3 = 76.5\ g$$

EXERCISE 3G

1. Find the density of a piece of wood weighing 6 g and having a volume of 8 cm^3.

2. Calculate the density of a metal if 12 cm^3 of it weighs 100 g.

3. Calculate the weight of a piece of plastic, 20 cm^3 in volume, if its density is 1.6 g/cm^3.

4. Calculate the volume of a piece of wood which weighs 102 g and has a density of 0.85 g/cm^3.

5. Find the weight of a marble model, 56 cm^3 in volume, if the density of marble is 2.8 g/cm^3.

6. Calculate the volume of a liquid weighing 4 kg and having a density of 1.25 g/cm^3.

7. Find the density of the material of a pebble which weighs 34 g and has a volume of 12.5 cm^3.

8. It is estimated that the statue of Queen Victoria in Endcliffe Park, Sheffield, has a volume of about 4 m^3. The density of the material used to make the statue is 9.2 g/cm^3. What is the estimated weight of the statue?

9. I bought a 50 kg bag of coal, and estimated the total volume of coal to be about 28 000 cm^3. What is the density of coal in g/cm^3?

10. A 1 kg bag of sugar has a volume of about 625 cm^3. What is the density of sugar in g/cm^3?

1 Three women earned a total of £36. They shared the £36 in the ratio 7 : 3 : 2.

Donna received the largest amount.

a Work out the amount Donna received.

A year ago, Donna weighed 51.5 kg. Donna now weighs $8\frac{1}{2}\%$ less.

b Work out how much Donna now weighs. Give your answer to an appropriate degree of accuracy.

Edexcel, Question 2, Paper 6 Higher, June 2005

  2 a How many 240 millilitre glasses can be filled from a 1.2-litre bottle of coke?

b A drink is made by mixing orange juice and soda in the ratio 9 : 1. How much orange juice is needed to make 500 ml of the drink?

 3 Share £34 800 in the ratio 1 : 5.

  4 Fred runs 200 metres in 21.2 seconds.

a Work out Fred's average speed. Write down all the figures on your calculator display.

b Round off your answer to part **a** to an appropriate degree of accuracy.

Edexcel, Question 6, Paper 6 Higher, November 2004

 5 Bill and Ben buy £10 worth of lottery tickets. Ben pays £7 and Bill pays £3. They decide to share any prize in the ratio of the money they each paid.

a They win £350. How much does Bill get?

b What percentage of the £350 does Ben get?

  6 The interior angles of a triangle are in the ratio

2 : 3 : 4

Calculate the size of the smallest angle.

  7 Rosa prepares the ingredients for pizzas.

She uses cheese, topping and dough in the ratio 2 : 3 : 5
Rose uses 70 grams of dough.

Work out the number of grams of cheese and the number of grams of topping Rosa uses.

Edexcel, Question 1, Paper 5 Higher, November 2004

  8 Mandy completes a journey in two stages. In stage 1 of her journey, she drives at an average speed of 96 km/h and takes 2 hours 15 minutes.

a How far does Mandy travel in stage 1 of her journey?

b Altogether, Mandy drives 370 km and takes a total time of 4 hours. What is her average speed, in km/h, in stage 2 of her journey?

WORKED EXAM QUESTION

To be on time, a train must complete a journey of 210 miles in 3 hours.
a Calculate the average speed of the train for the whole journey when it is on time.
b The train averages a speed of 56 mph over the first 98 miles of the journey. Calculate the average speed for the remainder of the journey so that the train arrives on time.

Solution

a 70 mph

Average speed = distance ÷ time = 210 ÷ 3. Note that one question in the examination will ask you to state the units of your answer. This is often done with a speed question.

b 98 ÷ 56 = 1.75 which is 1 hour and 45 minutes.

First find out how long the train took to do the first 98 miles.

(210 − 98) ÷ (3 − 1.75) = 112 ÷ 1.25 = 89.6 mph

Now work out the distance still to be travelled (112 miles) and the time left (1 hour 15 minutes = 1.25 hours). Divide distance by time to get the average speed.

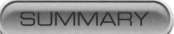

SUMMARY

GRADE YOURSELF

D Calculate average speeds from data

D Calculate distance from speed and time

D Calculate time from speed and distance

C Solve problems using ratio in appropriate situations

B Solve problems involving density

What you should know now

- How to divide any amount into a given ratio
- The relationships between speed, time and distance
- How to do problems involving direct proportion
- How to compare the prices of products
- How to work out the density of materials

Shape

1 Circumference and area of a circle

2 Area of a trapezium

3 Sectors

4 Volume of a prism

5 Cylinders

6 Volume of a pyramid

7 Cones

8 Spheres

This chapter will show you ...

- how to calculate the length of an arc
- how to calculate the area of a sector
- how to find the area of a trapezium
- how to calculate the surface area and volume of prisms, cylinders, pyramids, cones and spheres

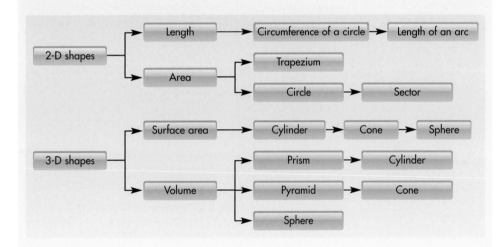

What you should already know

- The area of a rectangle is given by Area = length × width or $A = lw$
- The area of a parallelogram is given by Area = base × height or $A = bh$
- The area of a triangle is given by Area = $\frac{1}{2}$ × base × height or $A = \frac{1}{2}bh$
- The circumference of a circle is given by $C = \pi d$, where d is the diameter of the circle
- The area of a circle is given by $A = \pi r^2$, where r is the radius of the circle

continued

● The most accurate value of π that you can use is on your calculator. You should use it every time you have to work with π. Otherwise take π to be 3.142

● In problems using π, unless told otherwise, round off your answers to three significant figures

● The volume of a cuboid is given by Volume = length × width × height or $V = lwh$

● The common metric units to measure area, volume and capacity are shown in this table.

Area	Volume	Capacity
$100 \text{ mm}^2 = 1 \text{ cm}^2$	$1000 \text{ mm}^3 = 1 \text{ cm}^3$	$1000 \text{ cm}^3 = 1$ litre
$10\,000 \text{ cm}^2 = 1 \text{ m}^2$	$1\,000\,000 \text{ cm}^3 = 1 \text{ m}^3$	$1 \text{ m}^3 = 1000$ litres

Quick check

1 Find the areas of the following shapes.

a

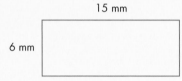

b

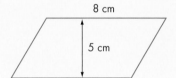

c

2 Find the volume of this cuboid.

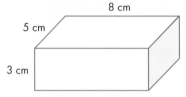

If you need to revise circle calculations, you should work through Exercise 4A.

4.1 Circumference and area of a circle

In this section you will learn how to:
- calculate the circumference and area of a circle

Key words

π
area
circumference

EXAMPLE 1

Calculate the **circumference** of the circle. Give your answer to three significant figures.

$C = \pi d$

$\quad = \pi \times 5 \text{ cm}$

$\quad = 15.7 \text{ cm (to 3 significant figures)}$

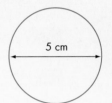

EXAMPLE 2

Calculate the **area** of the circle. Give your answer in terms of **π**.

$A = \pi r^2$

$\quad = \pi \times 6^2 \text{ m}^2$

$\quad = 36\pi \text{ m}^2$

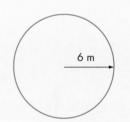

EXERCISE 4A

 1 Copy and complete the following table for each circle. Give your answers to 3 significant figures.

	Radius	Diameter	Circumference	Area
a	4 cm			
b	2.6 m			
c		12 cm		
d		3.2 m		

 2 Find the circumference of each of the following circles. Give your answers in terms of π.

    a Diameter 5 cm   **b** Radius 4 cm   **c** Radius 9 m   **d** Diameter 12 cm

 3 Find the area of each of the following circles. Give your answers in terms of π.

    a Radius 5 cm   **b** Diameter 12 cm   **c** Radius 10 cm   **d** Diameter 1 m

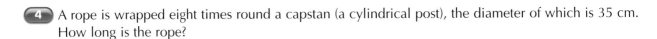

D

4 A rope is wrapped eight times round a capstan (a cylindrical post), the diameter of which is 35 cm. How long is the rope?

5 The roller used on a cricket pitch has a radius of 70 cm.

a What is the circumference of the roller?

b A cricket pitch has a length of 20 m. How many complete revolutions does the roller make when rolling the pitch?

6 The diameter of each of the following coins is as follows.

1p: 2 cm,   2p: 2.6 cm,   5p: 1.7 cm,   10p: 2.4 cm

Calculate the area of one face of each coin. Give your answers to 1 decimal place.

C

7 A circle has a circumference of 25 cm. What is its diameter?

8 What is the total perimeter of a semicircle of diameter 15 cm?

9 What is the total perimeter of a semicircle of radius 7 cm? Give your answer in terms of π.

10 Calculate the area of each of these shapes, giving your answers in terms of π.

a

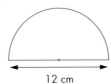

12 cm

b

4 cm

c

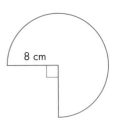

8 cm

11 Calculate the area of the shaded part of each of these diagrams, giving your answers in terms of π.

a

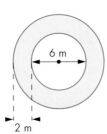

6 m

2 m

b

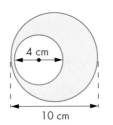

4 cm

10 cm

c

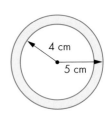

4 cm

5 cm

12 Assume that the human waist is circular.

a What are the distances around the waists of the following people?

Sue: waist radius of 10 cm   Dave: waist radius of 12 cm

Julie: waist radius of 11 cm   Brian: waist radius of 13 cm

b Compare differences between pairs of waist circumferences. What connection do they have to π?

c What would be the difference in length between a rope stretched tightly round the Earth and another rope always held 1 m above it?

In this section you will learn how to:
● find the area of a trapezium

Key word
trapezium

The area of a **trapezium** is calculated by finding the average of the lengths of its parallel sides and multiplying this by the perpendicular distance between them.

$$A = \tfrac{1}{2}(a + b)h$$

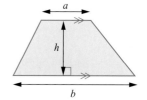

EXAMPLE 3

Find the area of the trapezium ABCD.

$$A = \tfrac{1}{2}(4 + 7) \times 3 \text{ cm}^2$$
$$= 16.5 \text{ cm}^2$$

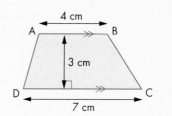

EXERCISE 4B

1 Copy and complete the following table for each trapezium.

	Parallel side 1	Parallel side 2	Vertical height	Area
a	8 cm	4 cm	5 cm	
b	10 cm	12 cm	7 cm	
c	7 cm	5 cm	4 cm	
d	5 cm	9 cm	6 cm	
e	3 m	13 m	5 m	
f	4 cm	10 cm		42 cm²
g	7 cm	8 cm		22.5 cm²
h	6 cm		5 cm	40 cm²

2 Calculate the perimeter and the area of each of these trapeziums.

a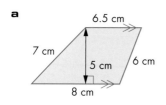

b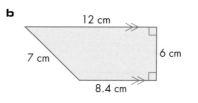

c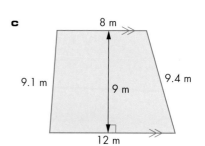

3 Calculate the area of each of these compound shapes.

a
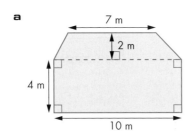

b
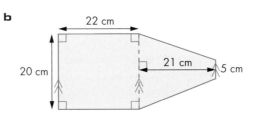

c
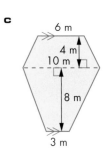

4 Calculate the area of the shaded part in each of these diagrams.

a
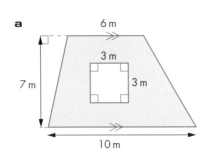

b
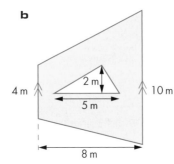

c
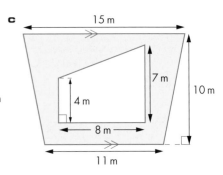

5 A trapezium has an area of 25 cm². Its vertical height is 5 cm. Write down five different possible pairs of lengths which the two parallel sides could be.

6 What percentage of this shape has been shaded?

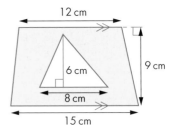

7 The shape of most of Egypt (see map) roughly approximates to a trapezium. The north coast is about 900 km long, the south boundary is about 1100 km long, and the distance from north to south is about 1100 km.

What is the approximate area of this part of Egypt?

8 A trapezium has parallel sides of a and b with a perpendicular height h. The trapezium is rotated by 180° and two trapezia are put together as shown.

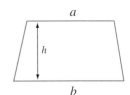

Use the diagram to prove that the area of a trapezium is $\frac{1}{2}h(a + b)$.

Sectors

In this section you will learn how to:

- calculate the length of an arc and the area of a sector

Key words

arc

sector

A **sector** is part of a circle, bounded by two radii of the circle and one of the **arcs** formed by the intersection of these radii with the circumference.

The angle subtended at the centre of the circle by the arc of a sector is known as the angle of the sector.

When a circle is divided into only two sectors, the larger one is called the major sector and the smaller one is called the minor sector.

Likewise, their arcs are called respectively the major arc and the minor arc.

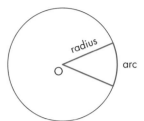

Length of an arc and area of a sector

A sector is a fraction of the whole circle, the size of the fraction being determined by the size of angle of the sector. The angle is often written as θ, a Greek letter pronounced *theta*. For example, the sector shown in the diagram represents the fraction $\frac{\theta°}{360°}$.

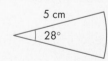

This applies to both its arc length and its area. Therefore,

Arc length $= \frac{\theta°}{360°} \times 2\pi r$ or $\frac{\theta°}{360°} \times \pi d$

Sector area $= \frac{\theta°}{360°} \times \pi r^2$

EXAMPLE 4

Find the arc length and the area of the sector in the diagram.

The sector angle is 28° and the radius is 5 cm. Therefore,

Arc length $= \frac{28°}{360°} \times \pi \times 2 \times 5 = 2.4$ cm (1 decimal place)

Sector area $= \frac{28°}{360°} \times \pi \times 5^2 = 6.1$ cm^2 (1 decimal place)

EXERCISE 4C

1 For each of these sectors, calculate **i** the arc length **ii** the sector area

a

40°
8 cm

b

95°
5 cm

c

78°
12 cm

d

130°
7 cm

2 Calculate the arc length and the area of a sector whose arc subtends an angle of 60° at the centre of a circle with a diameter of 12 cm. Give your answer in terms of π.

3 Calculate the total perimeter of each of these sectors.

a

11 cm

b

22°
8.5 cm

4 Calculate the area of each of these sectors.

a

110°
7 cm

b

50°
8 cm

c

120°
3 cm

d

250°
4 cm

5 Calculate the area of the shaded shape giving your answer in terms of π.

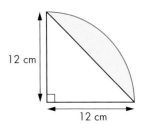

12 cm

12 cm

6 ABCD is a square of side length 8 cm. APC and AQC are arcs of the circles with centres D and B. Calculate the area of the shaded part.

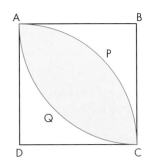

A   B

P

Q

D   C

7 A pendulum of length 72 cm swings through an angle of 15°. Through what distance does the bob swing? Give your answer in terms of π.

8 Find **i** the perimeter and **ii** the area of this shape.

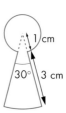

1 cm

30° 3 cm

4.4 Volume of a prism

In this section you will learn how to:
• calculate the volume of a prism

Key words
cross-section
prism

A **prism** is a 3-D shape which has the same **cross-section** running all the way through it.

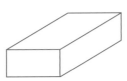

Name: Cuboid	Triangular prism	Cylinder
Cross-section: Rectangle	Isosceles triangle	Circle

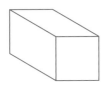

Name: Cuboid	Hexagonal prism
Cross-section: Square	Regular hexagon

The volume of a prism is found by multiplying the area of its cross-section by the length of the prism (or height if the prism is stood on end).

That is, Volume of prism = area of cross-section × length   **or** $V = Al$

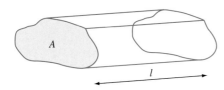

EXAMPLE 5

Find the volume of the triangular prism.

The area of the triangular cross-section = $A = \dfrac{5 \times 7}{2} = 17.5 \text{ cm}^2$

The volume is the area of its cross-section × length = Al

   $= 17.5 \times 9 = 157.5 \text{ cm}^3$

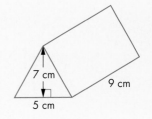

69

EXERCISE 4D

1 For each prism shown

    i sketch the cross-section   **ii** calculate the area of the cross-section

    iii calculate the volume.

a
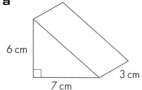

b
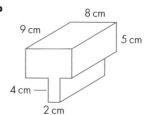

c
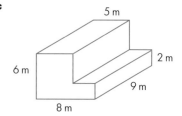

2 Calculate the volume of each of these prisms.

a
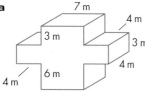

b
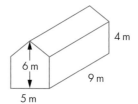

c
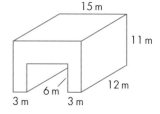

3 The uniform cross-section of a swimming pool is a trapezium with parallel sides, 1 m and 2.5 m, with a perpendicular distance of 30 m between them. The width of the pool is 10 m. How much water is in the pool when it is full? Give your answer in litres.

4 A lean-to is a prism. Calculate the volume of air inside the lean-to with the dimensions shown in the diagram. Give your answer in litres.

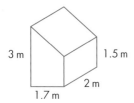

5 Each of these prisms has a regular cross-section in the shape of a right-angled triangle.

    a Find the volume of each prism.   **b** Find the total surface area of each prism.

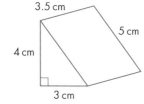

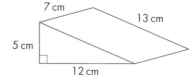

6 The top and bottom of the container shown here are the same size, both consisting of a rectangle, 4 cm by 9 cm, with a semicircle at each end. The depth is 3 cm. Find the volume of the container.

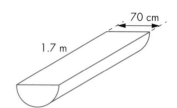

7 A tunnel is in the shape of a semicircle of radius 5 m, running for 500 m through a hill. Calculate the volume of soil removed when the tunnel was cut through the hill.

8 A horse trough is in the shape of a semicircular prism as shown. What volume of water will the trough hold when it is filled to the top? Give your answer in litres.

70 cm

1.7 m

9 The dimensions of the cross-section of a girder, 2 m in length, are shown on the diagram. The girder is made of iron with a density of 7.9 g/cm^3. What is the mass of the girder?

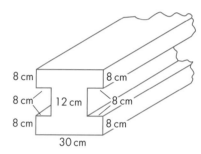

8 cm   8 cm

8 cm 12 cm 8 cm

8 cm   8 cm

30 cm

4.5 Cylinders

In this section you will learn how to:

- calculate the volume and surface area of a cylinder

Key words
cylinder
surface area
volume

Since a **cylinder** is an example of a prism, its **volume** is found by multiplying the area of one of its circular ends by the height.

That is, Volume = $\pi r^2 h$

where r is the radius of the cylinder and h is its height or length.

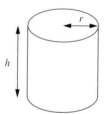

EXAMPLE 6

What is the volume of a cylinder having a radius of 5 cm and a height of 12 cm?

Volume = area of circular base × height

= $\pi r^2 h$

= $\pi \times 5^2 \times 12$ cm^3

= 942 cm^3 (3 significant figures)

Surface area

The total **surface area** of a cylinder is made up of the area of its curved surface plus the area of its two circular ends.

The curved surface area, when opened out, is a rectangle whose length is the circumference of the circular end.

Curved surface area = circumference of end × height of cylinder

$$= 2\pi rh \quad \textbf{or} \quad \pi dh$$

Area of one end $\quad = \pi r^2$

Therefore, total surface area = $2\pi rh + 2\pi r^2$ $\quad$ **or** $\quad \pi dh + 2\pi r^2$

EXAMPLE 7

What is the total surface area of a cylinder with a radius of 15 cm and a height of 2.5 m?

First, you must change the dimensions to a *common unit*. Use centimetres in this case.

$$\begin{aligned}
\text{Total surface area} &= \pi dh + 2\pi r^2 \\
&= \pi \times 30 \times 250 + 2 \times \pi \times 15^2 \text{ cm}^2 \\
&= 23\,562 + 1414 \text{ cm}^2 \\
&= 24\,976 \text{ cm}^2 \\
&= 25\,000 \text{ cm}^2 \text{ (3 significant figures)}
\end{aligned}$$

EXERCISE 4E

1 Find **i** the volume and **ii** the total surface area of each of these cylinders. Give your answers to 3 significant figures.

a 3 cm, 8 cm

b 1 cm, 19 cm

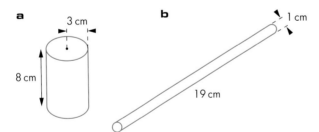

c 9 cm, 3.5 cm

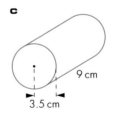

d 6 cm, 15 cm

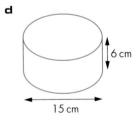

2 Find **i** the volume and **ii** the curved surface area of each of these cylinders. Give your answers in terms of π.

a base radius 3 cm and height 8 cm

b base diameter 8 cm and height 7 cm

c base diameter 12 cm and height 5 cm

d base radius of 10 m and length 6 m

3 The diameter of a marble, cylindrical column is 60 cm and its height is 4.2 m. The cost of making this column is quoted as £67.50 per cubic metre. What is the estimated total cost of making the column?

4 Find the mass of a solid iron cylinder 55 cm high with a base diameter of 60 cm. The density of iron is 7.9 g/cm^3.

5 What is the radius of a cylinder, height 8 cm, with a volume of 200π cm³?

 6 What is the radius of a cylinder, height 12 cm, with a curved surface area of 240π cm²?

 7 What is the height of a cylinder, diameter 12 cm, with a volume of 108π cm³?

 8 A cylindrical container is 65 cm in diameter. Water is poured into the container until it is 1 metre deep. How much water is in the container? Give your answer in litres.

 9 A cylindrical can of soup has a diameter of 7 cm and a height of 9.5 cm. It is full of soup, which weighs 625 g. What is the density of the soup?

 10 A metal bar, 1 m long, and with a diameter of 6 cm, has a mass of 22 kg. What is the density of the metal from which the bar is made?

 11 A block of wood has a hole of radius 2.5 cm drilled out as shown on the diagram. Calculate the mass of the wood if its density is 0.95 g/cm³.

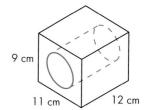

9 cm · 11 cm · 12 cm

4.6 Volume of a pyramid

In this section you will learn how to:
- calculate the volume of a pyramid

Key words
apex
frustum
pyramid
volume

A **pyramid** is a 3-D shape with a base from which triangular faces rise to a common vertex, called the **apex**. The base can be any polygon, but is usually a triangle, a rectangle or a square.

The **volume** of a pyramid is given by

Volume = $\frac{1}{3}$ × base area × vertical height

$V = \frac{1}{3}Ah$

where A is the base area and h is the vertical height.

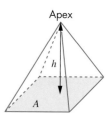

EXAMPLE 8

Calculate the volume of the pyramid on the right.

Base area = 5 × 4 = 20 cm²

Volume = $\frac{1}{3}$ × 20 × 6 = 40 cm³

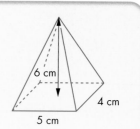

EXAMPLE 9

A pyramid, with a square base of side 8 cm, has a volume of 320 cm³. What is the vertical height of the pyramid?

Let h be the vertical height of the pyramid. Then,

$$\text{Volume} = \tfrac{1}{3} \times 64 \times h = 320 \text{ cm}^3$$

$$\frac{64h}{3} = 320 \text{ cm}^3$$

$$h = \frac{960}{64} \text{ cm}$$

$$h = 15 \text{ cm}$$

EXERCISE 4F

1 Calculate the volume of each of these pyramids, all with rectangular bases.

a
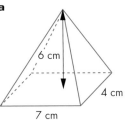
6 cm
4 cm
7 cm

b
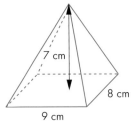
7 cm
8 cm
9 cm

c
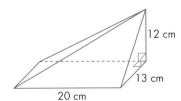
12 cm
13 cm
20 cm

d
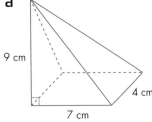
9 cm
4 cm
7 cm

e
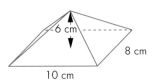
6 cm
8 cm
10 cm

2 Calculate the volume of a pyramid having a square base of side 9 cm and a vertical height of 10 cm.

3 Calculate the volume of each of these shapes.

a
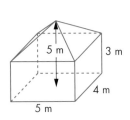
5 m
3 m
4 m
5 m

b
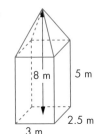
8 m
5 m
3 m
2.5 m

c
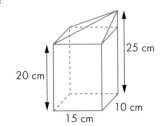
25 cm
20 cm
15 cm
10 cm

4 What is the mass of a solid pyramid having a square base of side 4 cm, a height of 3 cm and a density of 13 g/cm^3?

5 A crystal is in the form of two square-based pyramids joined at their bases (see diagram). The crystal has a mass of 31.5 grams. What is its density?

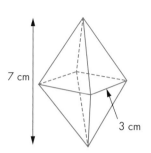

6 Find the mass of each of these pyramids.

a

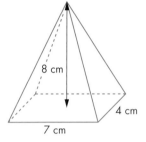

8 cm

4 cm

7 cm

Density 2.7 g/cm^3

b

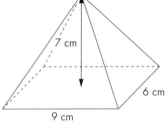

7 cm

6 cm

9 cm

Density 3.5 g/cm^3

c

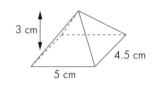

3 cm

4.5 cm

5 cm

Density 2.1 g/cm^3

7 Calculate the length x in each of these rectangular-based pyramids.

a

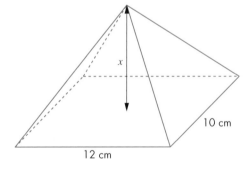

x

10 cm

12 cm

Weight 828 g
Density 2.3 g/cm^3

b

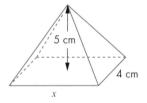

5 cm

4 cm

x

Weight 180 g
Density 4.5 g/cm^3

8 The pyramid in the diagram has its top 5 cm cut off as shown. The shape which is left is called a **frustum**. Calculate the volume of the frustum.

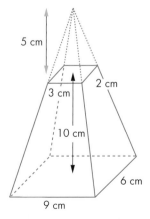

5 cm

2 cm

3 cm

10 cm

6 cm

9 cm

In this section you will learn how to:
- calculate the volume and surface area of a cone

Key words
slant height
surface area
vertical
    height
volume

A cone can be treated as a pyramid with a circular base. Therefore, the formula for the **volume** of a cone is the same as that for a pyramid.

Volume $= \frac{1}{3} \times$ base area $\times$ vertical height

$V = \frac{1}{3}\pi r^2 h$

where r is the radius of the base and h is the **vertical height** of the cone.

The curved **surface area** of a cone is given by

Curved surface area $= \pi \times$ radius $\times$ slant height

$S = \pi r l$

where l is the **slant height** of the cone.

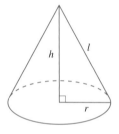

So the total surface area of a cone is given by the curved surface area plus the area of its circular base.

$A = \pi r l + \pi r^2$

EXAMPLE 10

For the cone in the diagram, calculate

i   its volume and

ii its total surface area.

Give your answers in terms of π.

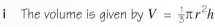

i   The volume is given by $V = \frac{1}{3}\pi r^2 h$

$= \frac{1}{3} \times \pi \times 36 \times 8 = 96\pi$ cm^3

ii The total surface area is given by $A = \pi r l + \pi r^2$

$= \pi \times 6 \times 10 + \pi \times 36 = 96\pi$ cm^2

EXERCISE 4G

1 For each cone, calculate **i** its volume and **ii** its total surface area. Give your answers to 3 significant figures.

a

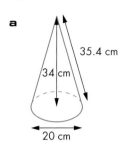

35.4 cm
34 cm
20 cm

b

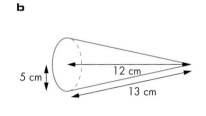

5 cm
12 cm
13 cm

c

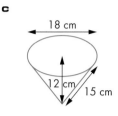

18 cm
12 cm
15 cm

2 A solid cone, base radius 6 cm and vertical height 8 cm, is made of metal whose density is 3.1 g/cm^3. Find the mass of the cone.

3 Find the total surface area of a cone whose base radius is 3 cm and slant height is 5 cm. Give your answer in terms of π.

4 Find the total surface area of a cone whose base radius is 5 cm and slant height is 13 cm.

5 Calculate the volume of each of these shapes. Give your answers in terms of π.

a

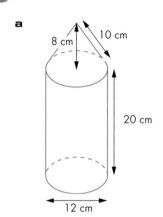

8 cm
10 cm
20 cm
12 cm

b

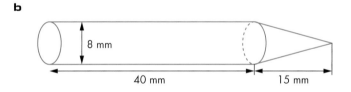

8 mm
40 mm
15 mm

6 The model shown on the right is made from aluminium. What is the mass of the model, given that the density of aluminium is 2.7 g/cm^3?

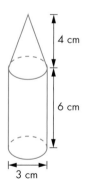

4 cm
6 cm
3 cm

7 A container in the shape of a cone, base radius 10 cm and vertical height 19 cm, is full of water. The water is poured into an empty cylinder of radius 15 cm. How high is the water in the cylinder?

4.8 Spheres

In this section you will learn how to:

- calculate the volume and surface area of a sphere

Key words
sphere
surface area
volume

The **volume** of a **sphere**, radius r, is given by

$$V = \tfrac{4}{3}\pi r^3$$

Its **surface area** is given by

$$A = 4\pi r^2$$

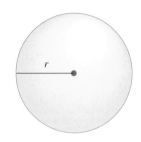

EXAMPLE 11

For a sphere of radius of 8 cm, calculate **i** its volume and **ii** its surface area.

i The volume is given by

$$V = \tfrac{4}{3}\pi r^3$$
$$= \tfrac{4}{3} \times \pi \times 8^3 = \tfrac{2048}{3} \times \pi = 2140 \text{ cm}^3 \text{ (3 significant figures)}$$

ii The surface area is given by $A = 4\pi r^2$

$$= 4 \times \pi \times 8^2 = 256 \times \pi = 804 \text{ cm}^2 \text{ (3 significant figures)}$$

EXERCISE 4H

 1 Calculate the volume of each of these spheres. Give your answers in terms of π.

    a Radius 3 cm   **b** Radius 6 cm   **c** Diameter 20 cm

 2 Calculate the surface area of each of these spheres. Give your answers in terms of π.

    a Radius 3 cm   **b** Radius 5 cm   **c** Diameter 14 cm

 3 Calculate the volume and the surface area of a sphere with a diameter of 50 cm.

 4 A sphere fits exactly into an open cubical box of side 25 cm. Calculate the following.

    a the surface area of the sphere   **b** the volume of the sphere

 5 A metal sphere of radius 15 cm is melted down and recast into a solid cylinder of radius 6 cm. Calculate the height of the cylinder.

 6 Lead has a density of 11.35 g/cm³. Calculate the maximum number of shot (spherical lead pellets) of radius 1.5 mm which can be made from 1 kg of lead.

 7 Calculate, correct to one decimal place, the radius of a sphere

    a whose surface area is 150 cm²   **b** whose volume is 150 cm³.

1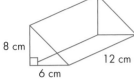

8 cm
12 cm
6 cm

The diagram shows a triangular prism.

a Work out the total surface area of the prism.

b Work out the volume of the prism.

2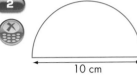

10 cm

A semi-circular protractor has a diameter of 10 cm.

Calculate its perimeter. Give your answer in terms of π.

3   A solid cylinder has a radius of 6 cm and a height of 20 cm.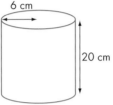

6 cm
20 cm

a Calculate the volume of the cylinder. Give your answer correct to 3 significant figures.

The cylinder is made of a material that has a density of 1.5 g/cm³.

b Calculate the mass of the cylinder. Give your answer correct to 3 significant figures.

Edexcel, Question 1, Paper 13B Higher, March 2005

4   OAB is a minor sector of a circle of radius 8 cm. Angle AOB = 120°

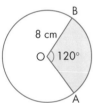

B
8 cm
O 120°
A

Calculate the area of the minor sector OAB. Give your answer to 1 decimal place.

5 The diagram shows a piece of wood. The piece of wood is a prism of length 350 cm. The cross-section of the prism is a semi-circle with diameter 1.2 cm.

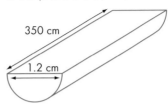

350 cm
1.2 cm

Calculate the volume of the piece of wood. Give your answer correct to 3 significant figures.

Edexcel, Question 1, Paper 13B Higher, January 2004

6 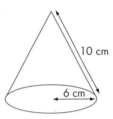 A solid cone has base radius 6 cm and slant height 10 cm. Calculate the *total* surface area of the cone. Give your answer in terms of π.

10 cm
6 cm

7   The diagram represents a large cone of height 6 cm and base diameter 18 cm.

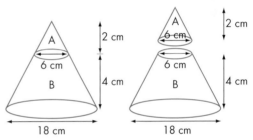

A
6 cm
2 cm
B
4 cm
18 cm

A
6 cm
2 cm
B
4 cm
18 cm

The large cone is made by placing a small cone A of height 2 cm and base diameter 6 cm on top of a frustum B.

Calculate the volume of the frustum B. Give your answer in terms of π.

Edexcel, Question 7, Paper 18 Higher, June 2003

WORKED EXAM QUESTION

The diagram shows a litter bin. The bin consists of a cylinder and a hemisphere. The cylinder has a diameter of 40 cm and a height of 60 cm.

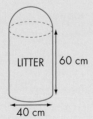

LITTER
60 cm
40 cm

Calculate the volume of the litter bin. Give your answer to 3 significant figures.

Solution

Volume of litter bin

$$= \pi r^2 h + \frac{2}{3}\pi r^3$$

(The volume of a sphere is $\frac{4}{3}\pi r^3$ so the volume of a hemisphere is half this.)

$$\pi \times 20^2 \times 60 + \frac{2}{3} \times \pi \times 20^3$$

Use the π button on your calculator.

$$= 92\,200 \text{ cm}^3 \text{ (to 3 sf)}$$

Mr and Mrs Jones have decided to "go green". They want to install a water purifying unit and water tank in their loft to collect rain water from their roof, and use this water for the washing machine, dishwasher, shower and toilet.

Copy the table below and help them to calculate their average total daily water usage for these four items.

BATHROOM

The toilet cistern has a cross section that is a trapezium. The diagram shows the amount of water that is used in one flush of the toilet.

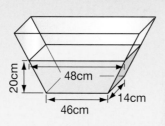

BATHROOM

The shower uses 2.5 gallons per minute.

An average shower takes 8 minutes.

Daily water usage			
	litres used each: flush/shower/load	frequency used	total litres per day
Toilet		12 times a day	
Shower		2 times a day	
Washing machine		3 times a week	
Dishwasher		once every 2 days	
		TOTAL:	

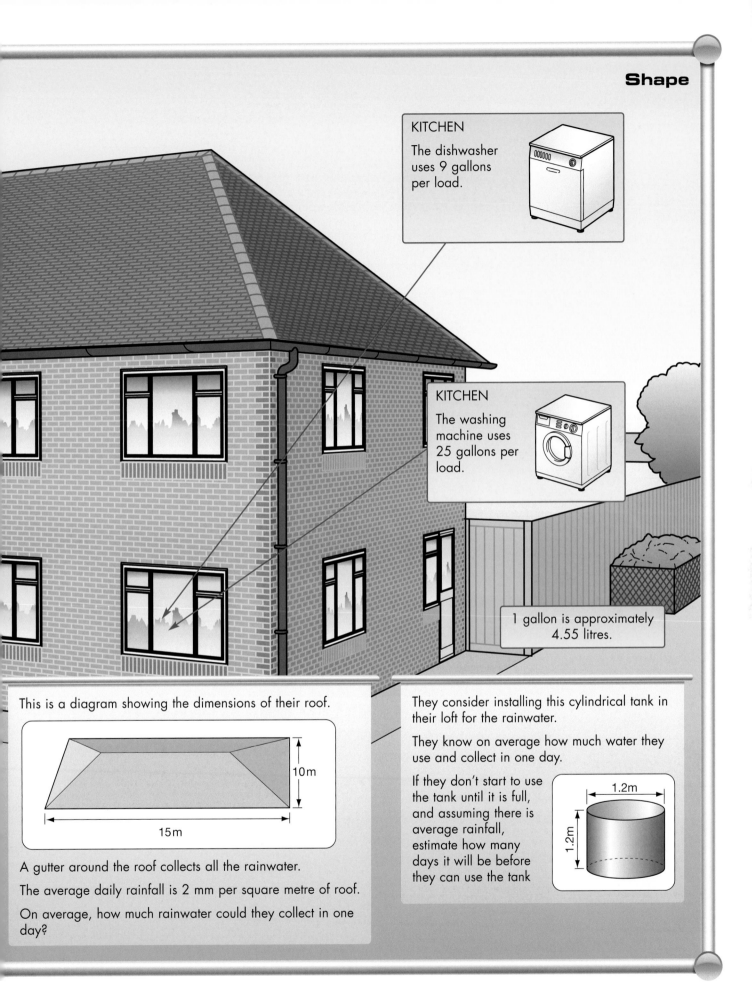

KITCHEN

The dishwasher uses 9 gallons per load.

KITCHEN

The washing machine uses 25 gallons per load.

1 gallon is approximately 4.55 litres.

This is a diagram showing the dimensions of their roof.

10m

15m

A gutter around the roof collects all the rainwater.

The average daily rainfall is 2 mm per square metre of roof.

On average, how much rainwater could they collect in one day?

They consider installing this cylindrical tank in their loft for the rainwater.

They know on average how much water they use and collect in one day.

If they don't start to use the tank until it is full, and assuming there is average rainfall, estimate how many days it will be before they can use the tank

1.2m

1.2m

GRADE YOURSELF

D Able to calculate the circumference and area of a circle

D Able to calculate the area of a trapezium

C Able to calculate the volume of prisms and cylinders

B Able to calculate the length of an arc and the area of a sector

B Able to calculate the surface area of cylinders, cones and spheres

B Able to calculate the volume of pyramids, cones and spheres

A Able to calculate volume and surface area of compound 3-D shapes

What you should know now

- For a sector of radius r and angle θ

  $$\text{Arc length} = \frac{\theta°}{360°} \times 2\pi r \text{ or } \frac{\theta°}{360°} \times \pi d$$

  $$\text{Area of a sector} = \frac{\theta°}{360°} \times \pi r^2$$

- The area of a trapezium is given by

  $$A = \tfrac{1}{2}(a + b)h$$

  where h is the vertical height, and a and b are the lengths of the two parallel sides

- The volume of a prism is given by $V = Al$, where A is the cross-section area and l is the length of the prism

- The volume of a cylinder is given by $V = \pi r^2 h$ where r is the radius and h is the height or length of the cylinder

- The curved surface area of a cylinder is given by $S = 2\pi rh$, where r is the radius and h is the height or length of the cylinder

- The volume of a pyramid is given by $V = \tfrac{1}{3}Ah$, where A is the area of the base and h is the vertical height of the pyramid

- The volume of a cone is given by $V = \tfrac{1}{3}\pi r^2 h$ where r is the base radius and h is the vertical height of the cone

- The curved surface area of a cone is given by $S = \pi rl$, where r is the base radius and l is the slant height of the cone

- The volume of a sphere is given by $V = \tfrac{4}{3}\pi r^3$ where r is its radius

- The surface area of a sphere is given by $A = 4\pi r^2$ where r is its radius

Chapter 5

Algebra 1

1 Basic algebra

2 Factorisation

3 Solving linear equations

4 Trial and improvement

5 Simultaneous equations

6 Rearranging formulae

This chapter will show you ...

- how to manipulate basic algebraic expressions by multiplying terms together, expanding brackets and collecting like terms
- how to factorise linear expressions
- how to solve linear equations
- how to solve simultaneous equations
- how to rearrange formulae

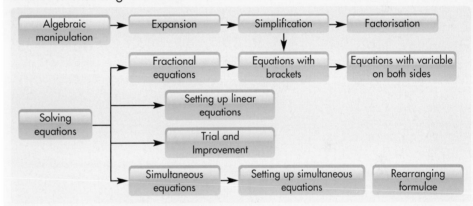

What you should already know

- The basic language of algebra
- How to collect together like terms
- How to multiply together terms such as $2m \times 3m$

Quick check

1 Expand the following.

  a $2(x + 6)$ **b** $4(x - 3)$ **c** $6(2x - 1)$

2 Simplify the following.

  a $4y + 2y - y$ **b** $3x + 2 + x - 5$ **c** $2(x + 1) - 3(x + 2)$

3 Simplify the following.

  a $3 \times 2x$ **b** $4y \times 2y$ **c** $c^2 \times 2c$

4 Solve the following equations

  a $2x + 4 = 6$ **b** $3x - 5 = 4$ **c** $\frac{x}{3} + 2 = 5$

  d $\frac{x}{2} = 4$ **e** $\frac{x}{3} = 8$ **f** $\frac{2x}{5} = 6$

Basic algebra

This section will show you how to:

- substitute into, manipulate and simplify algebraic expressions

Key words

bracket
coefficient
like terms
expand
expression
substitute
simplification
variable

Substitution

EXAMPLE 1

Find the value of $3x^2 - 5$ when **a** $x = 3$, **b** $x = -4$.

Whenever you **substitute** a number for a **variable** in an **expression** always put the value in a bracket before working it out. This will avoid errors in calculation, especially with negative numbers.

a When $x = 3$, $\quad 3(3)^2 - 5 = 3 \times 9 - 5 = 27 - 5 = 22$

b When $x = -4$, $\quad 3(-4)^2 - 5 = 3 \times 16 - 5 = 48 - 5 = 43$

EXAMPLE 2

Find the value of $L = a^2 - 8b^2$ when $a = -6$ and $b = \frac{1}{2}$.

Substitute for the letters.

$$L = (-6)^2 - 8\left(\tfrac{1}{2}\right)^2$$
$$L = 36 - 8 \times \tfrac{1}{4} = 36 - 2 = 34$$

Note: if you do not use brackets and write -6^2, this could be wrongly evaluated as -36.

EXERCISE 5A

1 Find the value of $4b + 3$ when $\quad$ **a** $b = 2.5$, $\quad$ **b** $b = -1.5$, $\quad$ **c** $b = \frac{1}{2}$.

2 Evaluate $\frac{x}{3}$ when $\quad$ **a** $x = 6$, $\quad$ **b** $x = 24$, $\quad$ **c** $x = -30$.

3 Find the value of $\frac{12}{y}$ when $\quad$ **a** $y = 2$, $\quad$ **b** $y = 4$, $\quad$ **c** $y = -6$.

4 Evaluate $3w - 4$ when $\quad$ **a** $w = -1$, $\quad$ **b** $w = -2$, $\quad$ **c** $w = 3.5$.

5 Find the value of $\frac{24}{x}$ when $\quad$ **a** $x = -5$, $\quad$ **b** $x = \frac{1}{2}$, $\quad$ **c** $x = \frac{3}{4}$.

6 Where $P = \dfrac{5w - 4y}{w + y}$, find P when

   a $w = 3$ and $y = 2$,   **b** $w = 6$ and $y = 4$,   **c** $w = 2$ and $y = 3$.

7 Where $A = b^2 + c^2$, find A when

   a $b = 2$ and $c = 3$,   **b** $b = 5$ and $c = 7$,   **c** $b = -1$ and $c = -4$.

8 Where $A = \dfrac{180(n - 2)}{n + 5}$, find A when

   a $n = 7$,   **b** $n = 3$,   **c** $n = -1$.

9 Where $Z = \dfrac{y^2 + 4}{4 + y}$, find Z when

   a $y = 4$,   **b** $y = -6$,   **c** $y = -1.5$.

Expansion

In mathematics, the term "**expand**" usually means "multiply out". For example, expressions such as $3(y + 2)$ and $4y^2(2y + 3)$ can be expanded by multiplying out.

You need to remember that there is an invisible multiplication sign between the outside number and the **bracket**. So that $3(y + 2)$ is really $3 \times (y + 2)$, and $4y^2(2y + 3)$ is really $4y^2 \times (2y + 3)$.

We expand by multiplying *everything inside* the bracket by what is outside the bracket.

So in the case of the two examples above,

$$3(y + 2) = 3 \times (y + 2) = 3 \times y + 3 \times 2 = 3y + 6$$
$$4y^2(2y + 3) = 4y^2 \times (2y + 3) = 4y^2 \times 2y + 4y^2 \times 3 = 8y^3 + 12y^2$$

Look at these next examples of expansion, which show clearly how the term outside the bracket has been multiplied with the terms inside it.

$2(m + 3) = 2m + 6$	$y(y^2 - 4x) = y^3 - 4xy$
$3(2t + 5) = 6t + 15$	$3x^2(4x + 5) = 12x^3 + 15x^2$
$m(p + 7) = mp + 7m$	$-3(2 + 3x) = -6 - 9x$
$x(x - 6) = x^2 - 6x$	$-2x(3 - 4x) = -6x + 8x^2$
$4t(t^3 + 2) = 4t^4 + 8t$	$3t(2 + 5t - p) = 6t + 15t^2 - 3pt$

Note: the signs change when a negative quantity is outside the bracket. For example,

$a(b + c) = ab + ac$	$a(b - c) = ab - ac$
$-a(b + c) = -ab - ac$	$-a(b - c) = -ab + ac$
$-(a - b) = -a + b$	$-(a + b - c) = -a - b + c$

Expand these expressions.

1 $2(3 + m)$ **2** $5(2 + l)$ **3** $3(4 - y)$ **4** $4(5 + 2k)$

5 $3(2 - 4f)$ **6** $2(5 - 3w)$ **7** $5(2k + 3m)$ **8** $4(3d - 2n)$

9 $t(t + 3)$ **10** $k(k - 3)$ **11** $4t(t - 1)$ **12** $2k(4 - k)$

13 $4g(2g + 5)$ **14** $5h(3h - 2)$ **15** $y(y^2 + 5)$ **16** $h(h^3 + 7)$

17 $k(k^2 - 5)$ **18** $3t(t^2 + 4)$ **19** $3d(5d^2 - d^3)$ **20** $3w(2w^2 + t)$

21 $5a(3a^2 - 2b)$ **22** $3p(4p^3 - 5m)$ **23** $4h^2(3h + 2g)$ **24** $2m^2(4m + m^2)$

Simplification

Simplification is the process whereby an expression is written down as simply as possible, any **like terms** being combined. Like terms are terms which have the same letter(s) raised to the same power and can differ only in their numerical **coefficients** (numbers in front). For example,

m, $3m$, $4m$, $-m$ and $76m$ are all like terms in m

t^2, $4t^2$, $7t^2$, $-t^2$, $-3t^2$ and $98t^2$ are all like terms in t^2

pt, $5tp$, $-2pt$, $7pt$, $-3tp$ and $103pt$ are all like terms in pt

Note also that all the terms in tp are also like terms to all the terms in pt.

In simplifying an expression, only like terms can be added or subtracted. For example,

$4m + 3m = 7m$ $3y + 4y + 3 = 7y + 3$ $4h - h = 3h$

$2t^2 + 5t^2 = 7t^2$ $2m + 6 + 3m = 5m + 6$ $7t + 8 - 2t = 5t + 8$

$3ab + 2ba = 5ab$ $5k - 2k = 3k$ $10g - 4 - 3g = 7g - 4$

Expand and simplify

When two brackets are expanded there are often like terms that can be collected together. Algebraic expressions should always be simplified as much as possible.

EXAMPLE 3

$$3(4 + m) + 2(5 + 2m) = 12 + 3m + 10 + 4m = 22 + 7m$$

EXAMPLE 4

$$3t(5t + 4) - 2t(3t - 5) = 15t^2 + 12t - 6t^2 + 10t = 9t^2 + 22t$$

EXERCISE 5C

1 Simplify these expressions.

    a $4t + 3t$ **b** $3d + 2d + 4d$ **c** $5e - 2e$ **d** $3t - t$

    e $2t^2 + 3t^2$ **f** $6y^2 - 2y^2$ **g** $3ab + 2ab$ **h** $7a^2d - 4a^2d$

2 Expand and simplify.

    a $3(4 + t) + 2(5 + t)$ **b** $5(3 + 2k) + 3(2 + 3k)$

    c $4(3 + 2f) + 2(5 - 3f)$ **d** $5(1 + 3g) + 3(3 - 4g)$

3 Expand and simplify.

    a $4(3 + 2h) - 2(5 + 3h)$ **b** $5(3g + 4) - 3(2g + 5)$

    c $5(5k + 2) - 2(4k - 3)$ **d** $4(4e + 3) - 2(5e - 4)$

> **HINTS AND TIPS**
>
> Be careful with minus signs. For example $-2(5e - 4) = -10e + 8$

4 Expand and simplify.

    a $m(4 + p) + p(3 + m)$ **b** $k(3 + 2h) + h(4 + 3k)$

    c $4r(3 + 4p) + 3p(8 - r)$ **d** $5k(3m + 4) - 2m(3 - 2k)$

5 Expand and simplify.

    a $t(3t + 4) + 3t(3 + 2t)$ **b** $2y(3 + 4y) + y(5y - 1)$

    c $4e(3e - 5) - 2e(e - 7)$ **d** $3k(2k + p) - 2k(3p - 4k)$

6 Expand and simplify.

    a $4a(2b + 3c) + 3b(3a + 2c)$ **b** $3y(4w + 2t) + 2w(3y - 4t)$

    c $5m(2n - 3p) - 2n(3p - 2m)$ **d** $2r(3r + r^2) - 3r^2(4 - 2r)$

5.2 Factorisation

This section will show you how to:
- factorise an algebraic expression

Key words
common factor
factorisation

Factorisation is the opposite of expansion. It puts an expression back into the brackets it may have come from.

In factorisation, we have to look for the **common factors** in *every* term of the expression.

EXAMPLE 5

Factorise.   **a** $6t + 9m$ **b** $6my + 4py$ **c** $5k^2 - 25k$ **d** $10a^2b - 15ab^2$

a First look at the numerical coefficients 6 and 9. These have a common factor of 3. Then look at the letters, *t* and *m*. These do not have any common factors as they do not appear in both terms. The expression can be thought of as $3 \times 2t + 3 \times 3m$, which gives the factorisation

$$6t + 9m = 3(2t + 3m)$$

Note: you can always check a factorisation by expanding the answer.

b First look at the numbers, these have a common factor of 2. *m* and *p* do not occur in both terms but *y* does, and is a common factor, so the factorisation is

$$6my + 4py = 2y(3m + 2p)$$

c 5 is a common factor of 5 and 25 and *k* is a common factor of k^2 and *k*.

$$5k^2 - 25k = 5k(k - 5)$$

d 5 is a common factor of 10 and 15, *a* is a common factor of a^2 and *a*, *b* is a common factor of *b* and b^2.

$$10a^2b - 15ab^2 = 5ab(2a - 3b)$$

Note: if you multiply out each answer, you will get the expressions you started with.

EXERCISE 5D

Factorise the following expressions.

1 $6m + 12t$ **2** $9t + 3p$ **3** $8m + 12k$

4 $4r + 8t$ **5** $mn + 3m$ **6** $5g^2 + 3g$

7 $4w - 6t$ **8** $3y^2 + 2y$ **9** $4t^2 - 3t$

10 $3m^2 - 3mp$ **11** $6p^2 + 9pt$ **12** $8pt + 6mp$

13 $8ab - 4bc$ **14** $5b^2c - 10bc$ **15** $8abc + 6bed$

16 $4a^2 + 6a + 8$

17 $6ab + 9bc + 3bd$ **18** $5t^2 + 4t + at$ **19** $6mt^2 - 3mt + 9m^2t$

20 $8ab^2 + 2ab - 4a^2b$ **21** $10pt^2 + 15pt + 5p^2t$

22 Factorise the following expressions where possible. List those which do not factorise.

a $7m - 6t$ **b** $5m + 2mp$ **c** $t^2 - 7t$

d $8pt + 5ab$ **e** $4m^2 - 6mp$ **f** $a^2 + b$

g $4a^2 - 5ab$ **h** $3ab + 4cd$ **i** $5ab - 3b^2c$

5.3 Solving linear equations

In this section you will learn how to:

- solve equations in which the variable appears as part of the numerator of a fraction
- solve equations where you have to expand brackets first
- solve equations where the variable (the letter) appears on both sides of the equals sign
- set up equations from given information, and then solve them

Key words
brackets
do the same to both sides
equation
rearrange
solution
solve

Fractional equations

EXAMPLE 6

Solve this **equation**. $\frac{x}{3} + 1 = 5$

First subtract 1 from both sides: $\frac{x}{3} = 4$

Now multiply both sides by 3: $x = 12$

EXAMPLE 7

Solve this equation. $\frac{x-2}{5} = 3$

First multiply both sides by 5: $x - 2 = 15$

Now add 2 to both sides: $x = 17$

EXAMPLE 8

Solve this equation. $\frac{3x}{4} - 3 = 1$

First add 3 to both sides: $\frac{3x}{4} = 4$

Now multiply both sides by 4: $3x = 16$

Now divide both sides by 3: $x = \frac{16}{3} = 5\frac{1}{3}$

EXERCISE 5E

Solve these equations.

1 $\dfrac{f}{5} + 2 = 8$

2 $\dfrac{w}{3} - 5 = 2$

3 $\dfrac{x}{8} + 3 = 12$

4 $\dfrac{5t}{4} + 3 = 18$

5 $\dfrac{3y}{2} - 1 = 8$

6 $\dfrac{2x}{3} + 5 = 12$

7 $\dfrac{t}{5} + 3 = 1$

8 $\dfrac{x+3}{2} = 5$

9 $\dfrac{t-5}{2} = 3$

10 $\dfrac{x+10}{2} = 3$

11 $\dfrac{2x+1}{3} = 5$

12 $\dfrac{5y-2}{4} = 3$

13 $\dfrac{6y+3}{9} = 1$

14 $\dfrac{2x-3}{5} = 4$

15 $\dfrac{5t+3}{4} = 1$

Brackets

When we have an equation which contains **brackets**, we first must multiply out the brackets and then solve the resulting equation.

EXAMPLE 9

Solve $5(x + 3) = 25$.

First multiply out the bracket to get:

$5x + 15 = 25$

Rearrange: $\quad 5x = 25 - 15 = 10$

Divide by 5: $\quad \dfrac{5x}{5} = \dfrac{10}{5}$

$x = 2$

EXAMPLE 10

Solve $3(2x - 7) = 15$.

Multiply out the bracket to get:

$6x - 21 = 15$

Add 21 to both sides: $\quad 6x = 36$

Divide both sides by 6: $\quad x = 6$

EXERCISE 5F

Solve each of the following equations. Some of the answers may be decimals or negative numbers. Remember to check that each answer works for its original equation. Use your calculator if necessary.

1 $2(x + 5) = 16$

2 $5(x - 3) = 20$

3 $3(t + 1) = 18$

4 $4(2x + 5) = 44$

5 $2(3y - 5) = 14$

6 $5(4x + 3) = 135$

7 $4(3t - 2) = 88$

8 $6(2t + 5) = 42$

9 $2(3x + 1) = 11$

10 $4(5y - 2) = 42$

11 $6(3k + 5) = 39$

12 $5(2x + 3) = 27$

13 $9(3x - 5) = 9$

14 $2(x + 5) = 6$

15 $5(x - 4) = -25$

16 $3(t + 7) = 15$

17 $2(3x + 11) = 10$

18 $4(5t + 8) = 12$

> **HINTS AND TIPS**
>
> Once the brackets have been expanded the equations become straightforward. Remember to multiply *everything* inside the bracket with what is outside.

Equations with the variable on both sides

When a letter (or variable) appears on both sides of an equation, it is best to use the "**do the same to both sides**" method of **solution**, and collect all the terms containing the letter on the left-hand side of the equation. But when there are more of the letter on the right-hand side, it is easier to turn the equation round. When an equation contains brackets, they must be multiplied out first.

EXAMPLE 11

Solve $5x + 4 = 3x + 10$.

There are more xs on the left-hand side, so leave the equation as it is.

Subtract $3x$ from both sides: $2x + 4 = 10$

Subtract 4 from both sides: $2x = 6$

Divide both sides by 2: $x = 3$

EXAMPLE 12

Solve $2x + 3 = 6x - 5$.

There are more xs on the right-hand side, so turn round the equation.

$6x - 5 = 2x + 3$

Subtract $2x$ from both sides: $4x - 5 = 3$

Add 5 to both sides: $4x = 8$

Divide both sides by 4: $x = 2$

EXAMPLE 13

Solve this equation. $3(2x + 5) + x = 2(2 - x) + 2$

Multiply out both brackets: $6x + 15 + x = 4 - 2x + 2$

Simplify both sides: $7x + 15 = 6 - 2x$

There are more xs on the left-hand side, so leave the equation as it is.

Add $2x$ to both sides: $9x + 15 = 6$

Subtract 15 from both sides: $9x = -9$

Divide both sides by 9: $x = -1$

EXERCISE 5G

Solve each of the following equations.

1 $2x + 3 = x + 5$ **2** $5y + 4 = 3y + 6$

3 $4a - 3 = 3a + 4$ **4** $5t + 3 = 2t + 15$

5 $7p - 5 = 3p + 3$ **6** $6k + 5 = 2k + 1$

7 $4m + 1 = m + 10$ **8** $8s - 1 = 6s - 5$

9 $2(d + 3) = d + 12$ **10** $5(x - 2) = 3(x + 4)$

11 $3(2y + 3) = 5(2y + 1)$ **12** $3(h - 6) = 2(5 - 2h)$

13 $4(3b - 1) + 6 = 5(2b + 4)$ **14** $2(5c + 2) - 2c = 3(2c + 3) + 7$

> **HINTS AND TIPS**
>
> Remember the rule "change sides, change signs".
> Show all your working on this type of question.
> **Rearrange** before you simplify. If you try to rearrange and simplify at the same time you will probably get it wrong.

Setting up linear equations

Equations are used to represent situations, so that we can solve real-life problems.

EXAMPLE 14

A milkman sets off from the dairy with eight crates of milk, each containing b bottles. He delivers 92 bottles to a large factory and finds that he has exactly 100 bottles left on his milk float. How many bottles were in each crate?

The equation is: $8b - 92 = 100$

                                             $8b = 192$ (Add 92 to both sides)

                                             $b = 24$ (Divide both sides by 8)

Checking the answer gives: $8 \times 24 - 92 = 192 - 92 = 100$

which is correct.

EXAMPLE 15

The rectangle shown has a perimeter of 40 cm.

Find the value of x.

The perimeter of the rectangle is:

$$3x + 1 + x + 3 + 3x + 1 + x + 3 = 40$$

This simplifies to: $\qquad 8x + 8 = 40$

$\qquad$ Subtract 8 $\qquad\qquad 8x = 32$

$\qquad$ Divide by 8 $\qquad\qquad\quad x = 4$

Checking the answer gives:

$$3x + 1 = 3 \times 4 + 1 = 13$$

$$x + 3 = 4 + 3 = 7$$

$$\text{perimeter} = 13 + 7 + 13 + 7$$

$$= 40$$

which is correct.

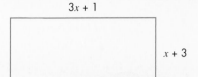

$3x + 1$

$x + 3$

EXERCISE 5H

Set up an equation to represent each situation described below. Then solve the equation. Do not forget to check each answer.

1 A man buys a daily paper from Monday to Saturday for d pence. On Sunday he buys the *Observer* for £1.60. His weekly paper bill is £4.90.

How much is his daily paper?

2 The diagram shows a rectangle.

$(10x - 1)$

6

$(4y - 2)$

14

a What is the value of x?

b What is the value of y?

3 In this rectangle, the length is 3 centimetres more than the width. The perimeter is 12 cm.

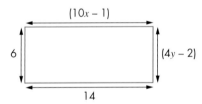

$(x + 3)$

x

a What is the value of x?

b What is the area of the rectangle?

4 Mary has two bags of sweets, each of which contains the same number of sweets. She eats four sweets. She then finds that she has 30 sweets left. How many sweets were in each bag to start with?

5 A boy is *Y* years old. His father is 25 years older than he is. The sum of their ages is 31. How old is the boy?

6 Another boy is *X* years old. His sister is twice as old as he is. The sum of their ages is 27. How old is the boy?

7 The diagram shows a square.
Find *x* if the perimeter is 44 cm.

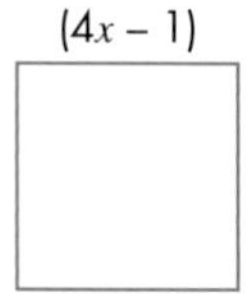

$(4x - 1)$

8 Max thought of a number. He then multiplied his number by 3. He added 4 to the answer. He then doubled that answer to get a final value of 38. What number did he start with?

5.4 Trial and improvement

In this section you will learn how to:

- estimate the answer to some equations that do not have exact solutions, using the method of trial and improvement

Key words

comment
decimal place
guess
trial and improvement

Certain equations cannot be solved exactly. However, a close enough solution to such an equation can be found by the **trial-and-improvement** method (sometimes wrongly called the trial-and-error method).

The idea is to keep trying different values in the equation which will take it closer and closer to its "true" solution. This step-by-step process is continued until a value is found which gives a solution that is close enough to the accuracy required.

The trial-and-improvement method is the way in which computers are programmed to solve equations.

EXAMPLE 16

Find a solution to the equation $x^3 + x = 105$, giving the solution to 1 **decimal place**.

The best way to do this is to set up a table to show working. There will be three columns: **guess** (the trial); the equation we are solving; and a **comment** whether the value of the guess is too high or too low.

Step 1 We must find the two consecutive whole numbers between which x lies. We do this by intelligent guessing.

Try $x = 5$: $125 + 5 = 130$ Too high – next trial needs to be smaller

Try $x = 4$: $64 + 4 = 68$ Too low

So we now know that a solution lies between $x = 4$ and $x = 5$.

Step 2 We must find the two consecutive one-decimal place numbers between which x lies. Try 4.5, which is halfway between 4 and 5.

This gives $91.125 + 4.5 = 95.625$ Too small

So we attempt to improve this by trying 4.6.

This gives $97.336 + 4.6 = 101.936$ Still too small

Try 4.7, which gives 108.523.   This is too high, so we know the solution is between 4.6 and 4.7.

It looks as though 4.6 is closer but there is a very important final step. Never assume that the one-decimal place number that gives the closest value to a solution is the answer.

Step 3 Now try the value that is halfway between the two one-decimal place values. In this case 4.65.

This gives 105.194 625   Too high

This means that an actual solution is between 4.60 and 4.65.

The diagram and table summarise our results.

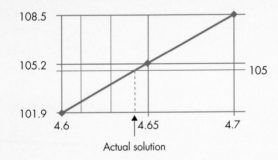

Guess	$x^3 + x$	Comment
4	68	Too low
5	130	Too high
4.5	95.625	Too low
4.6	101.936	Too low
4.7	108.523	Too high
4.65	105.194625	Too high

The approximate answer is $x = 4.6$ to 1 decimal place.

EXERCISE 5I

1 For each of the following equations, find a pair of consecutive *whole numbers*, between which a solution lies.

   a $x^2 + x = 24$ **b** $x^3 + 2x = 80$ **c** $x^3 - x = 20$

2 Copy and complete the table to find an approximate solution, using trial and improvement, to this equation.

   $x^3 + 2x = 50$

Give your answer to 1 decimal place.

Guess	$x^3 + 2x$	Comment
3	33	Too low
4	72	Too high

3 Copy and complete the table to find an approximate solution, using trial and improvement, to this equation.

   $x^3 - 3x = 40$

Give your answer to 1 decimal place.

Guess	$x^3 - 3x$	Comment
4	52	Too high

4 Use trial and improvement to find an approximate solution to this equation.

   $2x^3 + x = 35$

Give your answer to 1 decimal place.

You are given that the solution lies between 2 and 3.

> **HINTS AND TIPS**
>
> Set up a table to show your working.
> This makes it easier for you to show your method, and for the examiner to mark.

5 Use trial and improvement to find an exact solution to this equation.

   $4x^2 + 2x = 12$

Do not use a calculator.

6 Find a solution to each of the following equations to 1 decimal place.

   a $2x^3 + 3x = 35$ **b** $3x^3 - 4x = 52$ **c** $2x^3 + 5x = 79$

7 A rectangle has an area of 100 cm². Its length is 5 cm longer than its width.

   a Show that, if x is the width then $x^2 + 5x = 100$

   b Find, correct to 1 decimal place, the dimensions of the rectangle.

8 Use trial and improvement to find a solution to the equation $x^2 + x = 30$.

> I want to find a number that when you square it and add it to itself the answer is 30.

Simultaneous equations

In this section you will learn how to:

- solve simultaneous linear equations in two variables

Key words

balance
check
coefficient
eliminate
simultaneous
    equations
substitute
variable

A pair of **simultaneous equations** is exactly that – two equations (usually linear) for which we want the *same* solution, and which we therefore *solve together*. For example,

$x + y = 10$ has many solutions:

$\qquad x = 2, y = 8 \qquad x = 4, y = 6 \qquad x = 5, y = 5 \dots$

and $2x + y = 14$ has many solutions:

$\qquad x = 2, y = 10 \qquad x = 3, y = 8 \qquad x = 4, y = 6 \dots$

But only *one* solution, $x = 4$ and $y = 6$, satisfies *both* equations at the *same time*.

Elimination method

Here, we solve simultaneous equations by the *elimination method*. There are six steps in this method. Step 1 is to **balance** the **coefficients** of one of the **variables**. Step 2 is to **eliminate** this variable by adding or subtracting the equations. Step 3 is to solve the resulting linear equation in the other variable. Step 4 is to **substitute** the value found back into one of the previous equations. Step 5 is to solve the resulting equation. Step 6 is to **check** that the two values found satisfy the original equations.

EXAMPLE 17

Solve the equations $6x + y = 15$ and $4x + y = 11$.

The equations should be labelled so that the method can be clearly explained.

$\qquad 6x + y = 15 \qquad\qquad\qquad (1)$

$\qquad 4x + y = 11 \qquad\qquad\qquad (2)$

Step 1: Since the y-term in both equations has the same coefficient there is no need to balance them.

EXAMPLE 17 (contd)

Step 2: Subtract one equation from the other. (Equation (1) minus equation (2) will give positive values.) $6x - 4x = 2x$ $\quad 15 - 11 = 4$

$(1) - (2)$ $\qquad\qquad\qquad\qquad 2x = 4$

Step 3: Solve this equation: $\qquad\qquad\qquad x = 2$

Step 4: Substitute $x = 2$ into one of the original equations. (Usually the one with smallest numbers involved.)

So substitute into: $\qquad\qquad\qquad 4x + y = 11$

which gives: $\qquad\qquad\qquad\qquad 8 + y = 11$

Step 5: Solve this equation: $\qquad\qquad\qquad y = 3$

Step 6: Test our solution in the original equations. So substitute $x = 2$ and $y = 3$ into $6x + y$, which gives $12 + 3 = 15$ and into $4x + y$, which gives $8 + 3 = 11$. These are correct, so we can confidently say the solution is $x = 2$ and $y = 3$.

EXAMPLE 18

Solve these equations. $\qquad\qquad 5x + y = 22 \qquad\qquad (1)$

$\qquad\qquad\qquad\qquad\qquad\qquad 2x - y = 6 \qquad\qquad (2)$

Step 1: Both equations have the same y-coefficient but with *different* signs so there is no need to balance them.

Step 2: As the signs are different we *add* the two equations, to eliminate the y-terms.

$(1) + (2) \qquad\qquad\qquad\qquad 7x = 28$

Step 3: Solve this equation: $\qquad\qquad x = 4$

Step 4: Substitute $x = 4$ into one of the original equations, $5x + y = 22$,

which gives: $\qquad\qquad\qquad\qquad 20 + y = 22$

Step 5: Solve this equation: $\qquad\qquad\qquad y = 2$

Step 6: Test our solution by putting $x = 4$ and $y = 2$ into the original equations, $2x - y$, which gives $8 - 2 = 6$ and $5x + y$ which gives $20 + 2 = 22$. These are correct, so our solution is $x = 4$ and $y = 2$.

Substitution method

This is an alternative method (which is covered again in the Year 11 book, page 122). Which method you use depends very much on the coefficients of the variables and the way that the equations are written in the first place. There are five steps in the substitute method. Step 1 is to rearrange one of the equations into the form $y = \ldots$ or $x = \ldots$ Step 2 is to substitute the right hand side of this equation into the other equation in place of the variable on the left hand side. Step 3 is to expand and solve this equation. Step 4 is to substitute the value into the $y = \ldots$ or $x = \ldots$ equation. Step 5 is to check that the values work in both original equations.

EXAMPLE 19

Solve the simultaneous equations $y = 2x + 3$, $3x + 4y = 1$.

Because the first equation is in the form $y = \ldots$ it suggests that the substitution method should be used.

Equations should still be labelled to help with explaining the method

$$y = 2x + 3 \qquad\qquad (1)$$

$$3x + 4y = 1 \qquad\qquad (2)$$

Step 1: As equation (1) is in the form $y = \ldots$ there is no need to rearrange an equation.

Step 2: Substitute the right hand side of equation (1) into equation (2) for the variable y.

$$3x + 4(2x + 3) = 1$$

Step 3: Expand and solve the equation. $\qquad 3x + 8x + 12 = 1$, $11x = -11$, $x = -1$

Step 4: Substitute $x = -1$ into $y = 2x + 3$: $\qquad y = -2 + 3 = 1$

Step 5: Test the values in $y = 2x + 3$ which gives $1 = -2 + 3$ and $3x + 4y = 1$, which gives $-3 + 4 = 1$. These are correct so the solution is $x = -1$ and $y = 1$.

EXERCISE 5J

In this exercise the coefficients of one of the variables in questions **1** to **9** are the same so there is no need to balance them. Subtract the equations when the identical terms have the same sign. Add the equations when the identical terms have opposite signs. In questions **10** to **12** use the substitution method.

Solve these simultaneous equations.

1 $\quad 4x + y = 17$
$\quad\quad 2x + y = 9$

2 $\quad 5x + 2y = 13$
$\quad\quad x + 2y = 9$

3 $\quad 2x + y = 7$
$\quad\quad 5x - y = 14$

4 $\quad 3x + 2y = 11$
$\quad\quad 2x - 2y = 14$

5 $\quad 3x - 4y = 17$
$\quad\quad x - 4y = 3$

6 $\quad 3x + 2y = 16$
$\quad\quad x - 2y = 4$

7 $\quad x + 3y = 9$
$\quad\quad x + y = 6$

8 $\quad 2x + 5y = 16$
$\quad\quad 2x + 3y = 8$

9 $\quad 3x - y = 9$
$\quad\quad 5x + y = 11$

10 $\quad 2x + 5y = 37$
$\quad\quad\quad y = 11 - 2x$

11 $\quad 4x - 3y = 7$
$\quad\quad\quad x = 13 - 3y$

12 $\quad 4x - y = 17$
$\quad\quad\quad x = 2 + y$

You were able to solve all the pairs of equations in Exercise 5J simply by adding or subtracting the equations in each pair, or just by substituting without rearranging. This does not always happen. The next examples show you what to do when there are no identical terms to begin with, or when you need to rearrange.

EXAMPLE 20

Solve these equations.

$$3x + 2y = 18 \qquad (1)$$
$$2x - y = 5 \qquad (2)$$

Step 1: Multiply equation (2) by 2. There are other ways to balance the coefficients but this is the easiest and leads to less work later. You will get used to which will be the best way to balance the coefficients.

$$2 \times (2) \qquad 4x - 2y = 10 \qquad (3)$$

Label this equation as number (3).

Be careful to multiply every term and not just the y term, it sometimes helps to write:

$$2 \times (2x - y = 5) \quad \Rightarrow \quad 4x - 2y = 10 \qquad (3)$$

Step 2: As the signs of the y-terms are opposite, add the equations.

$$(1) + (3) \qquad 7x = 28$$

Be careful to add the correct equations. This is why labelling them is useful.

Step 3: Solve this equation: $\qquad x = 4$

Step 4: Substitute $x = 4$ into any equation, say $2x - y = 5 \quad \Rightarrow \quad 8 - y = 5$

Step 5: Solve this equation: $\qquad y = 3$

Step 6: Check: (1), $3 \times 4 + 2 \times 3 = 18$ and (2), $2 \times 4 - 3 = 5$, which are correct so the solution is $x = 4$ and $y = 3$.

EXAMPLE 21

Solve the simultaneous equations $3x + y = 5$ and $5x - 2y = 12$ using the substitution method.

Looking at the equations there is only one that could be sensibly rearranged without involving fractions.

Step 1: Rearrange $\qquad 3x + y = 5$ to get $y = 5 - 3x \qquad (1)$

Step 2: Substitute $\qquad y = 5 - 3x$ into $5x - 2y = 12 \qquad (2)$

$$5x - 2(5 - 3x) = 12$$

Step 3: Expand and solve $\qquad 5x - 10 + 6x = 12 \quad \Rightarrow \quad 11x = 22 \quad \Rightarrow \quad x = 2$

Step 4: Substitute into equation (1): $y = 5 - 3 \times 2 = 5 - 6 = -1$

Step 5: Check: (1), $3 \times 2 + -1 = 5$ and (2), $5 \times 2 - 2 \times -1 = 10 + 2 = 12$, which are correct so the solution is $x = 2$ and $y = -1$.

EXERCISE 5K

Solve questions **1** to **3** by the substitution method and the rest by first changing one of the equations in each pair to obtain identical terms, and then adding or subtracting the equations to eliminate those terms.

1 $5x + 2y = 4$

$4x - y = 11$

2 $4x + 3y = 37$

$2x + y = 17$

3 $x + 3y = 7$

$2x - y = 7$

4 $2x + 3y = 19$

$6x + 2y = 22$

5 $5x - 2y = 26$

$3x - y = 15$

6 $10x - y = 3$

$3x + 2y = 17$

7 $3x + 5y = 15$

$x + 3y = 7$

8 $3x + 4y = 7$

$4x + 2y = 1$

9 $5x - 2y = 24$

$3x + y = 21$

10 $5x - 2y = 4$

$3x - 6y = 6$

11 $2x + 3y = 13$

$4x + 7y = 31$

12 $3x - 2y = 3$

$5x + 6y = 12$

There are also cases where *both* equations have to be changed to obtain identical terms. The next example shows you how this is done.

Note the substitution method is not suitable for these type of equations as you end up with fractional terms.

EXAMPLE 22

Solve these equations.

$$4x + 3y = 27 \quad (1)$$

$$5x - 2y = 5 \quad (2)$$

Both equations have to be changed to obtain identical terms in either x or y. However, we can see that if we make the y-coefficients the same, we will add the equations. This is always safer than subtraction, so this is obviously the better choice. We do this by multiplying the first equation by 2 (the y-coefficient of the other equation) and the second equation by 3 (the y-coefficient of the other equation).

Step 1: (1) × 2 or 2 × (4x + 3y = 27) ⟹ $8x + 6y = 54$ (3)

(2) × 3 or 3 × (5x − 2y = 5) ⟹ $15x - 6y = 15$ (4)

Label the new equations (3) and (4).

Step 2: Eliminate one of the variables: (3) + (4) $23x = 69$

Step 3: Solve the equation: $x = 3$

Step 4: Substitute into equation (1): $12 + 3y = 27$

Step 5: Solve the equation: $y = 5$

Step 6: Check: (1), $4 \times 3 + 3 \times 5 = 12 + 15 = 27$, and (2), $5 \times 3 - 2 \times 5 = 15 - 10 = 5$, which are correct so the solution is $x = 3$ and $y = 5$.

EXERCISE 5L

Solve the following simultaneous equations.

1 $2x + 5y = 15$
    $3x - 2y = 13$

2 $2x + 3y = 30$
    $5x + 7y = 71$

3 $2x - 3y = 15$
    $5x + 7y = 52$

4 $3x - 2y = 15$
    $2x - 3y = 5$

5 $5x - 3y = 14$
    $4x - 5y = 6$

6 $3x + 2y = 28$
    $2x + 7y = 47$

7 $2x + y = 4$
    $x - y = 5$

8 $5x + 2y = 11$
    $3x + 4y = 8$

9 $x - 2y = 4$
    $3x - y = -3$

10 $3x + 2y = 2$
    $2x + 6y = 13$

11 $6x + 2y = 14$
    $3x - 5y = 10$

12 $2x + 4y = 15$
    $x + 5y = 21$

13 $3x - y = 5$
    $x + 3y = -20$

14 $3x - 4y = 4.5$
    $2x + 2y = 10$

15 $x - 5y = 15$
    $3x - 7y = 17$

Solving problems by using simultaneous equations

We are now going to meet a type of problem which has to be expressed as a pair of simultaneous equations so that it can be solved. The next example shows you how to tackle such a problem.

EXAMPLE 23

On holiday last year, I was talking over breakfast to two families about how much it cost them to go to the theatre. They couldn't remember how much was charged for each adult or each child, but they could both remember what they had paid altogether.

The Advani family, consisting of Mr and Mrs Advani with their daughter Rupa, paid £23.

The Shaw family, consisting of Mrs Shaw with her two children, Len and Sue, paid £17.50.

How much would I have to pay for my wife, my four children and myself?

We make a pair of simultaneous equations from the situation as follows.

Let x be the cost of an adult ticket, and y be the cost of a child's ticket. Then

$2x + y = 23$ for the Advani family

and $x + 2y = 17.5$ for the Shaw family

We solve these equations just as we have done in the previous examples, to obtain

$x = £9.50$ and $y = £4$. I can now find my cost, which will be

$(2 \times £9.50) + (4 \times £4) = £35$.

EXERCISE 5M

Read each situation carefully, then make a pair of simultaneous equations in order to solve the problem.

1 Amul and Kim have £10.70 between them. Amul has £3.70 more than Kim. Let x be the amount Amul has and y be the amount Kim has. Set up a pair of simultaneous equations. How much does each have?

2 The two people in front of me at the Post Office were both buying stamps. One person bought 10 second-class and five first-class stamps at a total cost of £3.45. The other bought eight second-class and 10 first-class stamps at a total cost of £4.38.

   a Let x be the cost of second-class stamps and y be the cost of first-class stamps. Set up two simultaneous equations.

   b How much did I pay for 3 second-class and 4 first-class stamps?

3 At a local tea room I couldn't help noticing that at one table, where the customers had eaten six buns and had three teas, the bill came to £4.35. At another table, the customers had eaten 11 buns and had seven teas at a total cost of £8.80.

   a Let x be the cost of a bun and y be the cost of a cup of tea. Show the situation as a pair of simultaneous equations.

   b My family and I had five buns and six teas. What did it cost us?

4 Three chews and four bubblies cost 72p. Five chews and two bubblies cost 64p. What would three chews and five bubblies cost?

5 On a nut-and-bolt production line, all the nuts weighed the same and all the bolts weighed the same. An order of 50 nuts and 60 bolts weighed 10.6 kg. An order of 40 nuts and 30 bolts weighed 6.5 kg. What should an order of 60 nuts and 50 bolts weigh?

6 A taxi firm charges a fixed amount plus so much per mile. A journey of 6 miles costs £3.70. A journey of 10 miles costs £5.10. What would be the cost of a journey of 8 miles?

7 Two members of the same church went to the same shop to buy material to make Christingles. One bought 200 oranges and 220 candles at a cost of £65.60. The other bought 210 oranges and 200 candles at a cost of £63.30. They only needed 200 of each. How much should it have cost them?

8 When you book Bingham Hall for a conference, you pay a fixed booking fee plus a charge for each delegate at the conference. The total charge for a conference with 65 delegates was £192.50. The total charge for a conference with 40 delegates was £180. What will be the charge for a conference with 70 delegates?

9 My mother-in-law uses this formula to cook a turkey:

$$T = a + bW$$

where T is the cooking time (minutes), W is the weight of the turkey (kg), and a and b are constants. She says it takes 4 hours 30 minutes to cook a 12 kg turkey, and 3 hours 10 minutes to cook an 8 kg turkey. How long will it take to cook a 5 kg turkey?

Rearranging formulae

In this section you will learn how to:

- rearrange formulae using the same methods as for solving equations

Key words

expression
rearrange
subject
transpose
variable

The **subject** of a formula is the **variable** (letter) in the formula which stands on its own, usually on the left-hand side of the equals sign. For example, x is the subject of each of the following equations.

$$x = 5t + 4 \qquad x = 4(2y - 7) \qquad x = \frac{1}{t}$$

If we wish to change the existing subject to a different variable, we have to **rearrange** (**transpose**) the formula to get that variable on the left-hand side. We do this by using the same rules as for solving equations. Move the terms concerned from one side of the equals sign to the other. The main difference is that when you solve an equation each step gives a numerical value. When you rearrange a formula each step gives an algebraic **expression**.

EXAMPLE 24

Make m the subject of this formula.	$T = m - 3$
Move the 3 away from the m.	$T + 3 = m$
Reverse the formula.	$m = T + 3$

EXAMPLE 25

From the formula $P = 4t$, express t in terms of P.

(This is another common way of asking you to make t the subject.)

Divide both sides by 4: $\qquad \dfrac{P}{4} = \dfrac{4t}{4}$

Reverse the formula: $\qquad t = \dfrac{P}{4}$

EXAMPLE 26

From the formula $C = 2m^2 + 3$, make m the subject.

Move the 3 away from the $2m^2$: $\qquad C - 3 = 2m^2$

Divide both sides by 2: $\qquad \dfrac{C - 3}{2} = \dfrac{2m^2}{2}$

Reverse the formula: $\qquad m^2 = \dfrac{C - 3}{2}$

Square root both sides: $\qquad m = \sqrt{\dfrac{C - 3}{2}}$

EXERCISE 5N

1 $T = 3k$ Make k the subject.

2 $X = y - 1$ Express y in terms of X.

3 $Q = \dfrac{p}{3}$ Express p in terms of Q.

4 $A = 4r + 9$ Make r the subject.

5 $W = 3n - 1$ Make n the subject.

6 $p = m + t$ **a** Make m the subject.   **b** Make t the subject.

7 $g = \dfrac{m}{v}$ Make m the subject.

8 $t = m^2$ Make m the subject.

9 $C = 2\pi r$ Make r the subject.

10 $A = bh$ Make b the subject.

11 $P = 2l + 2w$ Make l the subject.

12 $m = p^2 + 2$ Make p the subject.

13 $v = u + at$ **a** Make a the subject.   **b** Make t the subject.

14 $A = \dfrac{1}{4} \pi d^2,$ Make d the subject.

15 $W = 3n + t$ **a** Make n the subject.   **b** Express t in terms of n and W.

16 $x = 5y - w$ **a** Make y the subject.   **b** Express w in terms of x and y.

17 $k = 2p^2$ Make p the subject.

18 $v = u^2 - t$ **a** Make t the subject.   **b** Make u the subject.

19 $k = m + n^2$ **a** Make m the subject.   **b** Make n the subject.

20 $T = 5r^2$ Make r the subject.

21 $K = 5n^2 + w$ **a** Make w the subject.   **b** Make n the subject.

> **HINTS AND TIPS**
>
> Remember about inverse operations, and the rule "change sides, change signs".

1 **a** Multiply out $\qquad$ $3(4x - 5)$
   b Solve $\qquad$ $3(4x - 5) = 27$

2 Solve the equation $\qquad$ $7x - 1 = 3(x + 2)$

3 **a** Expand the brackets $\quad p(q - p^2)$
   b Expand and simplify $\quad 5(3p + 2) - 2(5p - 3)$
   Edexcel, Question 3, Paper 5 Higher, November 2004

4 **a** Expand and simplify $\quad 3(4x - 3) + 2(x + 5)$
   b Expand $\qquad$ $2x(x^2 - 3x)$
   c Expand and simplify $\quad (x + 2)(x - 1)$

5 **a** Make t the subject of the formula $\quad s = 2 - 3t$
   b Solve the equation $\qquad \frac{1}{3}x - 4 = \frac{1}{6}x + 2$

6 Solve the equations
   a $\dfrac{15 - x}{4} = 1.3$
   b $3(y - 2) = 15 - 4y$
   c $2(3x - 1) + 3(x + 4) = 4(3x - 1) + 2(x - 3)$

7 A cuboid has a square base of side x cm. The height of the cuboid is 1 cm more than the length x cm. The volume of the cuboid is 230 cm³.

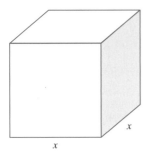

   a Show that $\qquad$ $x^3 + x^2 = 230$
   The equation $x^3 + x^2 = 230$ has a solution between $x = 5$ and $x = 6$.
   b Use a trial and improvement method to find this solution. Give your answer correct to 1 decimal place. You must show *all* your working.
   Edexcel, Question 4, Paper 6 Higher, June 2003

8 Solve the equations
   a $\dfrac{14 - t}{5} = 4$
   b $\dfrac{3x + 9}{3} - \dfrac{2x + 4}{5} = 4$

9 **a** Expand and simplify
   $3(4y - 2) + 2(y + 5)$
   b Expand
   $t^3(5 - 2t)$

10 Make t the subject of the formula $\quad t^2 + s = 10$

11 Make t the subject of the formula
   $5t + 3p = 5p - 7$
   Simplify your answer as much as possible.

12 A company bought a van that had a value of £12 000. Each year the value of the van depreciates by 25%.
   a Work out the value of the van at the end of three years.
   The company bought a new truck.
   Each year the value of the truck depreciates by 20%. The value of the new truck can be multiplied by a single number to find its value at the end of four years.
   b Find this single number as a decimal.
   Edexcel, Question 12, Paper 6 Higher, June 2004

13 Wendy does a 25 kilometre mountain race. She ran x kilometres to the top of the mountain at a speed of 9 km/h and then y kilometres to the finish at a speed of 12 km/h. She finishes the race in 2 hours and 20 minutes.
   By setting up two simultaneous equations in x and y, find how long it took Wendy to reach the top of the mountain.

14 Consider the simultaneous equations
   $y = x + 1$
   $y^2 = x + 6$
   a Show why x is the solution of the equation $x^2 + x - 5 = 0$
   b Use trial and improvement to find a positive solution to $x^2 + x - 5 = 0$. Give your answer to 1 decimal place.

WORKED EXAM QUESTIONS

1 $4x + 3y = 6$
$3x - 2y = 13$
Solve these simultaneous equations algebraically. Show your method clearly.

$4x + 3y = 23$ (1)

$3x - 2y = 13$ (2)

> Label the equations and decide on the best way to get the coefficients of one variable the same.

(1) × 2 $8x + 6y = 46$ (3)

(2) × 3 $9x - 6y = 39$ (4)

(3) + (4) $17x = 85$

> Making the y coefficients the same will be the most efficient way as the resulting equations will be added.

$x = 5$

Substitute into (1) $20 + 3y = 23$

$y = 1$

> Solve the resulting equation and substitute into one of the original equations to find the other value.

$4 \times 5 + 3 \times 1 = 23$ ✓

$3 \times 5 - 2 \times 1 = 13$ ✓

> Check that these values work in the original equations

2 Temperatures can be measured in degrees Celsius (°C), degrees Fahrenheit (°F) or degrees Kelvin (°K). The relationships between the scales of temperature are given by
$C = \dfrac{5(F - 32)}{9}$ and
$K = C + 273$

Express F
  i in terms of C
  ii in terms of K

i $9C = 5(F - 32)$
$9C = 5F - 160$
$5F = 9C + 160$
$F = \dfrac{9C + 160}{5}$

> Multiply both sides of the first equation by 9, then expand the bracket. Add 160 to both sides and change the equation round. Divide both sides by 5. Make sure you divide all of the right-hand side by 5.

ii $C = K - 273$
$F = \dfrac{9(K - 273) + 160}{5}$
$F = \dfrac{9K - 2457 + 160}{5}$
$F = \dfrac{9K - 2297}{5}$

> Make C the subject of the second equation. Substitute for C in the answer to part **i**, expand the bracket and tidy up the top line of the fraction.

Julia starts her new job at a riding stables, where she is responsible for six new horses. She measures the length and girth of each horse, and then uses the bodyweight calculator to work out its weight in kilograms. She then uses the feed chart and worming paste instructions to calculate how much feed and worming paste each horse needs.

Copy the stewardship table and help her to complete it for these six horses.

Summer
girth: 220 cm
length: 142 cm
work: medium

Sally
girth: 190 cm
length: 95 cm
work: hard

Skip
girth: 200 cm
length: 114 cm
work: hard

Simon
girth: 180 cm
length: 124 cm
work: medium

Stewardship table

Body weight of horse in (kg)	Weight of feed (in kg) at different levels of work		Horse	Weight in kg	Feed in kg	Worming paste in tubes
	Medium work	Hard work				
300	2.4	3.0	Summer			
350	2.8	3.5	Sally			
400	3.2	4.0	Skip			
450	3.6	4.5	Simon			
500	4.0	5.0	Barney			
Extra feed per 50 kg	300 g	400 g	Teddy			

Instructions for using the bodyweight calculator

Put a ruler from the girth line to the length line. Where the ruler crosses the weight line is the approximate weight of the horse. Give each horse's weight to the nearest 10 kg.

Barney
girth: 160 cm
length: 110 cm
work: medium

Teddy
girth: 190 cm
length: 140 cm
work: hard

Bodyweight Calculator

Girth (cm)	Weight (km)	Length (cm)
111.8		71.75
112	115.7	75
120	125	80
130	150	85
140	175	90
	200	
150	225	95
	250	100
160	275	
	300	105
170	325	
	350	110
180	400	115
	450	
190	500	120
	550	
200	600	125
	650	
210	700	130
	750	
220	800	135
	850	
230	900	140
	950	
	1000	145
240	1045.6	150
246.4		150.5

Worming paste instructions

Weight of horse (w) in kg	Amount of paste
w < 150	0.25 of tube
150 ≤ w < 300	0.5 of tube
300 ≤ w < 450	0.75 of tube
continue increasing dosage of paste, 0.25 of tube for every 150 kg	

During her first day, Julia sees a group of three adults and two children pay £136.50 for a 1½ hour ride. Then another group of four adults and five children pay £241.50 to go on the same ride.

Julia is hopeless at simultaneous equations. Work out for her the cost for an adult and the cost for a child to go on this ride.

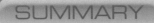

GRADE YOURSELF

D Able to expand a linear bracket

D Able to substitute numbers into expressions

D Able to factorise simple linear expresions

D Able to solve simple linear equations which include the variable inside a bracket

D Able to solve linear equations where the variable occurs in the numerator of a fraction

D Able to solve linear equations where the variable appears on both sides of the equals sign.

C Able to expand and simplify expressions

C Able to solve equations using trial and improvement

C Able to rearrange simple formulae

B Able to solve two simultaneous linear equations

B Able to rearrange more complicated formulae

A Able to set up and solve two simultaneous equations from a practical problem

What you should know now

- How to manipulate and simplify algebraic expressions, including those with linear brackets
- How to factorise linear expressions
- How to solve all types of linear equations
- How to find a solution to equations by trial and improvement
- How to set up and/or solve a pair of linear simultaneous equations

Pythagoras and trigonometry

This chapter will show you ...

● how to use Pythagoras' theorem in right-angled triangles

● how to solve problems using Pythagoras' theorem

● how to use trigonometric ratios in right-angled triangles

● how to use trigonometry to solve problems

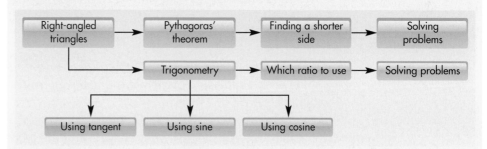

What you should already know

● how to find the square and square root of a number

● how to round numbers to a suitable degree of accuracy

Quick check

Use your calculator to evaluate the following, giving your answers to one decimal place.

1 2.3^2

2 15.7^2

3 0.78^2

4 $\sqrt{8}$

5 $\sqrt{260}$

6 $\sqrt{0.5}$

In this section you will learn how to:

- calculate the length of the hypotenuse in a right-angled triangle

Key words

hypotenuse
Pythagoras' theorem

Pythagoras, who was a philosopher as well as a mathematician, was born in 580 BC, on the island of Samos in Greece. He later moved to Crotona (Italy), where he established the Pythagorean Brotherhood, which was a secret society devoted to politics, mathematics and astronomy. It is said that when he discovered his famous theorem, he was so full of joy that he showed his gratitude to the gods by sacrificing a hundred oxen.

Consider squares being drawn on each side of a right-angled triangle, with sides 3 cm, 4 cm and 5 cm.

The longest side is called the **hypotenuse** and is always opposite the right angle.

Pythagoras' theorem can then be stated as follows:

For any right-angled triangle, the area of the square drawn on the hypotenuse is equal to the sum of the areas of the squares drawn on the other two sides.

The form in which most of your parents would have learnt the theorem when they were at school – and which is still in use today – is as follows:

In any right-angled triangle, the square of the hypotenuse is equal to the sum of the squares of the other two sides.

Pythagoras' theorem is more usually written as a formula:

$$c^2 = a^2 + b^2$$

Remember that Pythagoras' theorem can only be used in right-angled triangles.

Finding the hypotenuse

EXAMPLE 1

Find the length of the hypotenuse, marked x on the diagram.

Using Pythagoras' theorem gives

$$x^2 = 8^2 + 5.2^2 \text{ cm}^2$$
$$= 64 + 27.04 \text{ cm}^2$$
$$= 91.04 \text{ cm}^2$$

So $x = \sqrt{91.04} = 9.5$ cm (1 decimal place)

EXERCISE 6A

For each of the following triangles, calculate the length of the hypotenuse, x, giving your answers to one decimal place.

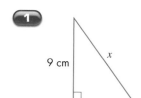

1

9 cm x

5 cm

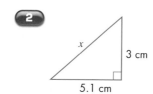

2

x 3 cm

5.1 cm

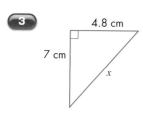

3

4.8 cm

7 cm

x

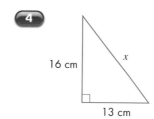

4

16 cm x

13 cm

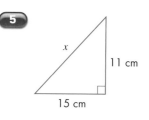

5

x 11 cm

15 cm

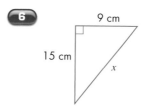

6

9 cm

15 cm

x

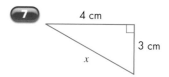

7

4 cm

3 cm

x

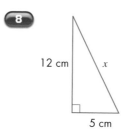

8

12 cm x

5 cm

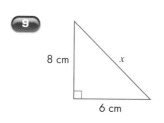

9

8 cm x

6 cm

The last three examples give whole number answers. Sets of whole numbers that obey Pythagoras' theorem are called Pythagorean triples. For example,

3, 4, 5   5, 12, 13   and   6, 8, 10.

Note that 6, 8, 10 are respectively multiples of 3, 4, 5.

Finding a shorter side

In this section you will learn how to:
- calculate the length of a shorter side in a right-angled triangle

Key word
Pythagoras' theorem

By rearranging the formula for **Pythagoras' theorem**, the length of one of the shorter sides can easily be calculated.

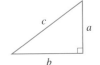

$$c^2 = a^2 + b^2$$

So, $a^2 = c^2 - b^2$ or $b^2 = c^2 - a^2$

EXAMPLE 2

Find the length x.

x is one of the shorter sides

So using Pythagoras' theorem gives

$$x^2 = 15^2 - 11^2 \text{ cm}^2$$
$$= 225 - 121 \text{ cm}^2$$
$$= 104 \text{ cm}^2$$

So $x = \sqrt{104} = 10.2$ cm (one decimal place)

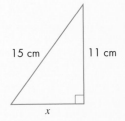

EXERCISE 6B

1 For each of the following triangles, calculate the length x, giving your answers to one decimal place.

a

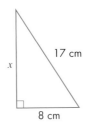

17 cm

x

8 cm

b

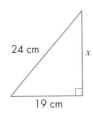

24 cm

x

19 cm

HINTS AND TIPS

In these examples you are finding a short side. The square of the other short side is subtracted from the square of the hypotenuse in every case.

c

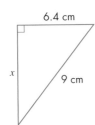

6.4 cm

x

9 cm

d

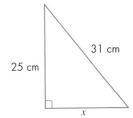

31 cm

25 cm

x

2 For each of the following triangles, calculate the length *x*, giving your answers to one decimal place.

a

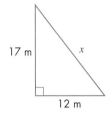

17 m

x

12 m

b

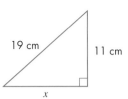

19 cm

11 cm

x

HINTS AND TIPS

These examples are a mixture. Make sure you combine the squares of the sides correctly.

c

17 m

x

23 m

d

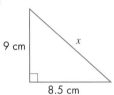

9 cm

x

8.5 cm

3 For each of the following triangles, find the length marked *x*.

a

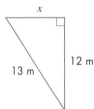

x

12 m

13 m

b

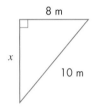

8 m

x

10 m

c

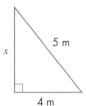

5 m

x

4 m

d

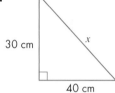

30 cm

x

40 cm

6.3

Solving problems using Pythagoras' theorem

In this section you will learn how to:
- solve problems using Pythagoras' theorem

Key words
3-D
isoceles
   triangle
Pythagoras'
   theorem

Pythagoras' theorem can be used to solve certain practical problems. When a problem involves two lengths only, follow these steps.

- Draw a diagram for the problem that includes a right-angled triangle.

- Look at the diagram and decide which side has to be found: the hypotenuse or one of the shorter sides. Label the unknown side *x*.

- If it's the hypotenuse, then square both numbers, add the squares and take the square root of the sum.

- If it's one of the shorter sides, then square both numbers, subtract the squares and take the square root of the difference.

- Finally, round off the answer to a suitable degree of accuracy.

EXAMPLE 3

A plane leaves Manchester airport heading due east. It flies 160 km before turning due north. It then flies a further 280 km and lands. What is the distance of the return flight if the plane flies straight back to Manchester airport?

First, sketch the situation.

Using Pythagoras' theorem gives

$$x^2 = 160^2 + 280^2 \text{ km}^2$$
$$= 25\,600 + 78\,400 \text{ km}^2$$
$$= 104\,000 \text{ km}^2$$

So $x = \sqrt{104\,000} = 322$ km (3 significant figures)

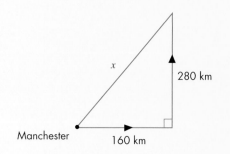

Remember the following tips when solving problems.

- Always sketch the right-angled triangle you need. Sometimes, the triangle is already drawn for you but some problems involve other lines and triangles that may confuse you. So identify which right-angled triangle you need and sketch it separately.

- Label the triangle with necessary information, such as the length of its sides, taken from the question. Label the unknown side x.

- Set out your solution as in Example 3. Avoid short cuts, since they often cause errors. You gain marks in your examination for clearly showing how you are applying Pythagoras' theorem to the problem.

- Round your answer off to a suitable degree of accuracy.

EXERCISE 6C

 A ladder, 12 metres long, leans against a wall. The ladder reaches 10 metres up the wall. How far away from the foot of the wall is the foot of the ladder?

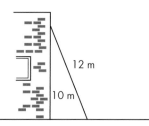

2 A model football pitch is 2 metres long and 0.5 metre wide. How long is the diagonal?

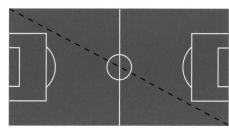

3 How long is the diagonal of a square with a side of 8 metres?

4 A ship going from a port to a lighthouse steams 15 km east and 12 km north. How far is the lighthouse from the port?

5 Some pedestrians want to get from point X on one road to point Y on another. The two roads meet at right angles.

a If they follow the roads, how far will they walk?

b Instead of walking along the road, they take the shortcut, XY. Find the length of the shortcut.

c How much distance do they save?

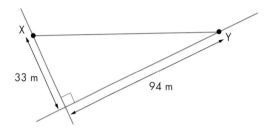

6 A mast on a sailboat is strengthened by a wire (called a stay), as shown on the diagram. The mast is 10 m tall and the stay is 11 m long. How far from the base of the mast does the stay reach?

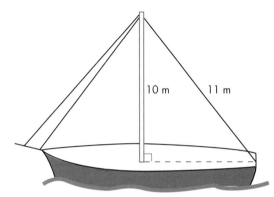

7 A ladder, 4 m long, is put up against a wall.

a How far up the wall will it reach when the foot of the ladder is 1 m away from the wall?

b When it reaches 3.6 m up the wall, how far is the foot of the ladder away from the wall?

8 A pole, 8 m high, is supported by metal wires, each 8.6 m long, attached to the top of the pole. How far from the foot of the pole are the wires fixed to the ground?

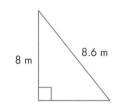

9 How long is the line that joins the two coordinates A(13, 6) and B(1, 1)?

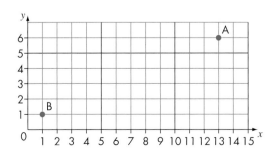

10 The regulation for safe use of ladders states that: *the foot of a 5 m ladder must be placed between 1.6 m and 2.1 m from the foot of the wall.*

   a What is the maximum height the ladder can safely reach up the wall?

   b What is the minimum height the ladder can safely reach up the wall?

11 Is the triangle with sides 7 cm, 24 cm and 25 cm, a right-angled triangle?

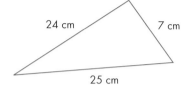

Pythagoras' theorem and isosceles triangles

This section shows you how to to use Pythagoras' theorem in isosceles triangles.

Every **isosceles triangle** has a line of symmetry that divides the triangle into two congruent right-angled triangles. So when you are faced with a problem involving an isosceles triangle, be aware that you are quite likely to have to split that triangle down the middle to create a right-angled triangle which will help you to solve the problem.

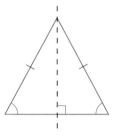

EXAMPLE 4

Calculate the area of this triangle.

It is an isosceles triangle and you need to calculate its height to find its area.

First split the triangle into two right-angled triangles to find its height.

Let the height be x.

Then, using Pythagoras' theorem,

$$x^2 = 7.5^2 - 3^2 \text{ cm}^2$$
$$= 56.25 - 9 \text{ cm}^2$$
$$= 47.25 \text{ cm}^2$$

So $x = \sqrt{47.25} \text{ cm}$

$x = 6.87 \text{ cm}$

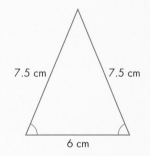

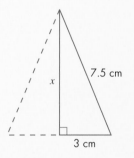

Keep the accurate figure in the calculator memory.

The area of the triangle is $\frac{1}{2} \times 6 \times 6.87 \text{ cm}^2$ (from the calculator memory), which is 20.6 cm^2 (1 decimal place)

EXERCISE 6D

1 Calculate the areas of these isosceles triangles.

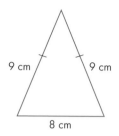
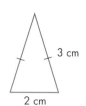
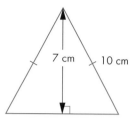

a 9 cm 9 cm 8 cm

b 3 cm 2 cm

c 7 cm 10 cm

2 Calculate the area of an isosceles triangle whose sides are 8 cm, 8 cm and 6 cm.

3 Calculate the area of an equilateral triangle of side 6 cm.

4 An isosceles triangle has sides of 5 cm and 6 cm.

   a Sketch the two different isosceles triangles that fit this data.

   b Which of the two triangles has the greater area?

5 a Sketch a regular hexagon, showing all its lines of symmetry.

   b Calculate the area of the hexagon if its side is 8 cm.

6 Calculate the area of a hexagon of side 10 cm.

7 Calculate the lengths marked x in these isosceles triangles.

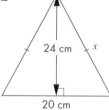
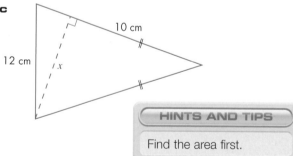

a 12 cm 13 cm x

b 24 cm x 20 cm

c 10 cm 12 cm x

> **HINTS AND TIPS**
>
> Find the area first.

Pythagoras' theorem in three dimensions

This section shows you how to solve problems in **3-D** using Pythagoras' theorem.

In your GCSE examinations, there may be questions which involve applying Pythagoras' theorem in 3-D situations. Such questions are usually accompanied by clearly labelled diagrams, which will help you to identify the lengths needed for your solutions.

You deal with these 3-D problems in exactly the same way as 2-D problems.

- Identify the right-angled triangle you need.

- Redraw this triangle and label it with the given lengths and the length to be found, usually x or y.

- From your diagram, decide whether it is the hypotenuse or one of the shorter sides which has to be found.

- Solve the problem, rounding off to a suitable degree of accuracy.

EXAMPLE 5

What is the longest piece of straight wire that can be stored in this box measuring 30 cm by 15 cm by 20 cm?

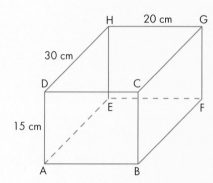

The longest distance across this box is any one of the diagonals AG, DF, CE or HB.

Let us take AG.

First, identify a right-angled triangle containing AG and draw it.

This gives a triangle AFG, which contains two lengths you do not know, AG and AF. Let AG = x and AF = y.

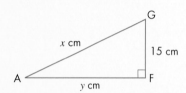

Next identify a right-angled triangle that contains the side AF and draw it.

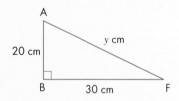

This gives a triangle ABF. You can now find AF.

By Pythagoras' theorem

$$y^2 = 30^2 + 20^2 \text{ cm}^2$$

$$y^2 = 1300 \text{ cm}^2 \text{ (there is no need to find } y)$$

Now find AG using triangle AFG.

By Pythagoras' theorem

$$x^2 = y^2 + 15^2 \text{ cm}^2$$

$$x^2 = 1300 + 225 = 1525 \text{ cm}^2$$

So $x = 39.1$ cm (1 decimal place)

So, the longest straight wire that can be stored in the box is 39.1 cm.

Note that in any cuboid with sides a, b and c, the length of a diagonal is given by

$$\sqrt{(a^2 + b^2 + c^2)}$$

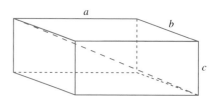

EXERCISE 6E

1 A box measures 8 cm by 12 cm by 5 cm.

    a Calculate the lengths of the following.

        i AC   **ii** BG   **iii** BE

    b Calculate the diagonal distance BH.

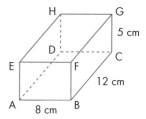

2 A garage is 5 m long, 3 m wide and 3 m high. Can a 7 m long pole be stored in it?

3 Spike, a spider, is at the corner S of the wedge shown in the diagram. Fred, a fly, is at the corner F of the same wedge.

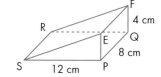

    a Calculate the two distances Spike would have to travel to get to Fred if she used the edges of the wedge.

    b Calculate the distance Spike would have to travel across the face of the wedge to get directly to Fred.

4 Fred is now at the top of a baked-beans can and Spike is directly below him on the base of the can. To catch Fred by surprise, Spike takes a diagonal route round the can. How far does Spike travel?

> **HINTS AND TIPS**
>
> Imagine the can opened out flat.

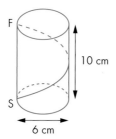

5 A corridor is 3 m wide and turns through a right angle, as in the diagram.

    a What is the longest pole that can be carried along the corridor horizontally?

    b If the corridor is 3 m high, what is the longest pole that can be carried along in any direction?

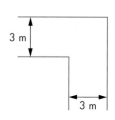

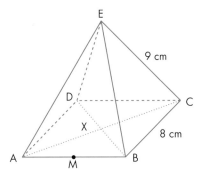

6 The diagram shows a square-based pyramid with base length 8 cm and sloping edges 9 cm. M is the mid-point of the side AB, X is the mid-point of the base, and E is directly above X.

a Calculate the length of the diagonal AC.

b Calculate EX, the height of the pyramid.

c Using triangle ABE, calculate the length EM.

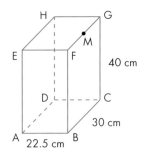

7 The diagram shows a cuboid with sides of 40 cm, 30 cm, and 22.5 cm. M is the mid-point of the side FG. Calculate (or write down) these lengths, giving your answers to three significant figures if necessary.

a AH   **b** AG   **c** AM   **d** HM

(6.4) Trigonometric ratios

In this section you will learn how to:

- use the three trigonometric ratios

Key words

adjacent side
cosine
hypotenuse
opposite side
sine
tangent
trigonometry

Trigonometry is concerned with the calculation of sides and angles in triangles, and involves the use of three important ratios: **sine**, **cosine** and **tangent**. These ratios are defined in terms of the sides of a right-angled triangle and an angle. The angle is often written as θ.

In a right-angled triangle

- the side opposite the right angle is called the **hypotenuse** and is the longest side

- the side opposite the angle θ is called the **opposite side**

- the other side next to both the right angle and the angle θ is called the **adjacent side**.

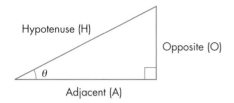

The sine, cosine and tangent ratios for θ are defined as

$$\text{sine } \theta = \frac{\text{Opposite}}{\text{Hypotenuse}} \qquad \text{cosine } \theta = \frac{\text{Adjacent}}{\text{Hypotenuse}} \qquad \text{tangent } \theta = \frac{\text{Opposite}}{\text{Adjacent}}$$

These ratios are usually abbreviated as

$$\sin \theta = \frac{O}{H} \qquad \cos \theta = \frac{A}{H} \qquad \tan \theta = \frac{O}{A}$$

These abbreviated forms are also used on calculator keys.

Memorising these formulae may be helped by a mnemonic such as

Silly **O**ld **H**itler **C**ouldn't **A**dvance **H**is **T**roops **O**ver **A**frica

in which the first letter of each word is taken in order to give

$$S = \frac{O}{H} \qquad C = \frac{A}{H} \qquad T = \frac{O}{A}$$

Using your calculator

You can use your calculator to find the sine, cosine and tangent of *any* angle.

To find the sine of an angle, press the key labelled *sin.*

To find the cosine of an angle, press the key labelled *cos.*

To find the tangent of an angle, press the key labelled *tan.*

Make sure you can find sin, cos and tan on your calculator.

Important: Make sure your calculator is working in *degrees.* Depending on the type of calculator used, you need to put it into *degree mode* before you start working on sines, cosines and tangents. This can be done either

- by using the MODE button

- or by pressing the key DRG until DEG is on display.

Try this *now* to make sure you can do it. When it is in degree mode, D or DEG appears on the calculator display.

EXAMPLE 6

Use your calculator to find the sine of 27°, written as sin 27°.

On some scientific calculators, the function is keyed in numbers first

[2] [7] [sin]

The display should read 0.453990499. (You may have more or fewer digits depending on your calculator.) This is 0.454 to three significant figures.

If you have a graphics calculator or an 'algebraic logic' (DAL) calculator, you key in the function as it reads

[sin] [2] [7]

You should get the same value as above. If you don't, then consult your calculator manual or your teacher.

EXAMPLE 7

Use your calculator to find the cosine of 56°, written as cos 56°.

cos 56° = 0.559 192 903 = 0.559 to 3 significant figures

Check that you agree with this, using as many digits as your calculator allows.

EXAMPLE 8

Use your calculator to work out 3 × cos 57°, written as 3 cos 57°.

Depending on your type of calculator, key in either

[3] [×] [5] [7] [cos] [=]   or   [3] [×] [cos] [5] [7] [=]

Check that you get an answer of 1.633 917 105 = 1.63 to 3 significant figures.

EXERCISE 6F

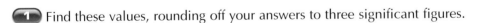

1 Find these values, rounding off your answers to three significant figures.

   a sin 43°   **b** sin 56°   **c** sin 67.2°   **d** sin 90°

   e sin 45°   **f** sin 20°   **g** sin 22°   **h** sin 0°

2 Find these values, rounding off your answers to three significant figures.

   a cos 43°   **b** cos 56°   **c** cos 67.2°   **d** cos 90°

   e cos 45°   **f** cos 20°   **g** cos 22°   **h** cos 0°

3 From your answers to questions **1** and **2**, what angle has the same value for sine and cosine?

4 **a** **i** What is sin 35°?   **ii** What is cos 55°?

     b **i** What is sin 12°?   **ii** What is cos 78°?

     c **i** What is cos 67°?   **ii** What is sin 23°?

     d What connects the values in parts **a**, **b** and **c**?

     e Copy and complete these sentences.

       i sin 15° is the same as cos …

       ii cos 82° is the same as sin …

       iii sin x is the same as cos …

5 Use your calculator to work out the values of

    a tan 43°   **b** tan 56°   **c** tan 67.2°   **d** tan 90°

    e tan 45°   **f** tan 20°   **g** tan 22°   **h** tan 0°

6 Use your calculator to work out the values of the following.

    a sin 73°   **b** cos 26°   **c** tan 65.2°   **d** sin 88°

    e cos 35°   **f** tan 30°   **g** sin 28°   **h** cos 5°

7 What is so different about tan compared with both sin and cos?

8 Use your calculator to work out the values of the following.

    a 5 sin 65°   **b** 6 cos 42°   **c** 6 sin 90°   **d** 5 sin 0°

9 Use your calculator to work out the values of the following.

    a 5 tan 65°   **b** 6 tan 42°   **c** 6 tan 90°   **d** 5 tan 0°

10 Use your calculator to work out the values of the following.

    a 4 sin 63°   **b** 7 tan 52°   **c** 5 tan 80°   **d** 9 cos 8°

11 Use your calculator to work out the values of the following.

    a $\dfrac{5}{\sin 63°}$ **b** $\dfrac{6}{\cos 32°}$ **c** $\dfrac{6}{\sin 90°}$ **d** $\dfrac{5}{\sin 30°}$

12 Use your calculator to work out the values of the following.

    a $\dfrac{3}{\tan 64°}$ **b** $\dfrac{7}{\tan 42°}$ **c** $\dfrac{5}{\tan 89°}$ **d** $\dfrac{6}{\tan 40°}$

13 Use your calculator to work out the values of the following.

    a 8 sin 75°   **b** $\dfrac{19}{\sin 23°}$ **c** 7 cos 71°   **d** $\dfrac{15}{\sin 81°}$

14 Use your calculator to work out the values of the following.

a 8 tan 75°   **b** $\dfrac{19}{\tan 23°}$ **c** 7 tan 71°   **d** $\dfrac{15}{\tan 81°}$

15 Using the following triangles calculate sin x, cos x, and tan x. Leave your answers as fractions.

a
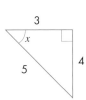

b
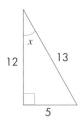

c
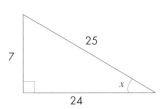

6.5 Calculating angles

In this section you will learn how to:
- use the trigonometric ratios to calculate an angle

Key word
inverse functions

The sine of 54° is 0.809 016 994 4 (to 10 decimal places).

The sine of 55° is 0.819 152 044 3 (to 10 decimal places).

What angle has a sine of 0.815?

Obviously, it is between 54° and 55°, so we could probably use a trial-and-improvement method to find it. But there is an easier way which uses the **inverse functions** on your calculator.

An inverse function can be accessed in several different ways. For example, the inverse function for sine may be any of these keys:

The inverse function printed above the sine key is usually given in either of the following ways:

You will need to find out how your calculator deals with inverse functions.

When you do the inverse sine of 0.815, you should get 54.587 361 89°.

It is normal in trigonometry to round off angles to one decimal place. So, the angle with a sine of 0.815 is 54.6° (1 decimal place).

This can be written as $\sin^{-1} 0.815 = 54.6°$.

EXAMPLE 9

Find the angle with a cosine of 0.654.

$\cos^{-1} 0.654 = 49.156\,131\,92° = 49.2°$ (1 decimal place)

EXAMPLE 10

Find the angle with a sine of (3 ÷ 4).

How you solve this will depend on your type of calculator. So key in either

$\boxed{3}\;\boxed{÷}\;\boxed{4}\;\boxed{=}\;\boxed{\text{INV}}\;\boxed{\text{sin}}$ or $\boxed{\text{INV}}\;\boxed{\text{sin}}\;\boxed{(}\;\boxed{3}\;\boxed{÷}\;\boxed{4}\;\boxed{)}\;\boxed{=}$

So $\sin^{-1}\left(\frac{3}{4}\right) = 48.590\,377\,89° = 48.6°$ (1 decimal place)

EXAMPLE 11

Find the angle with a tangent of 0.75.

$\tan^{-1} 0.75 = 36.869\,897\,65 = 36.9°$ (1 decimal place)

EXERCISE 6G

Use your calculator to find the answers to the following. Give your answers to one decimal place.

1 What angles have the following sines?

    a 0.5   **b** 0.785   **c** 0.64   **d** 0.877   **e** 0.999   **f** 0.707

2 What angles have the following cosines?

    a 0.5   **b** 0.64   **c** 0.999   **d** 0.707   **e** 0.2   **f** 0.7

3 What angles have the following tangents?

    a 0.6   **b** 0.38   **c** 0.895   **d** 1.05   **e** 2.67   **f** 4.38

4 What angles have the following sines?

    a 4 ÷ 5   **b** 2 ÷ 3   **c** 7 ÷ 10   **d** 5 ÷ 6   **e** 1 ÷ 24   **f** 5 ÷ 13

5 What angles have the following cosines?

    a 4 ÷ 5   **b** 2 ÷ 3   **c** 7 ÷ 10   **d** 5 ÷ 6   **e** 1 ÷ 24   **f** 5 ÷ 13

6 What angles have the following tangents?

    a 3 ÷ 5   **b** 7 ÷ 9   **c** 2 ÷ 7   **d** 9 ÷ 5   **e** 11 ÷ 7   **f** 6 ÷ 5

 7 What happens when you try to find the angle with a sine of 1.2? What is the largest value of sine you can put into your calculator without getting an error when you ask for the inverse sine? What is the smallest?

8 **a** **i** What angle has a sine of 0.3? (Keep the answer in your calculator memory.)

ii What angle has a cosine of 0.3?

iii Add the two accurate answers of parts **i** and **ii** together.

b Will you always get the same answer to the above no matter what number you start with?

6.6 Using the sine function

In this section you will learn how to:
- find lengths of sides and angles in right-angled triangles using the sine function

Key word
sine

Remember sine $\theta = \dfrac{\text{Opposite}}{\text{Hypotenuse}}$

We can use the **sine** ratio to calculate the lengths of sides and angles in right-angled triangles.

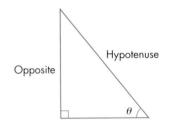

EXAMPLE 12

Find the angle θ, given that the opposite side is 7 cm and the hypotenuse is 10 cm.

Draw a diagram. (This is an essential step.)

From the information given, use sine.

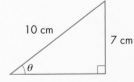

$$\sin \theta = \frac{O}{H} = \frac{7}{10} = 0.7$$

What angle has a sine of 0.7? To find out, use the inverse sine function on your calculator.

$$\sin^{-1} 0.7 = 44.4° \text{ (1 decimal place)}$$

EXAMPLE 13

Find the length of the side marked a in this triangle.

Side a is the opposite side, with 12 cm as the hypotenuse, so use sine.

$$\sin \theta = \frac{O}{H}$$

$$\sin 35° = \frac{a}{12}$$

So $a = 12 \sin 35° = 6.88$ cm (3 significant figures)

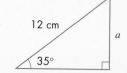

EXAMPLE 14

Find the length of the hypotenuse, h, in this triangle.

Note that although the angle is in the other corner, the opposite side is again given. So use sine.

$$\sin \theta = \frac{O}{H}$$

$$\sin 52° = \frac{8}{h}$$

So $h = \dfrac{8}{\sin 52°} = 10.2$ cm (3 significant figures)

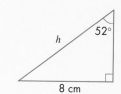

EXERCISE 6H

1 Find the angle marked x in each of these triangles.

a

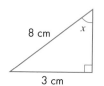
10 cm   3 cm x

b

8 cm x 3 cm

c

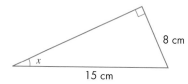
8 cm x 15 cm

2 Find the side marked x in each of these triangles.

a

13 cm x 24°

b

8 cm   46° x

c

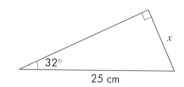
32°   25 cm x

3 Find the side marked x in each of these triangles.

a

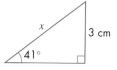
x 3 cm   41°

b

x 61°   6 cm

c

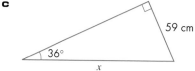
59 cm   36° x

129

4 Find the side marked *x* in each of these triangles.

a

b

c

d

5 Find the value of *x* in each of these triangles.

a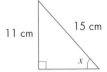

b

c

d

6 Angle θ has a sine of $\frac{3}{5}$. Calculate the missing lengths in these triangles.

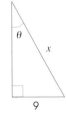

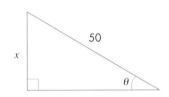

6.7 Using the cosine function

In this section you will learn how to:
- find lengths of sides and angles in right-angled triangles using the cosine function

Key word
cosine

Remember cosine $\theta = \dfrac{\text{Adjacent}}{\text{Hypotenuse}}$

We can use the **cosine** ratio to calculate the lengths of sides and angles in right-angled triangles.

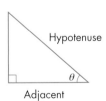

EXAMPLE 15

Find the angle θ, given that the adjacent side is 5 cm and the hypotenuse is 12 cm.

Draw a diagram. (This is an essential step.)

From the information given, use cosine.

$$\cos \theta = \frac{A}{H} = \frac{5}{12}$$

What angle has a cosine of $\frac{5}{12}$? To find out, use the inverse cosine function on your calculator.

$$\cos^{-1} = 65.4° \text{ (1 decimal place)}$$

EXAMPLE 16

Find the length of the side marked a in this triangle.

Side a is the adjacent side, with 9 cm as the hypotenuse, so use cosine.

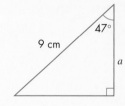

$$\cos \theta \quad = \frac{A}{H}$$

$$\cos 47° = \frac{a}{9}$$

So $a = 9 \cos 47° = 6.14$ cm (3 significant figures)

EXAMPLE 17

Find the length of the hypotenuse, h, in this triangle.

The adjacent side is given. So use cosine.

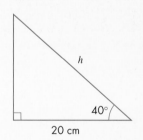

$$\cos \theta \quad = \frac{A}{H}$$

$$\cos 40° = \frac{20}{h}$$

So $h = \dfrac{20}{\cos 40°} = 26.1$ cm (3 significant figures)

EXERCISE 6I

1 Find the angle marked x in each of these triangles.

a

b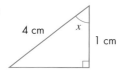

c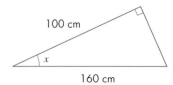

2 Find the side marked x in each of these triangles.

a

b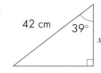

c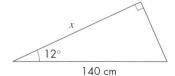

3 Find the side marked x in each of these triangles.

a

b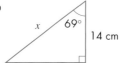

c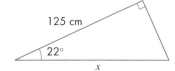

4 Find the side marked x in each of these triangles.

a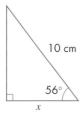

b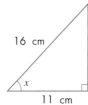

c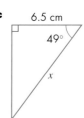

d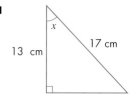

5 Find the value of x in each of these triangles.

a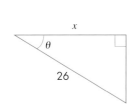

b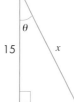

c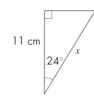

d

6 Angle θ has a cosine of $\frac{5}{13}$. Calculate the missing lengths in these triangles.

Using the tangent function

In this section you will learn how to:
- find lengths of sides and angles in right-angled triangles using the tangent function

Key word
tangent

Remember tangent $\theta = \dfrac{\text{Opposite}}{\text{Adjacent}}$

We can use the **tangent** ratio to calculate the lengths of sides and angles in right-angled triangles.

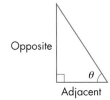

EXAMPLE 18

Find the angle θ, given that the opposite side is 3 cm and the adjacent side is 4 cm.

Draw a diagram. (This is an essential step.)

From the information given, use tangent.

$$\tan \theta = \frac{O}{A} = \frac{3}{4} = 0.75$$

What angle has a tangent of 0.75? To find out, use the inverse tangent function on your calculator.

$$\tan^{-1} 0.75 = 36.9° \text{ (1 decimal place)}$$

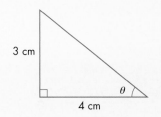

EXAMPLE 19

Find the length of the side marked x in this triangle.

Side x is the opposite side, with 9 cm as the adjacent side, so use tangent.

$$\tan \theta = \frac{O}{A}$$

$$\tan 62° = \frac{x}{9}$$

So $x = 9 \tan 62° = 16.9$ cm (3 significant figures)

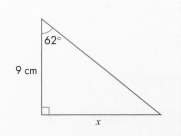

EXAMPLE 20

Find the length of the side marked a in this triangle.

Side a is the adjacent side and the opposite side is given.
So use tangent.

$$\tan \theta = \frac{O}{A}$$

$$\tan 35° = \frac{6}{a}$$

So $a = \dfrac{6}{\tan 35°} = 8.57$ cm (3 significant figures)

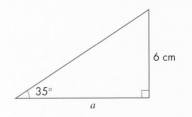

EXERCISE 6J

 1 Find the angle marked x in each of these triangles.

a
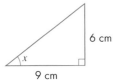

b
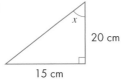

c

 2 Find the side marked x in each of these triangles.

a
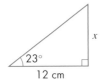

b
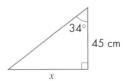

c

 3 Find the side marked x in each of these triangles.

a
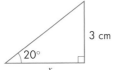

b
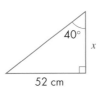

c

 4 Find the side marked x in each of these triangles.

a

b

c

d

5 Find the value x in each of these triangles.

a
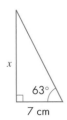

b
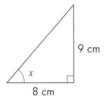

c

d
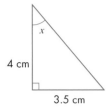

6 Angle θ has a tangent of $\frac{4}{3}$. Calculate the missing lengths in these triangles.

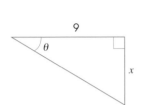

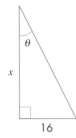

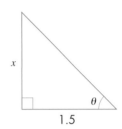

6.9 Which ratio to use

In this section you will learn how to:
- decide which trigonometric ratio to use in a right-angled triangle

Key words
sine
cosine
tangent

The difficulty with any trigonometric problem is knowing which ratio to use to solve it.

The following examples show you how to determine which ratio you need in any given situation.

EXAMPLE 21

Find the length of the side marked x in this triangle.

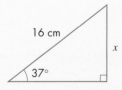

Step 1 Identify what information is given and what needs to be found. Namely, x is opposite the angle and 16 cm is the hypotenuse.

Step 2 Decide which ratio to use. Only one ratio uses opposite and hypotenuse: **sine**.

Step 3 Remember $\sin \theta = \dfrac{O}{H}$

Step 4 Put in the numbers and letters: $\sin 37° = \dfrac{x}{16}$

Step 5 Rearrange the equation and work out the answer: $x = 16 \sin 37° = 9.629\,040\,371$ cm

Step 6 Give the answer to an appropriate degree of accuracy: $x = 9.63$ cm (3 significant figures)

In reality, you do not write down every step as in Example 21. Step 1 can be done by marking the triangle. Steps 2 and 3 can be done in your head. Steps 4 to 6 are what you write down.

Remember that examiners will want to see evidence of working. Any reasonable attempt at identifying the sides and using a ratio will probably get you some method marks – but only if the fraction is the right way round.

The next examples are set out in a way that requires the *minimum* amount of working but gets *maximum* marks.

EXAMPLE 22

Find the length of the side marked x in this triangle.

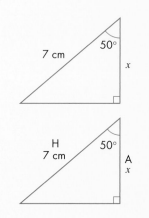

Mark on the triangle the side you know (H) and the side you want to find (A).

Recognise it is a **cosine** problem because you have A and H.

So $\cos 50° = \dfrac{x}{7}$

$x = 7 \cos 50° = 4.50$ cm (3 significant figures)

EXAMPLE 23

Find the angle marked x in this triangle.

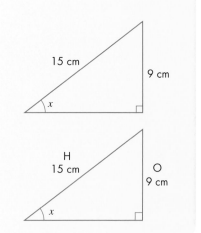

Mark on the triangle the sides you know.

Recognise it is a sine problem because you have O and H.

So $\sin x = \dfrac{9}{15} = 0.6$

$x = \sin^{-1} 0.6 = 36.9°$ (1 decimal place)

EXAMPLE 24

Find the angle marked x in this triangle.

12 cm   7 cm

x

Mark on the triangle the sides you know.

Recognise it is a **tangent** problem because you have O and A.

O   A
12 cm   7 cm

x

So $\tan x = \dfrac{12}{7}$

$x = \tan^{-1} \dfrac{12}{7} = 59.7°$ (1 decimal place)

EXERCISE 6K

1 Find the length marked x in each of these triangles.

a
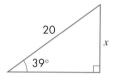
20
x
39°

b
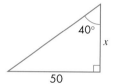
40°
x
50

c
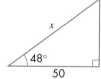
x
48°
50

d
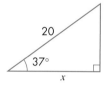
20
37°
x

e

x 40°
52

f
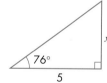
x
76°
5

2 Find the angle marked x in each of these triangles.

a

20
14
x

b
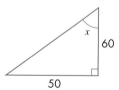
x
60
50

c
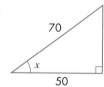
70
x
50

d
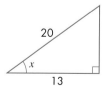
20
x
13

e
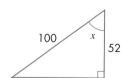
100   x
52

f
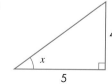
4
x
5

3 Find the angle or length marked x in each of these triangles.

a
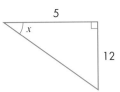

b
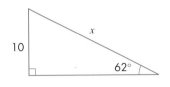

c
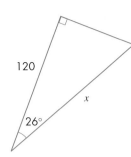

d
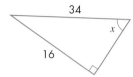

e

f
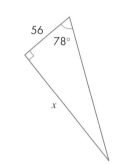

g
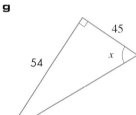

h
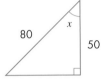

i
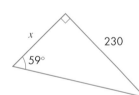

j
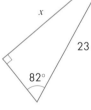

4 In a maths textbook it says:

The tangent of any angle is equal to the sine of the angle divided by the cosine of the angle.

a Show clearly that this is true for an angle of 30°.

b Prove, by using the definitions of sin θ and cos θ, that the statement is true for this right-angled triangle.

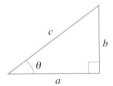

In this section you will learn how to:

- solve practical problems using trigonometry
- solve problems using an angle of elevation or an angle of depression
- solve bearing problems using trigonometry
- using trigonometry to solve problems involving isosceles triangles

Key words
angle of
    depression
angle of elevation
bearing
isosceles triangle
three-figure
    bearing
trigonometry

Most **trigonometry** problems in GCSE examination papers do not come as straightforward triangles. Usually, solving a triangle is part of solving a practical problem. You should follow these steps when solving a practical problem using trigonometry.

- Draw the triangle required.

- Put on the information given (angles and sides).

- Put on x for the unknown angle or side.

- Mark on two of O, A or H as appropriate.

- Choose which ratio to use.

- Write out the equation with the numbers in.

- Rearrange the equation if necessary, then work out the answer.

- Give your answer to a sensible degree of accuracy. Answers given to three significant figures or to the nearest degree are acceptable in exams.

EXAMPLE 25

A window cleaner has a ladder which is 7 m long. The window cleaner leans it against a wall so that the foot of the ladder is 3 m from the wall. What angle does the ladder make with the wall?

Draw the situation as a right-angled triangle.

Then mark the sides and angle.

Recognise it is a sine problem because you have O and H.

So $\sin x = \dfrac{3}{7}$

$x = \sin^{-1} \dfrac{3}{7} = 25°$ (to the nearest degree)

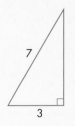

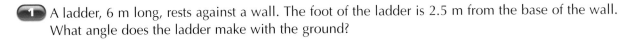

EXERCISE 6L

In these questions, give answers involving angles to the nearest degree.

1 A ladder, 6 m long, rests against a wall. The foot of the ladder is 2.5 m from the base of the wall. What angle does the ladder make with the ground?

2 The ladder in question **1** has a "safe angle" with the ground of between 60° and 70°. What are the safe limits for the distance of the foot of the ladder from the wall?

3 Another ladder, of length 10 m, is placed so that it reaches 7 m up the wall. What angle does it make with the ground?

4 Yet another ladder is placed so that it makes an angle of 76° with the ground. When the foot of the ladder is 1.7 m from the foot of the wall, how high up the wall does the ladder reach?

5 Calculate the angle that the diagonal makes with the long side of a rectangle which measures 10 cm by 6 cm.

6 This diagram shows a frame for a bookcase.

  a What angle does the diagonal strut make with the long side?

  b Use Pythagoras' theorem to calculate the length of the strut.

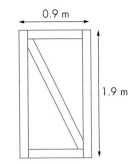

7 This diagram shows a roof truss.

  a What angle will the roof make with the horizontal?

  b Use Pythagoras' theorem to calculate the length of the sloping strut.

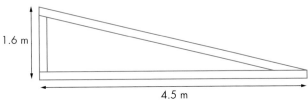

8 Alicia paces out 100 m from the base of a church. She then measures the angle to the top of the spire as 23°. How high is the church spire?

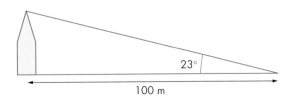

9 A girl is flying a kite on a string 32 m long. The string, which is being held at 1 m above the ground, makes an angle of 39° with the horizontal. How high is the kite above the ground?

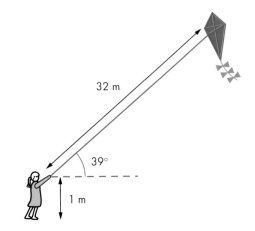

10 Angle θ has a sine of $\frac{3}{5}$.

a Use Pythagoras' theorem to calculate the missing side of this triangle.

b Write down the cosine and the tangent of θ.

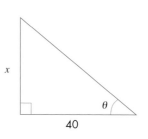

c Calculate the missing lengths marked x in these triangles.

i

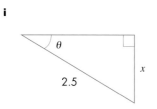

ii

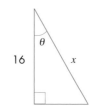

iii

Angles of elevation and depression

When you look *up* at an aircraft in the sky, the angle through which your line of sight turns from looking straight ahead (the horizontal) is called the **angle of elevation**.

When you are standing on a high point and look *down* at a boat, the angle through which your line of sight turns from looking straight ahead (the horizontal) is called the **angle of depression**.

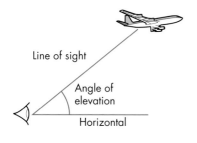

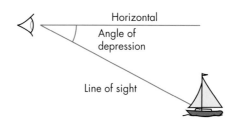

EXAMPLE 26

From the top of a vertical cliff, 100 m high, Andrew sees a boat out at sea. The angle of depression from Andrew to the boat is 42°. How far from the base of the cliff is the boat?

The diagram of the situation is shown in figure **i**.

From this, you get the triangle shown in figure **ii**.

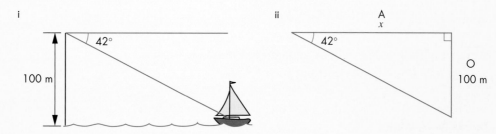

From figure **ii**, you see that this is a tangent problem.

So $\tan 42° = \dfrac{100}{x}$

$x = \dfrac{100}{\tan 42°} = 111$ m (3 significant figures)

EXERCISE 6M

In these questions, give any answers involving angles to the nearest degree.

1 Eric sees an aircraft in the sky. The aircraft is at a horizontal distance of 25 km from Eric. The angle of elevation is 22°. How high is the aircraft?

2 A passenger in an aircraft hears the pilot say that they are flying at an altitude of 4000 m and are 10 km from the airport. If the passenger can see the airport, what is the angle of depression?

3 A man standing 200 m from the base of a television transmitter looks at the top of it and notices that the angle of elevation of the top is 65°. How high is the tower?

4 From the top of a vertical cliff, 200 m high, a boat has an angle of depression of 52°. How far from the base of the cliff is the boat?

5 From a boat, the angle of elevation of the foot of a lighthouse on the edge of a cliff is 34°.

    a If the cliff is 150 m high, how far from the base of the cliff is the boat?

    b If the lighthouse is 50 m high, what would be the angle of elevation of the top of the lighthouse from the boat?

6 A bird flies from the top of a 12 m tall tree, at an angle of depression of 34°, to catch a worm on the ground.

    a How far does the bird actually fly?   **b** How far was the worm from the base of the tree?

7 Sunil stands about 50 m away from a building. The angle of elevation from Sunil to the top of the building is about 15°. How tall is the building?

8 The top of a ski run is 100 m above the finishing line. The run is 300 m long. What is the angle of depression of the ski run?

Trigonometry and bearings

A **bearing** is the direction to one place from another. The usual way of giving a bearing is as an angle measured from north in a clockwise direction. This is how a navigational compass and a surveyor's compass measure bearings.

A bearing is always written as a three-digit number, known as a **three-figure bearing**.

The diagram shows how this works, using the main compass points as examples.

When working with bearings, follow these three rules.

- Always start from *north*.

- Always measure *clockwise*.

- Always give a bearing in degrees and as a *three-figure bearing*.

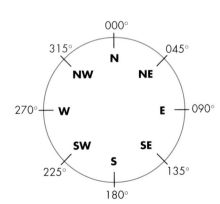

The difficulty with trigonometric problems involving bearings is dealing with those angles greater than 90° whose trigonometric ratios have negative values. To avoid this, we have to find a right-angled triangle that we can readily use. Example 27 shows you how to deal with such a situation.

EXAMPLE 27

A ship sails on a bearing of 120° for 50 km. How far east has it travelled?

The diagram of the situation is shown in figure **i**. From this, you can get the acute-angled triangle shown in figure **ii**.

From figure **ii**, you see that this is a cosine problem.

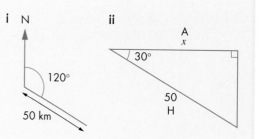

So $\cos 30° = \dfrac{x}{50}$

$x = 50 \cos 30° = 43.301 = 43.3$ km (3 significant figures)

EXERCISE 6N

1 A ship sails for 75 km on a bearing of 078°.

　a How far east has it travelled?　　　　**b** How far north has it travelled?

2 Lopham is 17 miles from Wath on a bearing of 210°.

　a How far south of Wath is Lopham?　　**b** How far east of Lopham is Wath?

3 A plane sets off from an airport and flies due east for 120 km, then turns to fly due south for 70 km before landing at Seddeth. What is the bearing of Seddeth from the airport?

4 A helicopter leaves an army base and flies 60 km on a bearing of 278°.

　a How far west has the helicopter flown?　**b** How far north has the helicopter flown?

5 A ship sails from a port on a bearing of 117° for 35 km before heading due north for 40 km and docking at Angle Bay.

　a How far south had the ship sailed before turning?

　b How far north had the ship sailed from the port to Angle Bay?

　c How far east is Angle Bay from the port?

　d What is the bearing from the port to Angle Bay?

6 Mountain A is due west of a walker. Mountain B is due north of the walker. The guidebook says that mountain B is 4.3 km from mountain A, on a bearing of 058°. How far is the walker from mountain B?

7 The diagram shows the relative distances and bearings of three ships A, B and C.

   a How far north of A is B? (Distance x on diagram.)

   b How far north of B is C? (Distance y on diagram.)

   c How far west of A is C? (Distance z on diagram.)

   d What is the bearing of A from C? (Angle $w°$ on diagram.)

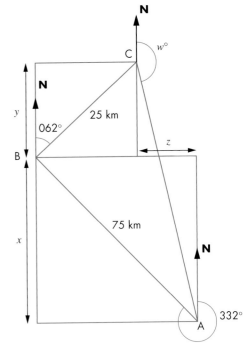

8 A ship sails from port A for 42 km on a bearing of 130° to point B. It then changes course and sails for 24 km on a bearing of 040° to point C, where it breaks down and anchors. What distance and on what bearing will a helicopter have to fly from port A to go directly to the ship at C?

Trigonometry and isosceles triangles

Isosceles triangles often feature in trigonometry problems because such a triangle can be split into two right-angled triangles that are congruent.

EXAMPLE 28

   a Find the length x in this isosceles triangle.

   b Calculate the area of the triangle.

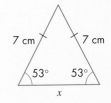

Draw a perpendicular from the apex of the triangle to its base, splitting the triangle into two congruent, right-angled triangles.

   a To find the length y, which is $\frac{1}{2}$ of x, use cosine.

   So, $\cos 53° = \dfrac{y}{7}$

   $y = 7 \cos 53° = 4.2127051$ cm

   So the length $x = 2y = 8.43$ cm (3 significant figures).

b To calculate the area of the original triangle, you first need to find its vertical height, h.

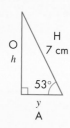

You have two choices, both of which involve the right-angled triangle of part a. We can use either Pythagoras' theorem ($h^2 + y^2 = 7^2$) or trigonometry. It is safer to use trigonometry again, since we are then still using known information.

This is a sine problem.

So, $\sin 53° = \dfrac{h}{7}$

$h = 7 \sin 53° = 5.590\,448\,6$ cm (Keep the accurate figure in the calculator.)

The area of the triangle $= \frac{1}{2} \times$ base $\times$ height. (We should use the most accurate figures we have for this calculation.)

$A = \frac{1}{2} \times 8.425\,410\,3 \times 5.590\,448\,6 = 23.6$ cm^2 (3 significant figures)

You are not expected to write down these eight-figure numbers, just to use them.

Note: If you use rounded-off values to calculate the area, the answer would be 23.5 cm^2, which is different from the one calculated using the most accurate data. So *never* use rounded-off data when you can use accurate data – unless you are just estimating.

EXERCISE 6P

In questions 1–4, find the side or angle marked x.

1

2

3

4

5 This diagram below shows a roof truss. How wide is the roof?

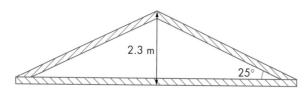

6 Calculate the area of each of these triangles.

a

b

c

d

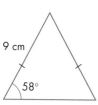
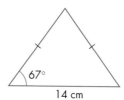
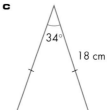
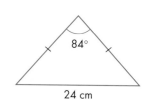

1 A football pitch ABCD is shown. The length of the pitch, AB = 120 m. The width of the pitch, BC = 90 m.

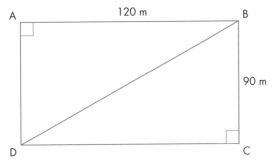

Calculate the length of the diagonal BD. Give your answer to 1 decimal place.

2 A ladder is leant against a wall. Its foot is 0.8 m from the wall and it reaches to a height of 4 m up the wall.

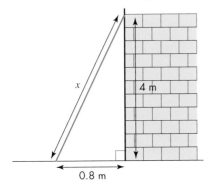

Calculate the length, in metres, of the ladder (marked *x* on the diagram). Give your answer to a suitable degree of accuracy.

3 In the diagram, ABC is a right-angled triangle. AC = 18 cm and AB = 12 cm.

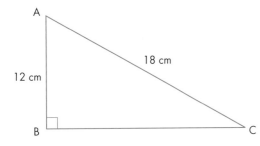

Calculate the length of BC.

4 **a** ABC is a right angled triangle. AB = 12 cm, BC = 8 cm. Find the size of angle CAB (marked *x* in the diagram). Give your answer to 1 decimal place.

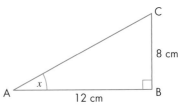

b PQR is a right-angled triangle. PQ = 15 cm, angle QPR = 32°. Find the length of PR (marked *y* in the diagram). Give your answer to 1 decimal place.

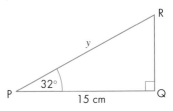

5

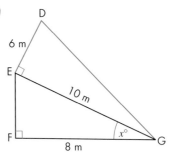

DE = 6 m.
EG = 10 m.
FG = 8 m.
Angle DEG = 90°.
Angle EFG = 90°.

a Calculate the length of DG. Give your answer correct to 3 significant figures.

b Calculate the size of the angle marked *x*°. Give your answer correct to 1 decimal place.

Edexcel, Question 9, Paper 6 Higher, June 2004

6 A lighthouse, L, is 3.2 km due West of a port, P. A ship, S, is 1.9 km due North of the lighthouse, L.

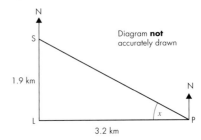

a Calculate the size of the angle marked *x*. Give your answer correct to 3 significant figures.

b Find the bearing of the port, P, from the ship, S. Give your answer correct to 3 significant figures.

Edexcel, Question 10, Paper 6 Higher, June 2005

7 The diagram represents a cuboid ABCDEFGH.

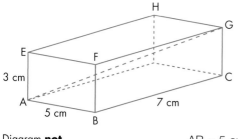

Diagram **not** accurately drawn

AB = 5 cm.
BC = 7 cm.
AE = 3 cm.

a Calculate the length of AG. Give your answer correct to 3 significant figures.

b Calculate the size of the angle between AG and the face ABCD. Give your answer correct to 1 decimal place.

Edexcel, Question 15, Paper 6 Higher, November 2004

WORKED EXAM QUESTION

a ABC is a right-angled triangle. AC = 19 cm and AB = 9 cm.

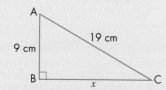

Calculate the length of BC.

b PQR is a right-angled triangle. PQ = 11 cm and QR = 24 cm.

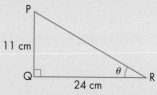

Calculate the size of angle PRQ.

c ABD and BCD are right-angled triangles. AB = 26 cm, AD = 24 cm and angle BCD = 35°.

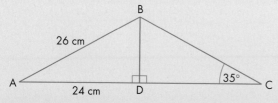

Calculate the length of BC. Give your answer to 3 significant figures.

Solution

a Let BC = x

By Pythagoras' theorem
$$x^2 = 19^2 - 9^2 \text{ cm}^2$$
$$= 280 \text{ cm}^2$$
So $x = \sqrt{280} = 16.7$ cm (3 sf)

b Let $\angle PRQ = \theta$

So $\tan \theta = \dfrac{11}{24}$

$\theta = \tan^{-1} \dfrac{11}{24} = 24.6°$ (1 dp)

c In triangle ABC, let BD = x

By Pythagoras' theorem
$$x^2 = 26^2 - 24^2$$
$$= 100$$
$$x = 10 \text{ cm}$$

In triangle BCD, let BC = y

So $\sin 35° = \dfrac{10}{y}$

$y = \dfrac{10}{\sin 35°}$

So BC = 17.4 cm (3 sf)

GRADE YOURSELF

C Able to use Pythagoras' theorem in right-angled triangles

C Able to solve problems in 2-D using Pythagoras' theorem

B Able to solve problems in 3-D using Pythagoras' theorem

B Able to use trigonometry to find lengths of sides and angles in right-angled triangles

B Able to use trigonometry to solve problems

What you should know now

- How to use Pythagoras' theorem

- How to solve problems using Pythagoras' theorem

- How to use the trigonometric ratios for sine, cosine and tangent in right-angled triangles

- How to solve problems using trigonometry

- How to solve problems using angles of elevation, angles of depression and bearings

Geometry

This chapter will show you ...

- how to find angles in triangles and quadrilaterals
- how to find interior and exterior angles in polygons
- how to find angles using circle theorems

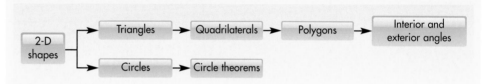

What you should already know

- Vertically opposite angles are equal.
  The angles labelled a and b are vertically opposite angles.

- The angles on a straight line add up to 180°, so $a + b = 180°$.
  This is true for any number of angles on a line.
  For example, $c + d + e + f = 180°$

- The sum of the angles around a point is 360°.
  For example, $a + b + c + d + e = 360°$

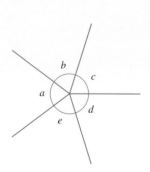

continued

- The three interior angles of a triangle add up to 180°. So, $a + b + c = 180°$

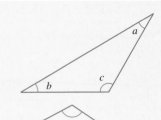

- The four interior angles of a quadrilateral add up to 360°.

  So, $a + b + c + d = 360°$

- A line which cuts parallel lines is called a transversal. The equal angles so formed are called alternate angles.

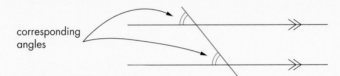

corresponding angles

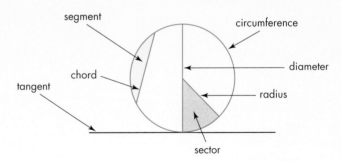

Because of their positions, the angles shown above are called corresponding angles.

Two angles positioned like a and b, which add up to 180°, are called allied angles.

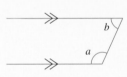

- A polygon is a 2-D shape with straight sides.
- Circle terms

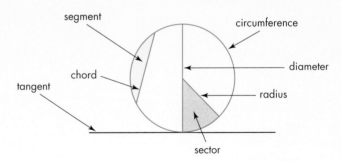

Quick check

Find the marked angles in these diagrams.

1

2

3

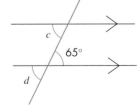

7.1 Special triangles and quadrilaterals

In this section you will learn how to:
- find angles in triangles and quadrilaterals

Key words
equilateral
  triangle
isosceles
  triangle
kite
parallelogram
rhombus
trapezium

Special triangles

An **equilateral triangle** is a triangle with all its sides equal.

Therefore, all three interior angles are 60°.

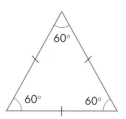

An **isosceles triangle** is a triangle with two equal sides, and therefore with two equal angles.

Notice how we mark the equal sides and equal angles.

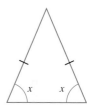

EXAMPLE 1

Find the angle marked a in the triangle.

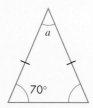

The triangle is isosceles, so both base angles are 70°.

So $a = 180° - 70° - 70° = 40°$

Special quadrilaterals

A **trapezium** has two parallel sides.

The sum of the interior angles at the ends of each non-parallel side is 180°: that is, ∠A + ∠D = 180° and ∠B + ∠C = 180°.

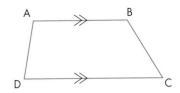

A **parallelogram** has opposite sides parallel.

Its opposite sides are equal. Its diagonals bisect each other. Its opposite angles are equal: that is, ∠A = ∠C and ∠B = ∠D.

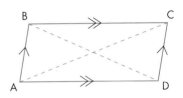

A **rhombus** is a parallelogram with all its sides equal.

Its diagonals bisect each other at right angles. Its diagonals also bisect the angles at the vertices.

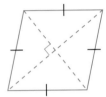

A **kite** is a quadrilateral with two pairs of equal adjacent sides.

Its longer diagonal bisects its shorter diagonal at right angles.
The opposite angles between the sides of different lengths are equal.

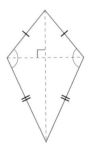

EXAMPLE 2

Find the angles marked x and y in this parallelogram.

$x = 55°$ (opposite angles are equal) and $y = 125°$ ($x + y = 180°$)

EXERCISE 7A

1 Calculate the lettered angles in each triangle.

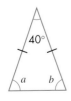

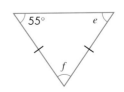

2 An isosceles triangle has an angle of 50°. Sketch the two different possible triangles that match this description, showing what each angle is.

3 Find the missing angles in these quadrilaterals.

a
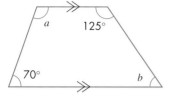

b
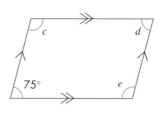

c
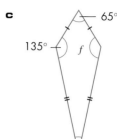

d
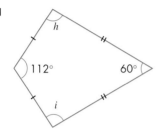

e

f
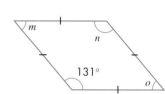

4 The three angles of an isosceles triangle are $2x$, $x - 10$ and $x - 10$. What is the actual size of each angle?

5 Calculate the lettered angles in these diagrams.

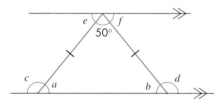

6 Calculate the values of x and y in each of these quadrilaterals.

a
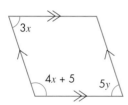

b
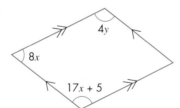

c
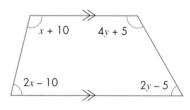

7 Find the value of x in each of these quadrilaterals and hence state the type of quadrilateral it is.

a a quadrilateral with angles $x + 10$, $x + 20$, $2x + 20$, $2x + 10$

b a quadrilateral with angles $x - 10$, $2x + 10$, $x - 10$, $2x + 10$

c a quadrilateral with angles $x - 10$, $2x$, $5x - 10$, $5x - 10$

d a quadrilateral with angles $4x + 10$, $5x - 10$, $3x + 30$, $2x + 50$

In this section you will learn how to:

● find interior angles and exterior angles in a polygon

Key words

exterior angle
heptagon
hexagon
interior angle
octagon
pentagon
polygon
regular
      polygon

A **polygon** has two kinds of angle.

● **Interior angles** are angles made by adjacent sides of the polygon and lying inside the polygon.

● **Exterior angles** are angles lying on the outside of the polygon, so that the interior angle + the exterior angle = 180°.

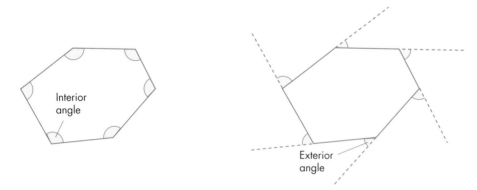

The *exterior* angles of *any* polygon add up to 360°.

Interior angles

You can find the sum of the interior angles of any polygon by splitting it into triangles.

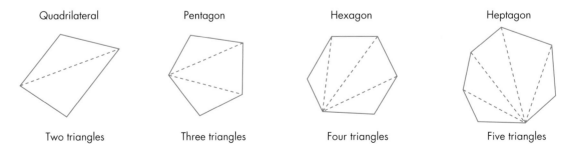

| Quadrilateral | Pentagon | Hexagon | Heptagon |
| Two triangles | Three triangles | Four triangles | Five triangles |

Since we already know that the angles in a triangle add up to 180°, the sum of the interior angles in a polygon is found by multiplying the number of triangles in the polygon by 180°, as shown in this table.

Shape	Name	Sum of interior angles
4-sided	Quadrilateral	2 × 180° = 360°
5-sided	Pentagon	3 × 180° = 540°
6-sided	Hexagon	4 × 180° = 720°
7-sided	Heptagon	5 × 180° = 900°
8-sided	Octagon	6 × 180° = 1080°

As you can see from the table, for an n-sided polygon, the sum of the interior angles, S, is given by the formula

$$S = 180(n - 2)°$$

Exterior angles

As you see from the diagram, the sum of an exterior angle and its adjacent interior angle is 180°.

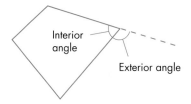

Regular polygons

A polygon is regular if all its interior angles are equal and all its sides have the same length. This means that all the exterior angles are also equal.

All regular polygons can be drawn by dividing the circumference of a circle into equal divisions, which means that the angle at the centre of a regular polygon is $\dfrac{360}{n}$

Here are two simple formulae for calculating the interior and the exterior angles of **regular polygons**.

The exterior angle, E, of a regular n-sided polygon is $E = \dfrac{360°}{n}$

The interior angle, I, of a regular n-sided polygon is $I = 180° - E = 180° - \dfrac{360°}{n}$

EXAMPLE 3

Find the exterior angle, x, and the interior angle, y, for this regular octagon.

$x = \dfrac{360°}{8} = 45°$ and $y = 180° - 45° = 135°$

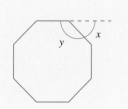

EXERCISE 7B

1 Calculate the sum of the interior angles of polygons with these numbers of sides.

   a 10 sides **b** 15 sides **c** 100 sides **d** 45 sides

2 Calculate the size of the interior angle of regular polygons with these numbers of sides.

   a 12 sides **b** 20 sides **c** 9 sides **d** 60 sides

3 Find the number of sides of polygons with these interior angle sums.

   a 1260° **b** 2340° **c** 18 000° **d** 8640°

4 Find the number of sides of regular polygons with these exterior angles.

   a 24° **b** 10° **c** 15° **d** 5°

5 Find the number of sides of regular polygons with these interior angles.

   a 150° **b** 140° **c** 162° **d** 171°

6 Calculate the size of the unknown angle in each of these polygons.

   a 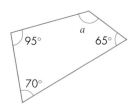 **b**  **c**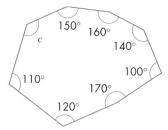

7 Find the value of x in each of these polygons.

   a 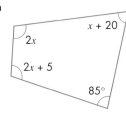 **b** 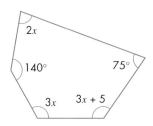 **c**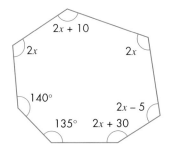

8 What is the name of the regular polygon whose interior angles are twice its exterior angles?

9 Wesley measured all the interior angles in a polygon. He added them up to make 991°, but he had missed out one angle.

   a What type of polygon did Wesley measure?

   b What is the size of the missing angle?

10 **a** In the triangle ABC, angle A is 42°, angle B is 67°.

    i Calculate the value of angle C.

    ii What is the value of the exterior angle at C.

    iii What connects the exterior angle at C with the sum of the angles at A and B?

  b Prove that any exterior angle of a triangle is equal to the sum of the two opposite interior angles.

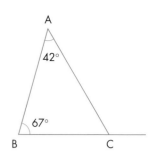

Circle theorems

In this section you will learn how to:

• find angles in circles

Key words

arc
circle
circumference
diameter
segment
semicircle
subtended

Here are three **circle** theorems you need to know.

• **Circle theorem 1**

The angle at the centre of a circle is twice the angle at the **circumference** **subtended** by the same **arc**.

$$\angle AOB = 2 \times \angle ACB$$

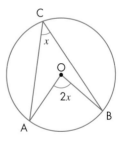

• **Circle theorem 2**

Every angle at the circumference of a **semicircle** that is subtended by the **diameter** of the semicircle is a right angle.

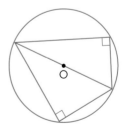

• **Circle theorem 3**

Angles at the circumference in the same **segment** of a circle are equal.

Points C_1, C_2, C_3 and C_4 on the circumference are subtended by the same arc AB.

So $\angle AC_1B = \angle AC_2B = \angle AC_3B = \angle AC_4B$

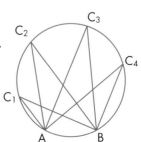

Follow through Examples 4–6 to see how these theorems are applied.

EXAMPLE 4

O is the centre of each circle. Find the angles marked *a* and *b* in each circle.

i

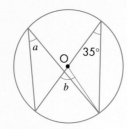

ii

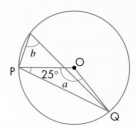

i $a = 35°$ (angles in same segment)

   $b = 2 \times 35°$ (angle at centre = twice angle at circumference)

   $= 70°$

ii With OP = OQ, triangle OPQ is isosceles and the sum of the angles in this triangle = 180°

   So $a + (2 \times 25°) = 180°$

   $a = 180° - (2 \times 25°)$

   $= 130°$

   $b = 130° \div 2$ (angle at centre = twice angle at circumference)

   $= 65°$

EXAMPLE 5

O is the centre of the circle. PQR is a straight line.

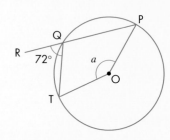

Find the angle labelled *a*.

   $\angle PQT = 180° - 72° = 108°$ (angles on straight line)

The reflex angle $\angle POT = 2 \times 108°$ (angle at centre = twice angle at circumference)

   $= 216°$

   $a + 216° = 360°$ (sum of angles around a point)

   $a = 360° - 216°$

   $a = 144°$

EXAMPLE 6

O is the centre of the circle. POQ is parallel to TR.

Find the angles labelled *a* and *b*.

$a = 64° \div 2$ (angle at centre = twice angle at circumference)

$a = 32°$

$\angle TQP = a$ (alternate angles)

$\quad = 32°$

$\angle PTQ = 90°$ (angle in a semicircle)

$b + 90° + 32° = 180°$ (sum of angles in $\triangle$PQT)

$\quad\quad b = 180° - 122°$

$\quad\quad b = 58°$

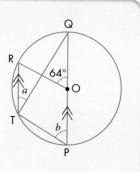

EXERCISE 7C

1 Find the angle marked *x* in each of these circles with centre O.

a
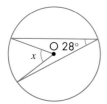
O 28°

b
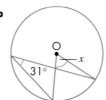
31°

c
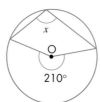
210°

d
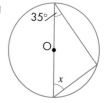
35°

e

f
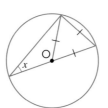

g
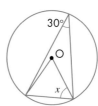
30°

h
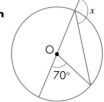
70°

2 Find the angle marked *x* in each of these circles with centre O.

a

35°

b
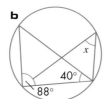
40°
88°

c

50°

d

95°
61°

e
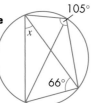
105°
66°

f
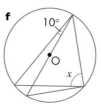
10°

g

68°

h
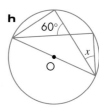
60°

3 In the diagram, O is the centre of the circle. Find these angles.

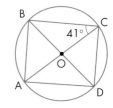

  a ∠ADB

  b ∠DBA

  c ∠CAD

4 In the diagram, O is the centre of the circle. Find these angles.

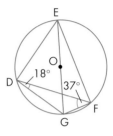

  a ∠EDF

  b ∠DEG

  c ∠EGF

5 Find the angles marked x and y in each of these circles. O is the centre where shown.

a
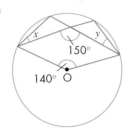

b
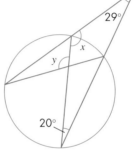

c
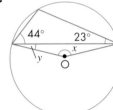

d
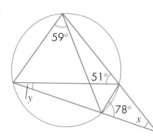

e
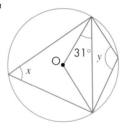

f
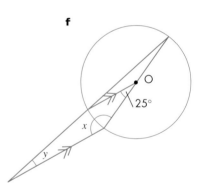

6 In the diagram, O is the centre and AD a diameter of the circle. Find x.

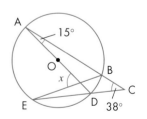

7 A, B, C and D are points on the circumference of a circle with centre O. Angle ABO is $x°$ and angle CBO is $y°$.

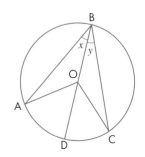

  a State the value of angle BAO.

  b State the value of angle AOD

  c Prove that the angle subtended by the chord AC at the centre of a circle is twice the angle subtended at the circumference.

Cyclic quadrilaterals

In this section you will learn how to:
• find angles in cyclic quadrilaterals

Key word
cyclic
   quadrilateral

A quadrilateral whose four vertices lie on the circumference of a circle is called a **cyclic quadrilateral**.

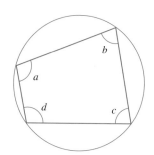

• **Circle theorem 4**

The sum of the opposite angles of a cyclic quadrilateral is 180°.

$a + c = 180°$ and $b + d = 180°$

EXAMPLE 7

Find the angles marked x and y in the diagram.

$x + 85° = 180°$ (angles in a cyclic quadrilateral)

So $x = 95°$

$y + 108° = 180°$ (angles in a cyclic quadrilateral)

So $y = 72°$

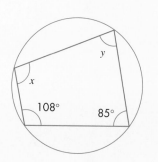

EXERCISE 7D

1 Find the sizes of the lettered angles in each of these circles.

a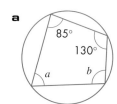

b

c

d

e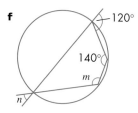

f

g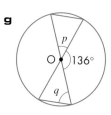

h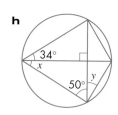

2 Find the values of *x* and *y* in each of these circles. Where shown, O marks the centre of the circle.

a 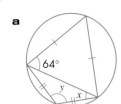 **b** 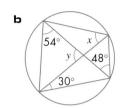 **c** 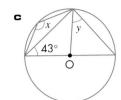 **d**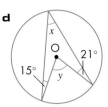

e 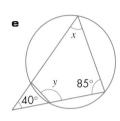 **f** 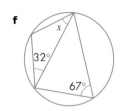 **g** 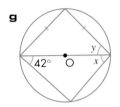 **h**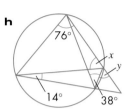

3 Find the values of *x* and *y* in each of these circles. Where shown, O marks the centre of the circle.

a 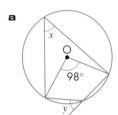 **b** **c** 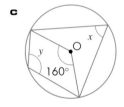 **d**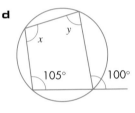

4 Find the values of *x* and *y* in each of these circles.

a 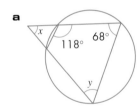 **b** **c** 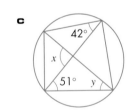 **d**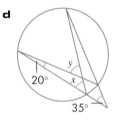

5 Find the values of *x* and *y* in each of these circles with centre O.

a 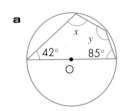 **b** 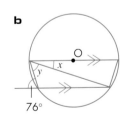 **c** 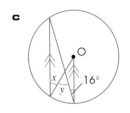 **d**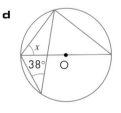

6 The cyclic quadrilateral PQRT has ∠ROQ equal to 38° where O is the centre of the circle. POT is a diameter and parallel to QR. Calculate these angles.

a ∠ROT　　　　**b** ∠QRT　　　　**c** ∠QPT

ABCD is a cyclic quadrilateral within a circle centre O and ∠AOC is $2x°$.

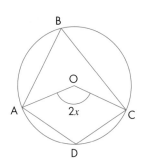

a Write down the value of ∠ABC.

b Write down the value of the reflex angle AOC.

c Prove that the sum of a pair of opposite angles of a cyclic quadrilateral is 180°.

7.5 Tangents and chords

In this section you will learn how to:

- find angles in circles when tangents or chords are used

Key words

chord
point of contact
radius
tangent

A **tangent** is a straight line that touches a circle at one point only. This point is called the **point of contact**. A **chord** is a line that joins two points on the circumference.

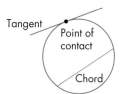

- **Circle theorem 5**

  A tangent to a circle is perpendicular to the **radius** drawn to the point of contact.

  The radius OX is perpendicular to the tangent AB.

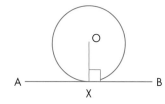

- **Circle theorem 6**

  Tangents to a circle from an external point to the points of contact are equal in length.

  AX = AY

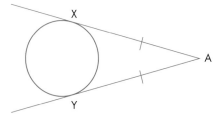

- **Circle theorem 7**

  The line joining an external point to the centre of the circle bisects the angle between the tangents.

  ∠OAX = ∠OAY

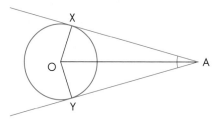

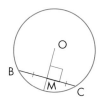

- **Circle theorem 8**

A radius bisects a chord at 90°.

If O is the centre of the circle

∠BMO = 90° and BM = CM.

EXAMPLE 8

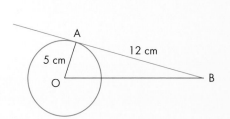

OA is the radius of the circle and AB is a tangent.

OA = 5 cm and AB = 12 cm.

Calculate the length OB.

∠OAB = 90° (radius is perpendicular to a tangent)

Let OB = x

By Pythagoras' theorem

$x^2 = 5^2 + 12^2$ cm^2

$x^2 = 169$ cm^2

So $x = \sqrt{169} = 13$ cm

EXERCISE 7E

1 In each diagram, TP and TQ are tangents to a circle with centre O. Find each value of x.

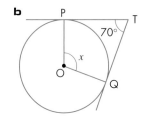
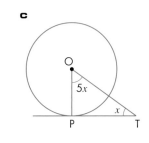
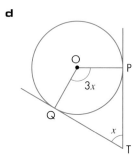

2 Each diagram shows tangents to a circle with centre O. Find each value of y.

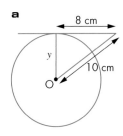
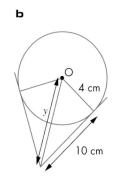
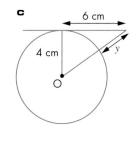
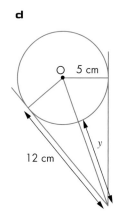

3 Each diagram shows a tangent to a circle with centre O. Find x and y in each case.

a

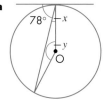

b

c

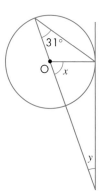

d

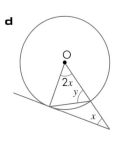

4 In each of the diagrams, TP and TQ are tangents to the circle with centre O. Find each value of x.

a

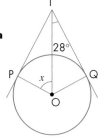

b

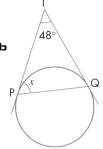

c

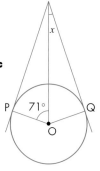

d

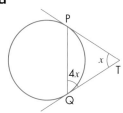

5 Two circles with the same centre have radii of 7 cm and 12 cm respectively. A tangent to the inner circle cuts the outer circle at A and B. Find the length of AB.

6 AB and CB are tangents from B to the circle with centre O. OA and OC are radii.

a Prove that angles AOB and COB are equal.

b Prove that OB bisects the angle ABC.

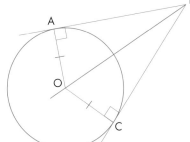

In this section you will learn how to:
- find angles in circles using the alternate segment theorem

Key words

alternate
  segment
chord
tangent

PTQ is the **tangent** to a circle at T. The segment containing ∠TBA is known as the **alternate segment** of ∠PTA, because it is on the other side of the **chord** AT from ∠PTA.

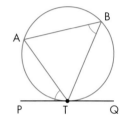

- **Circle theorem 9**

  The angle between a tangent and a chord through the point of contact is equal to the angle in the alternate segment.

  ∠PTA = ∠TBA

EXAMPLE 9

In the diagram, find **a** ∠ATS and **b** ∠TSR.

a ∠ATS = 80° (angle in alternate segment)

b ∠TSR = 70° (angle in alternate segment)

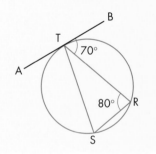

EXERCISE 7F

1 Find the size of each lettered angle.

a

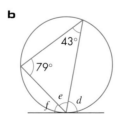

b

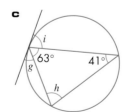

c

d

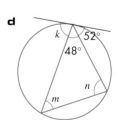

2 In each diagram, find the size of each lettered angle.

a
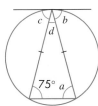

b
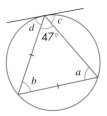

c
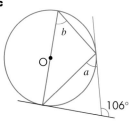

d
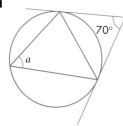

3 In each diagram, find the value of *x*.

a
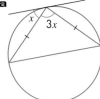

b
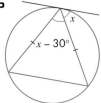

4 ATB is a tangent to each circle with centre O. Find the size of each lettered angle.

a
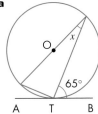

b
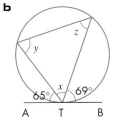

c
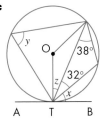

d
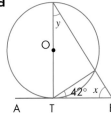

5 PT is a tangent to a circle with centre O.
AB are points on the circumference. Angle PBA is *x*°.

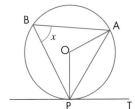

    a Write down the value of angle AOP.

    b Calculate the angle OPA in terms of *x*.

    c Prove that the angle APT is equal to the angle PBA.

1 The diagram shows a regular pentagon.

Calculate the size of the exterior angle of the regular pentagon, marked x on the diagram.

2 The diagram shows part of a regular polygon. Each interior angle is 150°.

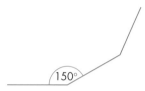

Calculate the number of sides of the polygon.

3 A, B, C and D are points on a circle, centre O. Angle BOD = 116°

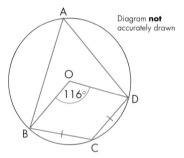

Diagram **not** accurately drawn

a Calculate the size of angle BAD.

BC = CD.

b Calculate the size of angle DBC.

Edexcel, Question 6, Paper 19 Higher, June 2003

4 In the diagram, A, B and C are points on the circumference of a circle, centre O. PA and PB are tangents to the circle. Angle ACB = 75°.

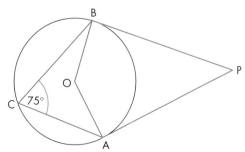

a i Work out the size of angle AOB.

ii Give a reason for your answer.

b Work out the size of angle APB.

Edexcel, Question 14, Paper 6 Higher, June 2005

5 In the diagram, AOB is a diameter of the circle, centre O. TS is a tangent to the circle at C. Angle ABC = 52°.

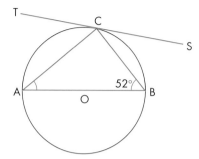

a Write down the size of angle ACB.

b Calculate the size of angle BCS.

6 R, S and T are points on the circumference of a circle, centre O. PS and PT are tangents to the circle. PSN and TORN are straight lines.

PO is parallel to SR.
SR = NR.
Angle OPT = angle OPS.

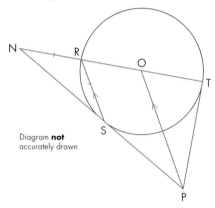

Diagram **not** accurately drawn

a Work out the size of angle PNT.

b Show that PS = SN.

Edexcel, Question 5, Paper 10B Higher, March 2003

WORKED EXAM QUESTIONS

1

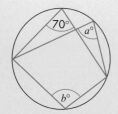

a Write down the value of a.
b Calculate the value of b.

2 A and C are points on the circumference of a circle centre O.
AD and CD are tangents. Angle ADO = 40°.

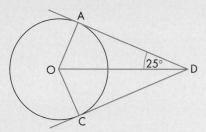

Explain why angle AOC is 130°.

3 ABCD is a cyclic quadrilateral.
PAQ is a tangent to the circle at A.
BC = CD.
AD is parallel to BC.
Angle BAQ = 42°.

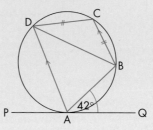

Explain why angle BAD is 84°.

Solutions

1 a $a = 70°$ (angle in same segment)
  b $b = 110°$ (opposite angles in cyclic quadrilateral = 180°)

2 ∠OAD = 90° (radius is perpendicular to tangent)
  ∠AOD = 65° (angles in a triangle)
  Similarly:
  ∠OCD = 90° (radius is perpendicular to tangent)
  ∠COD = 65° (angles in a triangle)
  So ∠AOC = 130°

3 ∠ADB = 42° (alternate segment theorem)
  ∠DBC = 42° (alternate angles in parallel lines)
  ∠BDC = 42° (isosceles triangle)
  ∠DCB = 96° (angles in a triangle)
  So ∠BAD = 84° (opposite angles in cyclic quadrilateral = 180°)

GRADE YOURSELF

D Able to find angles in triangles and quadrilaterals

C Able to find interior angles and exterior angles in polygons

B Able to find angles in circles

A Able to find angles in circles using the alternate segment theorem

A* Can use circle theorems to prove geometrical results

What you should know now

- How to find angles in any triangle or in any quadrilateral
- How to calculate interior and exterior angles in polygons
- How to use circle theorems to find angles

Chapter

Transformation geometry

1 Congruent triangles

2 Translations

3 Reflections

4 Rotations

5 Enlargements

6 Combined transformations

This chapter will show you ...

- how to show that two triangles are congruent
- what is meant by a transformation
- how to translate, reflect, rotate and enlarge 2-D shapes

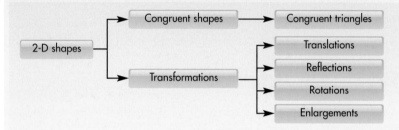

What you should already know

- How to find the lines of symmetry of a 2-D shape
- How to find the order of rotational symmetry of a 2-D shape
- How to recognise congruent shapes
- How to draw the lines with equations $y = x$ and $y = -x$, and lines with equations like $x = 2$ and $y = 3$

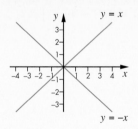 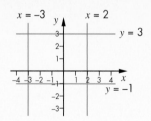

Quick check

Which of these shapes is not congruent to the others?

a **b** **c** **d**

171

Congruent triangles

Two shapes are **congruent** if they are exactly the same size and shape.

For example, these triangles are all congruent.

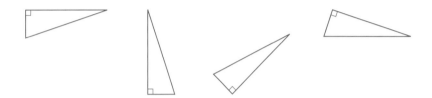

Notice that the triangles can be differently orientated (reflected or rotated).

Conditions for congruent triangles

Any one of the following four conditions is sufficient for two triangles to be congruent.

- **Condition 1**

All three sides of one triangle are equal to the corresponding sides of the other triangle.

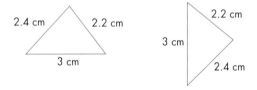

This condition is known as SSS (side, side, side).

- **Condition 2**

Two sides and the angle between them of one triangle are equal to the corresponding sides and angle of the other triangle.

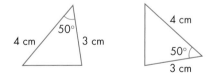

This condition is known as SAS (side, angle, side).

- **Condition 3**

Two angles and a side of one triangle are equal to the corresponding angles and side of the other triangle.

This condition is known as ASA (angle, side, angle) or AAS (angle, angle, side).

- **Condition 4**

Both triangles have a right angle, an equal hypotenuse and another equal side.

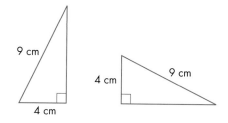

This condition is known as RHS (right angle, hypotenuse, side).

Notation

Once you have shown that triangle ABC is congruent to triangle PQR by one of the above conditions, it means that

$\angle A = \angle P$	$AB = PQ$
$\angle B = \angle Q$	$BC = QR$
$\angle C = \angle R$	$AC = PR$

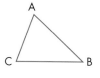

In other words, the points ABC correspond exactly to the points PQR in that order. Triangle ABC is congruent to triangle PQR can be written as $\triangle ABC \equiv \triangle PQR$.

EXAMPLE 1

ABCD is a kite. Show that triangle ABC is congruent to triangle ADC.

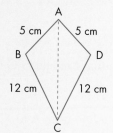

AB = AD

BC = CD

AC is common

So $\triangle ABC \equiv \triangle ADC$ (SSS)

EXERCISE 8A

1. State whether each pair of triangles in **a** to **h** is congruent. If a pair is congruent, give the condition which shows that the triangles are congruent.

a
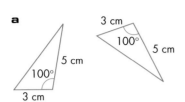

b
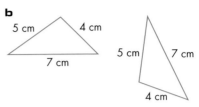

c
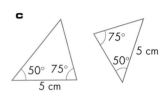

d
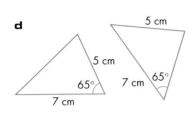

e
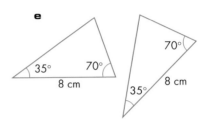

f
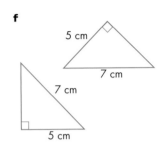

g
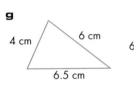

h
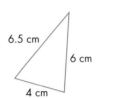
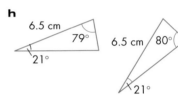

2. State whether each pair of triangles given below is congruent or not. If the triangles are congruent, give the reason and state which points correspond to which.

   a ABC where AB = 8 cm, BC = 9 cm, AC = 7.4 cm
   PQR where PQ = 9 cm, QR = 7.4 cm, PR = 8 cm

   b ABC where AB = 7.5 cm, AC = 8 cm, angle A = 50°
   PQR where PQ = 8 cm, QR = 75 mm, angle R = 50°

   c ABC where AB = 5 cm, BC = 6 cm, angle B = 35°
   PQR where PQ = 6 cm, QR = 50 mm, angle Q = 35°

   d ABC where AB = 6 cm, angle B = 35°, angle C = 115°
   PQR where PQ = 6 cm, angle Q = 115°, angle R = 35°

3. Triangle ABC is congruent to triangle PQR, ∠A = 60°, ∠B = 80° and AB = 5 cm. Find these.

   i ∠P   **ii** ∠Q   **iii** ∠R   **iv** PQ

4. ABCD is congruent to PQRS, ∠A= 110°, ∠B = 55°, ∠C = 85° and RS = 4 cm. Find these.

   i ∠P   **ii** ∠Q   **iii** ∠R   **iv** ∠S   **v** CD

5. Draw a rectangle EFGH. Draw in the diagonal EG. Prove that triangle EFG is congruent to triangle EHG.

6. Draw an isosceles triangle ABC where AB = AC. Draw the line from A to X, the mid-point of BC. Prove that triangle ABX is congruent to triangle ACX.

Translations

In this section you will learn how to:

- translate a 2-D shape

A **transformation** changes the position or the size of a shape.

There are four basic ways of changing the position and size of 2-D shapes: a translation, a reflection, a rotation or an enlargement. All of these transformations, except enlargement, keep shapes congruent.

A **translation** is the "movement" of a shape from one place to another without reflecting it or rotating it. It is sometimes called a glide, since the shape appears to glide from one place to another. Every point in the shape moves in the same direction and through the same distance.

We describe translations by using **vectors**. A vector is represented by the combination of a horizontal shift and a vertical shift.

EXAMPLE 2

Use vectors to describe the translations of the following triangles.

a A to B

b B to C

c C to D

d D to A

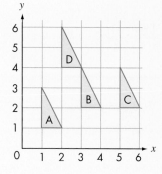

a The vector describing the translation from A to B is $\begin{pmatrix} 2 \\ 1 \end{pmatrix}$.

b The vector describing the translation from B to C is $\begin{pmatrix} 2 \\ 0 \end{pmatrix}$.

c The vector describing the translation from C to D is $\begin{pmatrix} -3 \\ 2 \end{pmatrix}$.

d The vector describing the translation from D to A is $\begin{pmatrix} -1 \\ -3 \end{pmatrix}$.

Note:

- The top number in the vector describes the horizontal movement. To the right +, to the left −.

- The bottom number in the vector describes the vertical movement. Upwards +, downwards −.

EXERCISE 8B

1 Use vectors to describe the following translations.

a i A to B   **ii** A to C   **iii** A to D   **iv** A to E   **v** A to F   **vi** A to G

b i B to A   **ii** B to C   **iii** B to D   **iv** B to E   **v** B to F   **vi** B to G

c i C to A   **ii** C to B   **iii** C to D   **iv** C to E   **v** C to F   **vi** C to G

d i D to E   **ii** E to B   **iii** F to C   **iv** G to D   **v** F to G   **vi** G to E

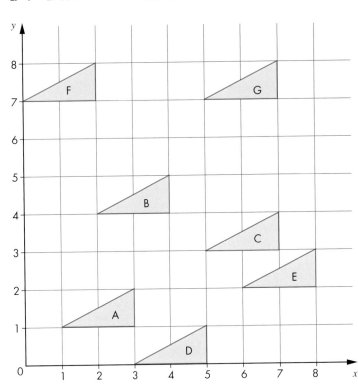

2 **a** Draw the triangle with coordinates A(1,1), B(2,1) and C(1,3).

b Draw the image of ABC after a translation with vector $\begin{pmatrix} 2 \\ 3 \end{pmatrix}$. Label this triangle P.

c Draw the image of ABC after a translation with vector $\begin{pmatrix} -1 \\ 2 \end{pmatrix}$. Label this triangle Q.

d Draw the image of ABC after a translation with vector $\begin{pmatrix} 3 \\ -2 \end{pmatrix}$. Label this triangle R.

e Draw the image of ABC after a translation with vector $\begin{pmatrix} -2 \\ -4 \end{pmatrix}$. Label this triangle S.

3 Using your diagram from question **2**, use vectors to describe the translation that will move

a P to Q   **b** Q to R   **c** R to S   **d** S to P

e R to P   **f** S to Q   **g** R to Q   **e** P to S

4 Take a 10 × 10 grid and the triangle A(0, 0), B(1, 0) and C(0, 1). How many different translations are there that use integer values only and will move the triangle ABC to somewhere in the grid?

In this section you will learn how to:

- reflect a 2-D shape in a mirror line

Key words

image
mirror line
object
reflection

A **reflection** transforms a shape so that it becomes a mirror image of itself.

EXAMPLE 3

Object

Mirror line

Image

Notice the reflection of each point in the original shape, called the **object**, is perpendicular to the **mirror line**. So if you "fold" the whole diagram along the mirror line, the object will coincide with its reflection, called its **image**.

EXERCISE 8C

1 Copy the diagram below and draw the reflection of the given triangle in the following lines.

    a $x = 2$ **b** $x = -1$ **c** $x = 3$ **d** $y = 2$ **e** $y = -1$ **f** y-axis

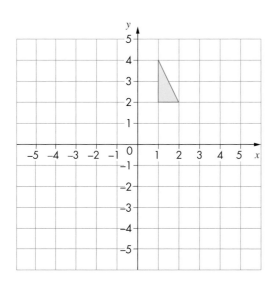

D

2 a Draw a pair of axes, x-axis from –5 to 5, y-axis from –5 to 5.

b Draw the triangle with coordinates A(1, 1), B(3, 1), C(4, 5).

c Reflect the triangle ABC in the x-axis. Label the image P.

d Reflect triangle P in the y-axis. Label the image Q.

e Reflect triangle Q in the x-axis. Label the image R.

f Describe the reflection that will move triangle ABC to triangle R.

3 a Draw a pair of axes, x-axis from –5 to +5 and y-axis from –5 to +5.

b Reflect the points A(2, 1), B(5, 0), C(–3, 3), D(3, –2) in the x-axis.

c What do you notice about the values of the coordinates of the reflected points?

d What would the coordinates of the reflected point be if the point (a, b) were reflected in the x-axis?

4 a Draw a pair of axes, x-axis from –5 to +5 and y-axis from –5 to +5.

b Reflect the points A(2, 1), B(0, 5), C(3, –2), D(–4, –3) in the y-axis.

c What do you notice about the values of the coordinates of the reflected points?

d What would the coordinates of the reflected point be if the point (a, b) were reflected in the y-axis?

5 Draw each of these triangles on squared paper, leaving plenty of space on the opposite side of the given mirror line. Then draw the reflection of each triangle.

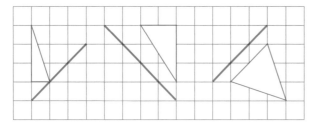

HINTS AND TIPS

Turn the page so that the mirror line is horizontal or vertical.

6 a Draw a pair of axes and the lines y = x and y = –x, as shown.

b Draw the triangle with coordinates A(2, 1), B(5, 1), C(5, 3).

c Draw the reflection of triangle ABC in the x-axis and label the image P.

d Draw the reflection of triangle P in the line y = –x and label the image Q.

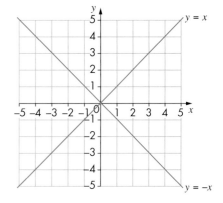

e Draw the reflection of triangle Q in the y-axis and label the image R.

f Draw the reflection of triangle R in the line y = x and label the image S.

g Draw the reflection of triangle S in the x-axis and label the image T.

h Draw the reflection of triangle T in the line y = –x and label the image U.

i Draw the reflection of triangle U in the y-axis and label the image W.

j What single reflection will move triangle W to triangle ABC?

Copy the diagram and reflect the triangle in these lines.

a $y = x$

b $x = 1$

c $y = -x$

d $y = -1$

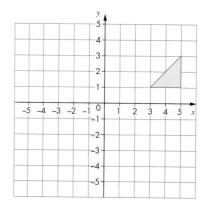

8 **a** Draw a pair of axes, x-axis from -5 to $+5$ and y-axis from -5 to $+5$.

b Draw the line $y = x$.

c Reflect the points A(2, 1), B(5, 0), C(−3, 2), D(−2, −4) in the line $y = x$.

d What do you notice about the values of the coordinates of the reflected points?

e What would the coordinates of the reflected point be if the point (a, b) were reflected in the line $y = x$?

9 **a** Draw a pair of axes, x-axis from -5 to $+5$ and y-axis from -5 to $+5$.

b Draw the line $y = -x$.

c Reflect the points A(2, 1), B(0, 5), C(3, −2), D(−4, −3) in the line $y = -x$.

d What do you notice about the values of the coordinates of the reflected points?

e What would the coordinates of the reflected point be if the point (a, b) were reflected in the line $y = -x$?

8.4 Rotations

In this section you will learn how to:
- rotate a 2-D shape about a point

Key words
angle of rotation
anticlockwise
centre of rotation
clockwise
rotation

A **rotation** transforms a shape to a new position by turning it about a fixed point called the **centre of rotation**.

EXAMPLE 4

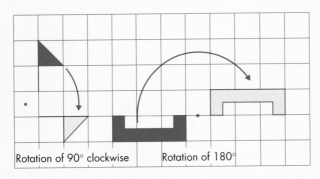

Rotation of 90° clockwise   Rotation of 180°

Note:

- The direction of turn or the **angle of rotation** is expressed as **clockwise** or **anticlockwise**.
- The position of the centre of rotation is always specified.
- The rotations 180° clockwise and 180° anticlockwise are the same.

The rotations which most often appear in examination questions are 90° and 180°.

EXERCISE 8D

1 On squared paper, draw each of these shapes and its centre of rotation, leaving plenty of space all round the shape.

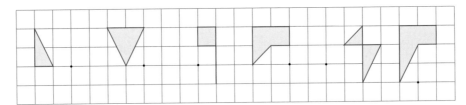

a Rotate each shape about its centre of rotation

i first by 90° clockwise (call the image A)   **ii** then by 90° anticlockwise (call the image B).

b Describe, in each case, the rotation that would take

i A back to its original position   **ii** A to B.

2 Copy the diagram and rotate the given triangle by the following.

a 90° clockwise about (0, 0)

b 180° about (3, 3)

c 90° anticlockwise about (0, 2)

d 180° about (−1, 0)

e 90° clockwise about (−1, −1)

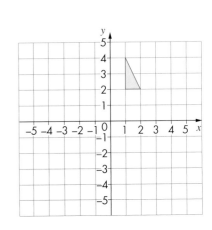

3 What other rotations are equivalent to these rotations?

a 270° clockwise b 90° clockwise c 60° anticlockwise d 100° anticlockwise

4 a Draw a pair of axes where both the x and y values are from –5 to 5.

b Draw the triangle ABC, where A = (1, 2), B = (2, 4) and C = (4, 1).

c i Rotate triangle ABC 90° clockwise about the origin (0, 0) and label the image A′, B′, C′, where A′ is the image of A, etc.

ii Write down the coordinates of A′, B′, C′.

iii What connection is there between A, B, C and A′, B′, C′?

iv Will this connection always be so for a 90° clockwise to rotation about the origin?

5 Repeat question **4**, but rotate triangle ABC through 180°.

6 Repeat question **4**, but rotate triangle ABC 90° anticlockwise.

7 Show that a reflection in the x-axis followed by a reflection in the y-axis is equivalent to a rotation of 180° about the origin.

8 Show that a reflection in the line y = x followed by a reflection in the line y = –x is equivalent to a rotation of 180° about the origin.

9 a Draw a regular hexagon ABCDEF with centre O.

b Using O as the centre of rotation, describe a transformation that will result in the following movements.

i triangle AOB to triangle BOC ii triangle AOB to triangle COD

iii triangle AOB to triangle DOE iv triangle AOB to triangle EOF

c Describe the transformations that will move the rhombus ABCO to these positions.

i rhombus BCDO ii rhombus DEFO

Enlargements

In this section you will learn how to:
- enlarge a 2-D shape by a scale factor

Key words

centre of
   enlargement
enlargement
scale factor

An **enlargement** changes the size of a shape to give a similar image. It always has a **centre of enlargement** and a **scale factor**. Every length of the enlarged shape will be

Original length × Scale factor

The distance of each image point on the enlargement from the centre of enlargement will be

Distance of original point from centre of enlargement × Scale factor

---

EXAMPLE 5

The diagram shows the enlargement of triangle ABC by scale factor 3 about the centre of enlargement X.

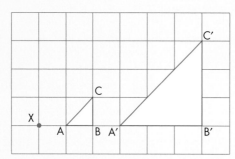

Note:

- Each length on the enlargement A'B'C' is three times the corresponding length on the original shape.

  This means that the corresponding sides are in the same ratio:

  AB:A'B' = AC:A'C' = BC:B'C' = 1:3

- The distance of any point on the enlargement from the centre of enlargement is three times longer than the distance from the corresponding point on the original shape to the centre of enlargement.

There are two distinct ways to enlarge a shape: the ray method and the coordinate method.

Ray method

This is the *only* way to construct an enlargement when the diagram is not on a grid.

EXAMPLE 6

Enlarge triangle ABC by scale factor 3 about the centre of enlargement X.

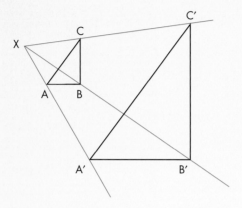

Notice that the rays have been drawn from the centre of enlargement to each vertex and beyond.

The distance from X to each vertex on triangle ABC is measured and multiplied by 3 to give the distance from X to each vertex A′, B′ and C′ for the enlarged triangle A′B′C′.

Once each image vertex has been found, the whole enlarged shape can then be drawn.

Check the measurements and see for yourself how the calculations have been done.

Notice again that the length of each side on the enlarged triangle is three times longer than the length of the corresponding side on the original triangle.

Counting squares method

EXAMPLE 7

Enlarge the triangle ABC by scale factor 3 from the centre of enlargement (1, 2).

To find the coordinates of each image vertex, first work out the horizontal and vertical distances from each original vertex to the centre of enlargement.

Then multiply each of these distances by 3 to find the position of each image vertex.

For example, to find the coordinates of C′ work out the distance from the centre of enlargement (1, 2) to the point C(3, 5).

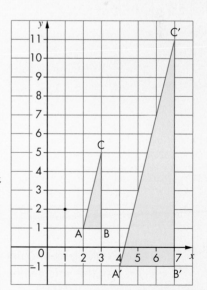

    horizontal distance = 2

    vertical distance = 3

Make these 3 times longer to give

    new horizontal distance = 6

    new vertical distance = 9

So the coordinates of C′ are

    (1 + 6, 2 + 9) = (7, 11)

Notice again that the length of each side is three times longer in the enlargement.

Negative enlargement

A negative enlargement produces an image shape on the opposite side of the centre of enlargement to the original shape.

EXAMPLE 8

Triangle ABC has been enlarged by scale factor −2, with the centre of enlargement at (1, 0).

You can enlarge triangle ABC to give triangle A′B′C′ by either the ray method or the coordinate method. You calculate the new lengths on the opposite side of the centre of enlargement to the original shape.

Notice how a negative scale factor also inverts the original shape.

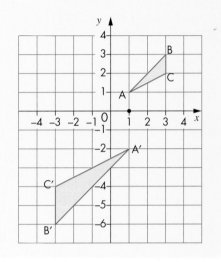

Fractional enlargement

Strange but true … you can have an enlargement in mathematics that is actually smaller than the original shape!

EXAMPLE 9

Triangle ABC has been enlarged by a scale factor of $\frac{1}{2}$ about the centre of enlargement O to give triangle A′B′C′.

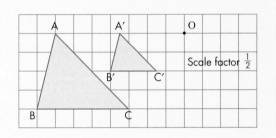

EXERCISE 8E

1. Make larger copies of each of these figures with its centre of enlargement, leaving plenty of space for the enlargement. Then enlarge it by the given scale factor, using the ray method.

Scale factor 2

Scale factor 3

Scale factor 2

Scale factor −3

2 **a** Draw a triangle ABC on squared paper.

   b Mark four different centres of enlargement on your diagram as follows.

   one above your triangle   one to the left of your triangle
   one below your triangle   one to the right of your triangle

   c Enlarge the triangle by a scale factor of 2 from each centre.

   d What do you notice about each enlarged shape?

3 Enlarge each of these shapes by a scale factor of $\frac{1}{2}$ about the given centre of enlargement.

4 Copy this diagram onto squared paper.

   a Enlarge the rectangle A by scale factor $\frac{1}{3}$ about the origin.
   Label the image B.

   b Write down the ratio of the lengths of the sides of
   rectangle A to the lengths of the sides of rectangle B.

   c Work out the ratio of the perimeter of rectangle A to the
   perimeter of rectangle B.

   d Work out the ratio of the area of rectangle A to the
   area of rectangle B.

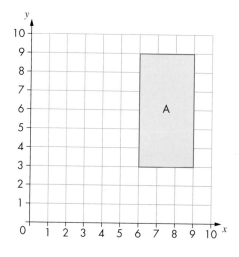

5 Copy the diagram onto squared paper.

   a Enlarge A by a scale factor of 3 about a centre (4, 5).

   b Enlarge B by a scale factor $\frac{1}{2}$ about a centre (−1, −3).

   c Enlarge B by scale factor $-\frac{1}{2}$ about a centre (−3, −1).

   d What is the centre of enlargement and scale factor
   which maps B onto A?

   e What is the centre of enlargement and scale factor
   which maps A onto B?

   f What is the centre of enlargement and scale factor
   which maps the answer to part **b** to the answer to
   part **c**?

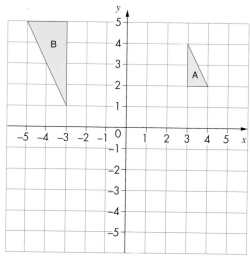

   g What is the centre of enlargement and scale factor which maps the answer to part **c** to the
   answer to part **b**?

   h What is the connection between the scale factors and the centres of enlargement in parts **d**
   and **e**, and in parts **f** and **g**?

Combined transformations

In this section you will learn how to:

• combine transformations

Key words
enlargement
reflection
rotation
transformation
translation

Examination questions often require you to use more than one transformation in a question. This exercise will revise the transformations you have met in this chapter.

EXERCISE 8F

C

1 Describe fully the transformations that will map the shaded triangle onto each of the triangles A–F.

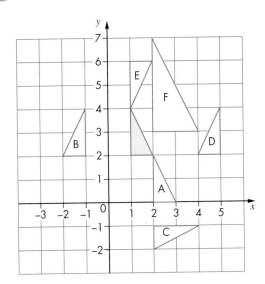

2 Describe fully the transformations that will result in the following movements.

a T_1 to T_2

b T_1 to T_6

c T_2 to T_3

d T_6 to T_2

e T_6 to T_5

f T_5 to T_4

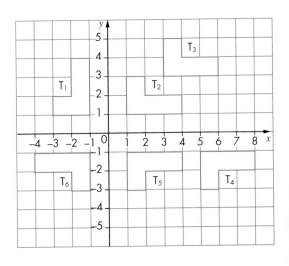

3 **a** Plot a triangle T with vertices (1,1), (2,1), (1,3).

   b Reflect triangle T in the *y*-axis and label the image T_b.

   c Rotate triangle T_b 90° anticlockwise about the origin and label the image T_c.

   d Reflect triangle T_c in the *y*-axis and label the image T_d.

   e Describe fully the transformation that will move triangle T_d back to triangle T.

4 The point P(3, 4) is reflected in the *x*-axis, then rotated by 90° clockwise about the origin. What are the coordinates of the image of P?

5 A point Q(5, 2) is rotated by 180°, then reflected in the *x*-axis.

   a What are the coordinates of the image point of Q?

   b What single transformation would have taken point Q directly to the image point?

6 Find the coordinates of the image of the point (3, 5) after a clockwise rotation of 90° about the point (1, 3).

7 Describe fully at least three different transformations that could move the square labelled S to the square labelled T.

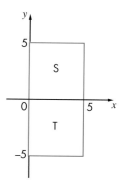

8 The point A(4, 4) has been transformed to the point A′(4, −4). Describe as many different transformations as you can that could transform point A to point A′.

9 Describe the single transformation equivalent to a reflection in the *y*-axis followed by a reflection in the *x*-axis.

1

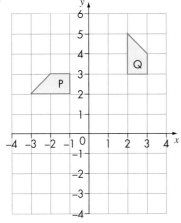

Describe fully the single transformation that maps shape P onto shape Q.

Edexcel, Question 2, Paper 10A Higher, January 2003

2

a Copy the grid below.

  i Reflect the shaded triangle in the line $y = -x$. Label it A.

  ii Rotate the shaded triangle 90° clockwise about (−1, 1). Label it B.

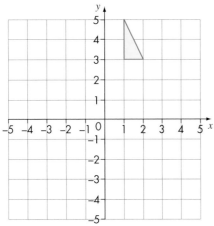

b Describe the *single* transformation that takes triangle A to triangle B.

3

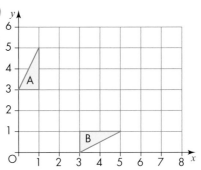

Triangle A and triangle B have been drawn on the grid.

Describe fully the single transformation which will map triangle A onto triangle B.

Edexcel, Question 3, Paper 5 Higher, June 2005

4

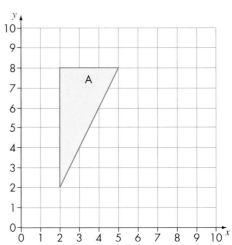

a On a copy of the grid, translate triangle A by the vector $\begin{pmatrix} 4 \\ -2 \end{pmatrix}$. Label the triangle B.

b On the copy of the grid, enlarge triangle A by a scale factor of $\frac{1}{3}$ about the point (5, 2).

5 PQRS is a parallelogram.
Prove that triangle PQS is congruent to triangle RSQ.

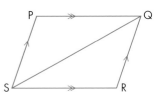

Edexcel, Question 15a, Paper 5 Higher, November 2004

WORKED EXAM QUESTION

The grid shows two congruent shapes, A and B.

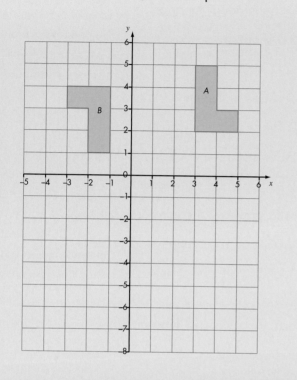

a Describe the single transformation of shape A to shape B.

b On a copy of the grid, draw the enlargement of shape A by scale factor −2, centre of enlargement (2, 1).

Solution

a A rotation of 180° about the point (1, 3). Use tracing paper to rotate the triangle until the centre of rotation is located.

b Use the ray method or the counting squares method. Remember a negative scale factor inverts the shape on the other side of the centre of enlargement.

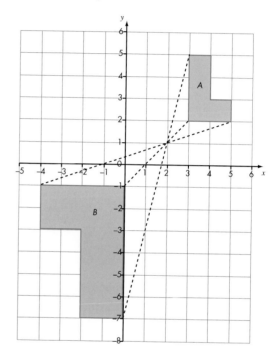

GRADE YOURSELF

D Able to reflect a 2-D shape in a line $x = a$ or $y = b$

D Able to rotate a 2-D shape about the origin

D Able to enlarge a 2-D shape by a whole number scale factor

C Able to translate a 2-D shape by a vector

C Able to reflect a 2-D shape in the line $y = x$ or $y = -x$

C Able to rotate a 2-D shape about any point

C Able to enlarge a 2-D shape by a fractional scale factor

C Able to enlarge a 2-D shape about any point

B Know the conditions to show two triangles are congruent

B Able to enlarge a 2-D shape by a negative scale factor

A Able to prove two triangles are congruent

What you should know now

- How to translate a 2-D shape by a vector
- How to reflect a 2-D shape in any line
- How to rotate a 2-D shape about any point and through any angle
- How to enlarge a 2-D shape about any point using a positive, fractional or negative scale factor
- How to show that two triangles are congruent

Constructions

This chapter will show you ...

- how to bisect a line and an angle
- how to construct perpendiculars
- how to define a locus
- how to solve locus problems

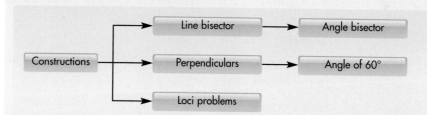

What you should already know

- How to construct triangles using a protractor and a pair of compasses
- How to use scale drawings

Quick check

Construct these triangles using a ruler, protractor and a pair of compasses.

1

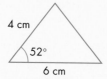

4 cm

52°

6 cm

2

65° 75°

4 cm

3

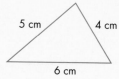

5 cm   4 cm

6 cm

In this section you will learn how to:

- bisect a line and an angle

Key words

angle bisector
bisector
line bisector
perpendicular
  bisector

To bisect means to divide in half. So a **bisector** divides something into two equal parts.

- A **line bisector** divides a straight line into two equal lengths.

- An **angle bisector** is the straight line which divides an angle into two equal angles.

EXAMPLE 1

To construct a line bisector

It is usually more accurate to construct a line bisector than to measure its position (the midpoint of the line).

Bisect the line AB.   A ———————— B

- Open your compasses to a radius of about three quarters of the length of the line. Using A and B as centres, draw two intersecting arcs without changing the radius of your compasses.

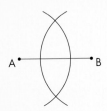

- Join the two points at which the arcs intersect to meet AB at X. This line is known as the **perpendicular bisector** of AB.

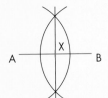

          X is the midpoint of AB.

EXAMPLE 2

To construct an angle bisector

It is much more accurate to construct an angle bisector than to measure with a protractor.

Bisect ∠BAC.

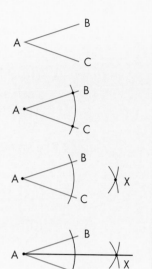

- Open your compasses to any reasonable radius. If in doubt, go for about 3 cm. With centre at A, draw an arc through both lines of the angle.

- With centres at the two points at which this arc intersects the lines, draw two more arcs so that they intersect at X. (The radius of the compasses may have to be increased to do this.)

- Join AX.

  This line is the **angle bisector** of ∠BAC.

  So ∠BAX = ∠CAX.

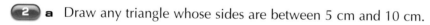

EXERCISE 9A

In this exercise, it is important to leave in all your construction lines.

1 Draw a line 7 cm long. Bisect it using a pair of compasses and a ruler only. Check your accuracy by measuring to see if each half is 3.5 cm.

2 a Draw any triangle whose sides are between 5 cm and 10 cm.

b On each side construct the perpendicular bisector as on the diagram. All your perpendicular bisectors should intersect at the same point.

c Use this point as the centre of a circle that touches each vertex of the triangle. Draw this circle. This circle is known as the *circumscribed circle* of the triangle.

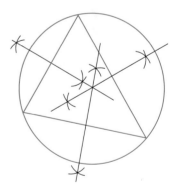

3 Repeat question **2** with a different triangle and check that you get a similar result.

4 a Draw a quadrilateral whose opposite angles add up to 180°.

b On each side construct the perpendicular bisectors. They all should intersect at the same point.

c Use this point as the centre of a circle that touches the quadrilateral at each vertex. Draw this circle.

5 a Draw an angle of 50°.

b Construct the angle bisector.

c Use a protractor to check how accurate you have been. Each angle should be 25°.

6 **a** Draw any triangle whose sides are between 5 cm and 10 cm.

b At each angle construct the angle bisector as on the diagram. All three bisectors should intersect at the same point.

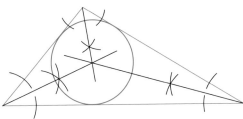

c Use this point as the centre of a circle that touches each side of the triangle once. Draw this circle. This circle is known as the *inscribed circle* of the triangle.

7 Repeat question **6** with a different triangle and check that you get a similar result.

9.2 Other angle constructions

In this section you will learn how to:
- construct perpendiculars from a point
- construct an angle of 60°

Key words
construct
perpendicular

EXAMPLE 3

To construct a perpendicular from a point on a line

This construction will produce a perpendicular from a point A on a line.

- Open your compasses to about 2 or 3 cm. With point A as centre, draw two short arcs to intersect the line at each side of the point.

- Now extend the radius of your compasses to about 4 cm. With centres at the two points at which the arcs intersect the line, draw two arcs to intersect at X above the line.

- Join AX.

  AX is perpendicular to the line.

Note: If you needed to construct a 90° angle at the end of a line, you would first have to extend the line.

You could be even more accurate by also drawing two arcs underneath the line, which would give three points in line.

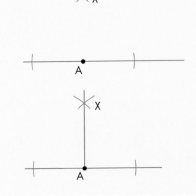

EXAMPLE 4

To construct a perpendicular from a point to a line

This construction will produce a perpendicular from a point A to a line.

- With point A as centre, draw an arc which intersects the line at two points.

- With centres at these two points of intersection, draw two arcs to intersect each other both above and below the line.

- Join the two points at which the arcs intersect. The resulting line passes through point A and is perpendicular to the line.

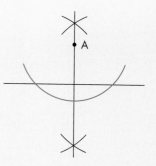

Examination note: When a question says *construct*, you must only use compasses – no protractor. When it says *draw*, you may use whatever you can to produce an accurate diagram. But also note, when constructing you may use your protractor to check your accuracy.

EXAMPLE 5

To construct an angle of 60°

This construction will produce an angle of 60° from a point A on a line.

- Open your compasses to about 3 cm. With point A as centre, draw an arc from above to intersect the line at point B.

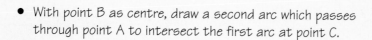

- With point B as centre, draw a second arc which passes through point A to intersect the first arc at point C.

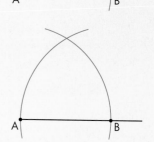

- Join AC.

    ∠CAB = 60°

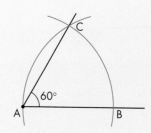

EXERCISE 9B

In this exercise, it is important to leave in all your construction lines.

1 Construct these triangles accurately without using a protractor.

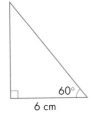 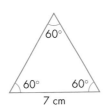

2 **a** Without using a protractor, construct a square of side 6 cm.

b See how accurate you have been by constructing an angle bisector on any of the right angles and seeing whether this also cuts through the opposite right angle.

3 **a** Construct an angle of 90°.

b Bisect this angle to construct an angle of 45°.

4 **a** Construct these angles.　　**i** 30°　　**ii** 15°　　**iii** 22.5°　　**iv** 75°

b Check your accuracy by measuring with a protractor. (The allowable error is ±1°.)

5 With ruler and compasses only, construct these triangles.

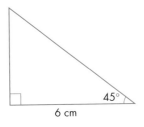 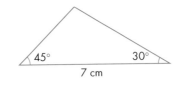 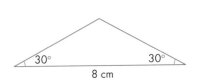

6 Construct an isosceles triangle ABC, where AB = AC = 7 cm and ∠CAB = 120°.

7 Construct a trapezium whose parallel sides are 8 cm and 6 cm, and having an angle of 60° at each end of the longer side.

8 **a** Construct the triangle ABC, where AB = 7 cm, ∠BAC = 60° and ∠ABC = 45°.

b Measure the lengths of AC and BC.

9 **a** Construct the triangle PQR, where PQ = 8 cm, ∠RPQ = 30° and ∠PQR = 45°.

b Measure the lengths of PR and RQ.

10 Construct a parallelogram which has sides of 6 cm and 8 cm and with an angle of 105°.

11 Draw a straight line and mark a point above the line. Construct the perpendicular which passes through that point to the line.

Defining a locus

In this section you will learn how to:
● draw a locus for a given rule

Key words
loci
locus

A **locus** (plural **loci**) is the movement of a point according to a given rule.

EXAMPLE 6

A point P that moves so that it is always at a distance of 5 cm from a fixed point A will have a locus that is a circle of radius 5 cm.

You can express this mathematically by saying

the locus of the point P is such that AP = 5 cm.

EXAMPLE 7

A point P that moves so that it is always the same distance from two fixed points A and B will have a locus that is the perpendicular bisector of the line joining A and B.

You can express this mathematically by saying

the locus of the point P is such that AP = BP.

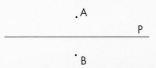

EXAMPLE 8

A point that moves so that it is always 5 cm from a line AB will have a locus that is a racetrack shape around the line.

This is difficult to express mathematically.

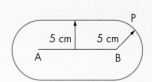

In your GCSE examination, you will usually get practical situations rather than abstract mathematical ones.

EXAMPLE 9

A point that is always 5 m from a long, straight wall will have a locus that is a line parallel to the wall and 5 m from it.

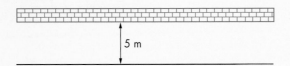

EXAMPLE 10

Imagine a grassy, flat field in which a horse is tethered to a stake by a rope that is 10 m long. What is the shape of the area that the horse can graze?

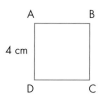

In reality, the horse may not be able to reach the full 10 m if the rope is tied round its neck but ignore fine details like that. You "model" the situation by saying that the horse can move around in a 10 m circle and graze all the grass within that circle.

In this example, the locus is the whole of the area inside the circle.

You can express this mathematically as

the locus of the point P is such that AP ⩽ 10 m.

EXERCISE 9C

1. A is a fixed point. Sketch the locus of the point P in each of these situations.

   a AP = 2 cm   b AP = 4 cm   c AP = 5 cm

2. A and B are two fixed points 5 cm apart. Sketch the locus of the point P for each of these situations.

   a AP = BP

   b AP = 4 cm and BP = 4 cm

   c P is always within 2 cm of the line AB

3. A horse is tethered in a field on a rope 4 m long. Describe or sketch the area that the horse can graze.

4. The horse is still tethered by the same rope but there is now a long, straight fence running 2 m from the stake. Sketch the area that the horse can now graze.

5. ABCD is a square of side 4 cm. In each of the following loci, the point P moves only inside the square. Sketch the locus in each case.

   a AP = BP   b AP < BP   c AP = CP

   d CP < 4 cm   e CP > 2 cm   f CP > 5 cm

6. One of the following diagrams is the locus of a point on the rim of a bicycle wheel as it moves along a flat road. Which is it?

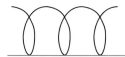 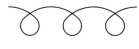  

7. Draw the locus of the centre of the wheel for the bicycle in question 6.

Loci problems

In this section you will learn how to:
- solve practical problems using loci

Key words
loci
scale

Most of the **loci** problems in your GCSE examination will be of a practical nature, as in the next example.

EXAMPLE 11

Imagine that a radio company wants to find a site for a transmitter. The transmitter must be the same distance from Doncaster and Leeds and within 20 miles of Sheffield.

In mathematical terms, this means they are concerned with the perpendicular bisector between Leeds and Doncaster and the area within a circle of radius 20 miles from Sheffield.

The map, drawn to a **scale** of 1 cm = 10 miles, illustrates the situation and shows that the transmitter can be built anywhere along the thick part of the blue line.

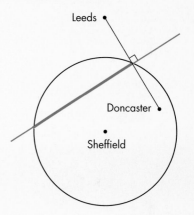

EXERCISE 9D

For questions **1** to **7**, you should start by sketching the picture given in each question on a 6 × 6 grid, each square of which is 1 cm by 1 cm. The scale for each question is given.

1 A goat is tethered by a rope, 7 m long, in a corner of a field with a fence at each side. What is the locus of the area that the goat can graze? Use a scale of 1 cm ≡ 2 m.

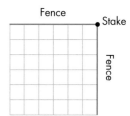

2 In a field a horse is tethered to a stake by a rope 6 m long. What is the locus of the area that the horse can graze? Use a scale of 1 cm ≡ 2 m.

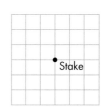

3 A cow is tethered to a rail at the top of a fence 6 m long. The rope is 3 m long. Sketch the area that the cow can graze. Use a scale of 1 cm ≡ 2 m.

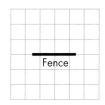

4 A horse is tethered to a stake near a corner of a fenced field, at a point 4 m from each fence. The rope is 6 m long. Sketch the area that the horse can graze. Use a scale of 1 cm ≡ 2 m.

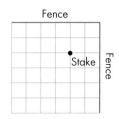

5 A horse is tethered to a corner of a shed, 2 m by 1 m. The rope is 2 m long. Sketch the area that the horse can graze. Use a scale of 1 cm ≡ 1 m.

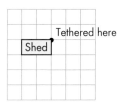

6 A goat is tethered by a 4 m rope to a stake at one corner of a pen, 4 m by 3 m. Sketch the area of the pen on which the goat cannot graze. Use a scale of 1 cm ≡ 1 m.

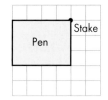

7 A puppy is tethered to a stake by a rope, 1.5 m long, on a flat lawn on which are two raised brick flower beds. The stake is situated at one corner of a bed, as shown. Sketch the area that the puppy is free to roam in. Use a scale of 1 cm ≡ 1 m.

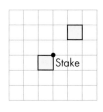

For questions **8** to **15**, you should use a copy of the map opposite. For each question, trace the map and mark on those points that are relevant to that question.

8 A radio station broadcasts from London on a frequency of 1000 kHz with a range of 300 km. Another radio station broadcasts from Glasgow on the same frequency with a range of 200 km.

  a Sketch the area to which each station can broadcast.

  b Will they interfere with each other?

  c If the Glasgow station increases its range to 400 km, will they then interfere with each other?

9 The radar at Leeds airport has a range of 200 km. The radar at Exeter airport has a range of 200 km.

  a Will a plane flying over Birmingham be detected by the Leeds radar?

  b Sketch the area where a plane can be picked up by both radars at the same time.

10 A radio transmitter is to be built according to these rules.

    i   It has to be the same distance from York and Birmingham.

    ii It must be within 350 km of Glasgow.

    iii It must be within 250 km of London.

  a Sketch the line that is the same distance from York and Birmingham.

  b Sketch the area that is within 350 km of Glasgow and 250 km of London.

  c Show clearly the possible places at which the transmitter could be built.

11 A radio transmitter centred at Birmingham is designed to give good reception in an area greater than 150 km and less than 250 km from the transmitter. Sketch the area of good reception.

12 Three radio stations pick up a distress call from a boat in the Irish Sea. The station at Glasgow can tell from the strength of the signal that the boat is within 300 km of the station. The station at York can tell that the boat is between 200 km and 300 km from York. The station at London can tell that it is less than 400 km from London. Sketch the area where the boat could be.

13 Sketch the area that is between 200 km and 300 km from Newcastle upon Tyne, and between 150 km and 250 km from Bristol.

14 An oil rig is situated in the North Sea in such a position that it is the same distance from Newcastle upon Tyne and Manchester. It is also the same distance from Sheffield and Norwich. Draw the line that shows all the points that are the same distance from Newcastle upon Tyne and Manchester. Repeat for the points that are the same distance from Sheffield and Norwich and find out where the oil rig is located.

15 Whilst looking at a map, Fred notices that his house is the same distance from Glasgow, Norwich and Exeter. Where is it?

16 Wathsea Harbour is as shown in the diagram.
A boat sets off from point A and steers so that it keeps the same distance from the sea wall and the West Pier. Another boat sets off from B and steers so that it keeps the same distance from the East Pier and the sea wall. Copy the diagram below, and on your diagram show accurately the path of each boat.

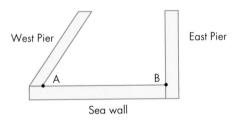

17 The curve $x^2 + y^2 = 25$ is a circle of radius 5 centred on the origin.

  a Show that the points (3, 4) and (–4, 3) lie on the curve.

  b Sketch the loci of the curve $x^2 + y^2 = 16$ showing clearly the values where it crosses the axes.

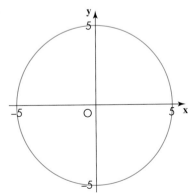

1 Make an accurate drawing of this triangle.

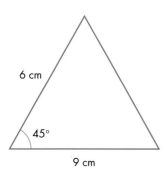

2 Construct an accurate drawing of this triangle.

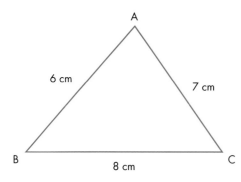

3 a Construct an accurate drawing of this triangle

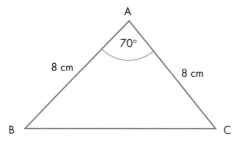

b Measure the length BC.

4 a Construct an angle of 60°.

b Copy the line AB and then construct the perpendicular bisector of the points A and B.

5 The map shows a small island with two towns A and B. Town B is north west of town A. The map is drawn to a scale of 1 square to 10 km.

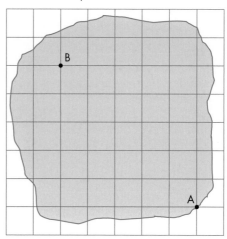

a What bearing is the direction north·west?

b A mobile phone mast is to be built. It has to be within 40 km of both towns. Copy the map and shade the area in which the mast could be built.

6 The diagram represents a triangular garden ABC.

The scale of the diagram is 1 cm represents 1 m.

A tree is to be planted in the garden so that it is nearer to AB than to AC, within 5 m of point A.

Copy the diagram and shade the region where the tree may be planted.

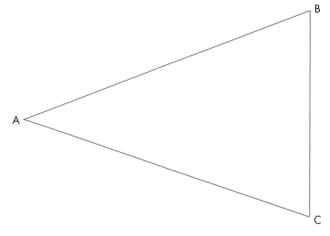

Edexcel, Question 7, Paper 5 Higher, June 2003

7

—P

X ———————————————————— Y

Use a ruler and compasses to construct the perpendicular from P to the line segment XY. You must show all construction lines.

8 This is a map of part of Northern England.

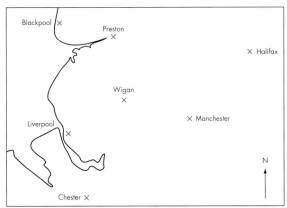

Scale: 1 cm represents 10 km

A radio station in Manchester transmits programmes. Its programmes can be received anywhere within a distance of 30 km.

On a copy of the diagram, shade the region in which the programmes can be received.

Edexcel, Question 2, Paper 6 Higher, June 2004

9 Use a ruler and compasses to construct the bisector of angle ABC. You must show all construction lines.

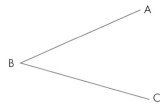

10 The diagram shows three points A, B and C on a centimetre grid.

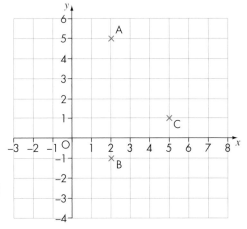

a On a copy of the grid, draw the locus of points which are equidistant from A and B.

b On a copy of the grid, draw the locus of points that are 3 cm from C.

c On a copy of the grid, shade the region in which points are nearer to A than B and also less than 3 cm from C.

Edexcel, Question 1, Paper 13A Higher, January 2004

WORKED EXAM QUESTION

The map shows two trees, A and B, in a park. At the edge of the park there is a straight path.

A new tree, C, is to be planted in the park.

The tree must be:

more than 60 m from the path,

closer to A than B,

more than 100 m from A.

Using a ruler and compasses only, shade the region where the tree could be planted.

You must show all construction lines.

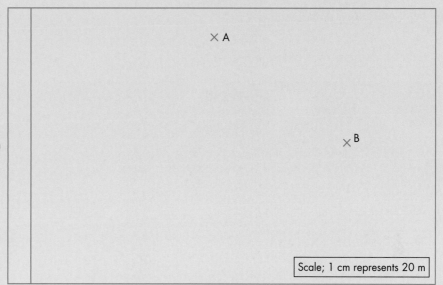

Solution

Draw a parallel line 3 cm from the path.

Draw the perpendicular bisector of AB.

Draw a circle of radius 5 cm at A.

The region required is shaded on the diagram.

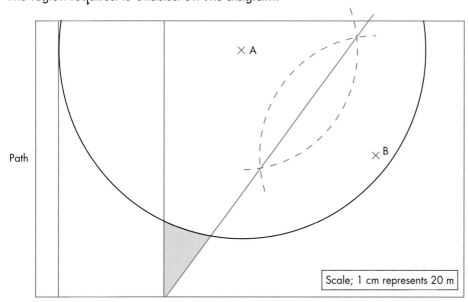

Bill the builder builds a street of 100 bungalows, 50 on each side of the street.

He builds them in blocks of 5.

The bungalows at the end of the blocks are called end-terraced, and the other bungalows are called mid-terraced.

3.2m

Key:
■ gate
■ door
■ window
— fence
□ garden shed

Here is the plan of one block of five.

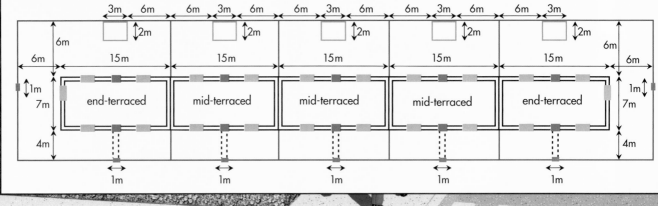

A tree is to be planted in the back garden of each mid-terraced house. The tree must be at least 2 m from the back of the house, at least 1 m from the back fence of the garden, and at least 3.5 m from each of the bottom corners of the garden. It must also be at least 1.5 m from the garden shed.

Draw an accurate scale drawing, using a scale of 1 cm ≡ 1 m, of a mid-terraced house and garden. Shade the region in which Bill can plant the tree.

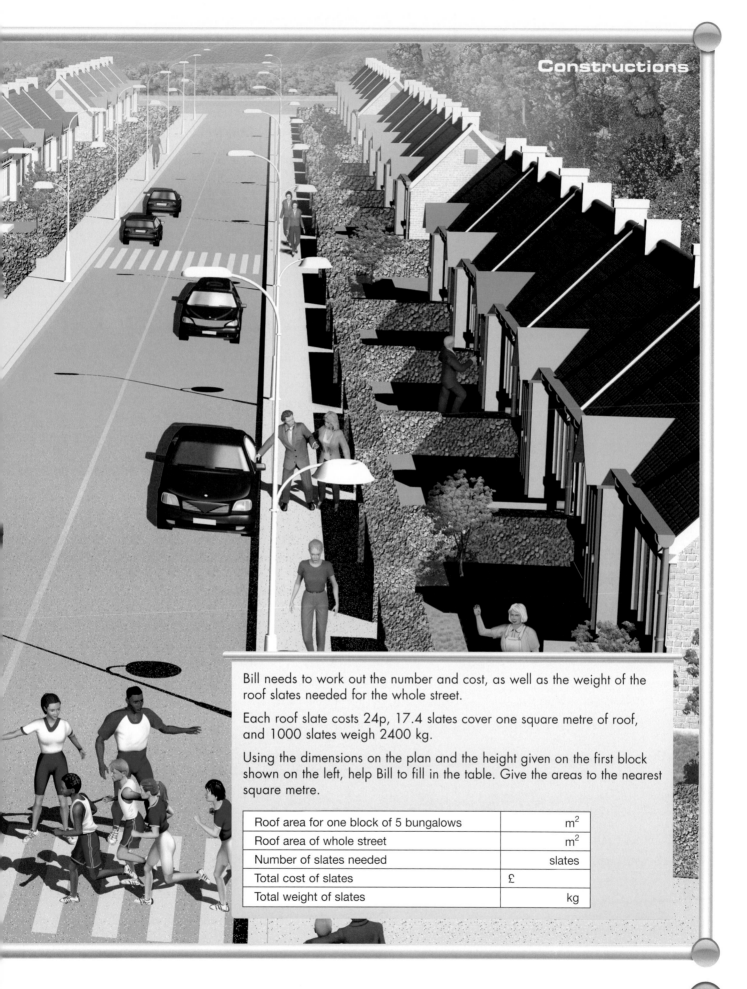

Bill needs to work out the number and cost, as well as the weight of the roof slates needed for the whole street.

Each roof slate costs 24p, 17.4 slates cover one square metre of roof, and 1000 slates weigh 2400 kg.

Using the dimensions on the plan and the height given on the first block shown on the left, help Bill to fill in the table. Give the areas to the nearest square metre.

Roof area for one block of 5 bungalows		m^2
Roof area of whole street		m^2
Number of slates needed		slates
Total cost of slates	£	
Total weight of slates		kg

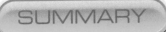

GRADE YOURSELF

c Able to construct line and angle bisectors

c Able to draw and describe the locus of a point from a given rule

c Able to solve problems using loci

B Able to construct a perpendicular from a point on a line

B Able to construct a perpendicular from a point to a line

B Able to construct an angle of 60°

What you should know now

- How to construct line and angle bisectors
- How to construct perpendiculars
- How to construct angles without a protractor
- Understand what is meant by a locus
- How to solve problems using loci

Powers, standard form and surds

This chapter will show you ...

- how to calculate with indices
- how to write numbers in standard form and how to calculate with standard form
- how to convert fractions to terminating and recurring decimals, and vice versa
- how to work out a reciprocal
- how to calculate with surds

Visual overview

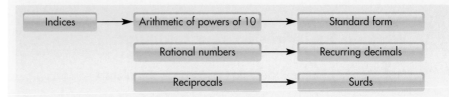

What you should already know

- How to convert a fraction to a decimal
- How to convert a decimal to a fraction
- How to find the lowest common denominator of two fractions
- The meaning of square root and cube root

Quick check

1 Convert the following fractions to decimals.

  a $\frac{6}{10}$ **b** $\frac{11}{25}$ **c** $\frac{3}{8}$

2 Convert the following decimals to fractions.

  a 0.17   **b** 0.64   **c** 0.858

3 Work these out.   **a** $\frac{2}{3} + \frac{1}{5}$ **b** $\frac{5}{8} - \frac{2}{5}$

4 Write down the values.   **a** $\sqrt{25}$ **b** $\sqrt[3]{64}$

The **index** is the number of times a number is multiplied by itself. For example,

$$4^6 = 4 \times 4 \times 4 \times 4 \times 4 \times 4, \ 6^4 = 6 \times 6 \times 6 \times 6, \ 7^3 = 7 \times 7 \times 7, \ 12^2 = 12 \times 12$$

Here, 4 has an index of 6, 6 has an index of 4, 7 has an index of 3 and 12 has an index of 2.

Indices (or **powers**) can also be used to simplify the writing of repetitive multiplications, For example,

$$3 \times 3 \times 3 \times 3 \times 3 \times 3 \times 3 \times 3 = 3^8, \ 13 \times 13 \times 13 \times 13 \times 13 = 13^5, \ 7 \times 7 \times 7 \times 7 = 7^4$$

A commonly used power is "2", which has the special name "squared". The only other power with a special name is "3", which is called "cubed".

The value of "7 squared" is $7^2 = 7 \times 7 = 49$ and the value of "5 cubed" is $5^3 = 5 \times 5 \times 5 = 125$.

Working out indices on your calculator

How do we work out the value of 5^7 on a calculator?

We could do the calculation as $5 \times 5 \times 5 \times 5 \times 5 \times 5 \times 5 =$. But if we tried to key this in, we would probably end up missing a "× 5" or pressing a wrong key. Instead, we use the power key x^y (or, on some calculators, y^x). So

$$5^7 = \boxed{5} \ \boxed{x^y} \ \boxed{7} \ \boxed{=} \ = 78\,125$$

Make sure you know where to find the power key on your calculator. It may be an INV or SHIFT function.

Two special powers

Choose any number, say 5, and use your calculator to raise it to the power 1. You will find that $5^1 = 5$. That is, a number raised to the power 1 stays the same number. This is true for *any* number, so we do not normally write down the power 1.

Choose any number, say 9, and use your calculator to raise it to the power 0. You will find that $9^0 = 1$. This is true for *any* number raised to the power 0. The answer is *always* 1.

EXERCISE 10A

1 Write these expressions using power notation. Do not work them out yet.

 a $2 \times 2 \times 2 \times 2$ **b** $3 \times 3 \times 3 \times 3 \times 3$

 c 7×7 **d** $5 \times 5 \times 5$

 e $10 \times 10 \times 10 \times 10 \times 10 \times 10 \times 10$ **f** $6 \times 6 \times 6 \times 6$

 g 4 **h** $1 \times 1 \times 1 \times 1 \times 1 \times 1 \times 1$

 i $0.5 \times 0.5 \times 0.5 \times 0.5$ **j** $100 \times 100 \times 100$

2 Write these power terms out in full. Do not work them out yet.

 a 3^4 **b** 9^3 **c** 6^2 **d** 10^5 **e** 2^{10}

 f 8^1 **g** 0.1^3 **h** 2.5^2 **i** 0.7^3 **j** 1000^2

3 Using the power key on your calculator (or another method), work out the values of the power terms in question **1**.

4 Using the power key on your calculator (or another method), work out the values of the power terms in question **2**.

5 Without using a calculator, work out the values of these power terms.

 a 2^0 **b** 4^1 **c** 5^0 **d** 1^9 **e** 1^{235}

6 The answers to question **5**, parts **d** and **e**, should tell you something special about powers of 1. What is it?

7 Write the answer to question **1**, part **j** as a power of 10.

8 Write the answer to question **2**, part **j** as a power of 10.

9 Using your calculator, or otherwise, work out the values of these power terms.

 a $(-1)^0$ **b** $(-1)^1$ **c** $(-1)^2$ **d** $(-1)^4$ **e** $(-1)^5$

10 Using your answers to question **9**, write down the answers to these power terms.

 a $(-1)^8$ **b** $(-1)^{11}$ **c** $(-1)^{99}$ **d** $(-1)^{80}$ **e** $(-1)^{126}$

Negative indices

A negative index is a convenient way of writing the **reciprocal** of a number or term. (That is, one divided by that number or term.) For example,

$$x^{-a} = \frac{1}{x^a}$$

Here are some other examples:

$$5^{-2} = \frac{1}{5^2} \qquad 3^{-1} = \frac{1}{3} \qquad 5x^{-2} = \frac{5}{x^2}$$

EXAMPLE 1

Rewrite the following in the form 2^n.

a 8   **b** $\frac{1}{4}$ **c** -32 **d** $-\frac{1}{64}$

a $8 = 2 \times 2 \times 2 = 2^3$ **b** $\frac{1}{4} = \frac{1}{2^2} = 2^{-2}$

c $-32 = -2^5$ **d** $-\frac{1}{64} = -\frac{1}{2^6} = -2^{-6}$

EXERCISE 10B

1 Write down each of these in fraction form.

a 5^{-3} **b** 6^{-1} **c** 10^{-5} **d** 3^{-2} **e** 8^{-2}

f 9^{-1} **g** w^{-2} **h** t^{-1} **i** x^{-m} **j** $4m^{-3}$

> **HINTS AND TIPS**
>
> If you move a power from top to bottom, or vice versa, the sign changes. Negative power means the reciprocal: it does not mean the answer is negative.

2 Write down each of these in negative index form.

a $\frac{1}{3^2}$ **b** $\frac{1}{5}$ **c** $\frac{1}{10^3}$ **d** $\frac{1}{m}$ **e** $\frac{1}{t^n}$

3 Change each of the following expressions into an index form of the type shown.

a all of the form 2^n

   i 16   **ii** $\frac{1}{2}$ **iii** $\frac{1}{16}$ **iv** -8

b all of the form 10^n

   i 1000   **ii** $\frac{1}{10}$ **iii** $\frac{1}{100}$ **iv** 1 million

c all of the form 5^n

   i 125   **ii** $\frac{1}{5}$ **iii** $\frac{1}{25}$ **iv** $\frac{1}{625}$

d all of the form 3^n

   i 9   **ii** $\frac{1}{27}$ **iii** $\frac{1}{81}$ **iv** -243

4 Rewrite each of the following expressions in fraction form.

a $5x^{-3}$ **b** $6t^{-1}$ **c** $7m^{-2}$ **d** $4q^{-4}$ **e** $10y^{-5}$

f $\frac{1}{2}x^{-3}$ **g** $\frac{1}{2}m^{-1}$ **h** $\frac{3}{4}t^{-4}$ **i** $\frac{4}{5}y^{-3}$ **j** $\frac{7}{8}x^{-5}$

5 Change each fraction to index form.

a $\dfrac{7}{x^3}$ **b** $\dfrac{10}{p}$ **c** $\dfrac{5}{t^2}$ **d** $\dfrac{8}{m^5}$ **e** $\dfrac{3}{y}$

6 Find the value of each of the following, where the letters have the given values.

a Where $x = 5$

   i x^2 **ii** x^{-3} **iii** $4x^{-1}$

b Where $t = 4$

   i t^3 **ii** t^{-2} **iii** $5t^{-4}$

c Where $m = 2$

   i m^3 **ii** m^{-5} **iii** $9m^{-1}$

d Where $w = 10$

   i w^6 **ii** w^{-3} **iii** $25w^{-2}$

Rules for multiplying and dividing numbers in index form

When we *multiply* together powers of the same number or variable, we *add* the indices. For example,

$$3^4 \times 3^5 = 3^{(4 + 5)} = 3^9$$

$$2^3 \times 2^4 \times 2^5 = 2^{12}$$

$$10^4 \times 10^{-2} = 10^2$$

$$10^{-3} \times 10^{-1} = 10^{-4}$$

$$a^x \times a^y = a^{(x + y)}$$

When we *divide* powers of the same number or variable, we *subtract* the indices. For example,

$$a^4 \div a^3 = a^{(4 - 3)} = a^1 = a$$

$$b^4 \div b^7 = b^{-3}$$

$$10^4 \div 10^{-2} = 10^6$$

$$10^{-2} \div 10^{-4} = 10^2$$

$$a^x \div a^y = a^{(x - y)}$$

When we *raise* a power term to a further power, we *multiply* the indices. For example,

$$(a^2)^3 = a^{2 \times 3} = a^6$$

$$(a^{-2})^4 = a^{-8}$$

$$(a^2)^6 = a^{12}$$

$$(a^x)^y = a^{xy}$$

Here are some examples of different kinds of power expressions.

$$2a^2 \times 3a^4 = (2 \times 3) \times (a^2 \times a^4) = 6 \times a^6 = 6a^6$$

$$4a^2b^3 \times 2ab^2 = (4 \times 2) \times (a^2 \times a) \times (b^3 \times b^2) = 8a^3b^5$$

$$12a^5 \div 3a^2 = (12 \div 3) \times (a^5 \div a^2) = 4a^3$$

$$(2a^2)^3 = (2)^3 \times (a^2)^3 = 8 \times a^6 = 8a^6$$

EXERCISE 10C

1 Write these as single powers of 5.

  a $5^2 \times 5^2$ **b** 5×5^2 **c** $5^{-2} \times 5^4$ **d** $5^6 \times 5^{-3}$ **e** $5^{-2} \times 5^{-3}$

2 Write these as single powers of 6.

  a $6^5 \div 6^2$ **b** $6^4 \div 6^4$ **c** $6^4 \div 6^{-2}$ **d** $6^{-3} \div 6^4$ **e** $6^{-3} \div 6^{-5}$

3 Simplify these and write them as single powers of a.

  a $a^2 \times a$ **b** $a^3 \times a^2$ **c** $a^4 \times a^3$

  d $a^6 \div a^2$ **e** $a^3 \div a$ **f** $a^5 \div a^4$

4 Write these as single powers of 4.

  a $(4^2)^3$ **b** $(4^3)^5$ **c** $(4^1)^6$

  d $(4^3)^{-2}$ **e** $(4^{-2})^{-3}$ **f** $(4^7)^0$

5 Simplify these expressions.

  a $2a^2 \times 3a^3$ **b** $3a^4 \times 3a^{-2}$ **c** $(2a^2)^3$

  d $-2a^2 \times 3a^2$ **e** $-4a^3 \times -2a^5$ **f** $-2a^4 \times 5a^{-7}$

> **HINTS AND TIPS**
>
> Deal with numbers and indices separately and do not confuse the rules. For example $12a^5 \div 4a^2 = (12 \div 4) \times (a^5 \div a^2)$

6 Simplify these expressions.

  a $6a^3 \div 2a^2$ **b** $12a^5 \div 3a^2$ **c** $15a^5 \div 5a$

  d $18a^{-2} \div 3a^{-1}$ **e** $24a^5 \div 6a^{-2}$ **f** $30a \div 6a^5$

7 Simplify these expressions.

  a $2a^2b^3 \times 4a^3b$ **b** $5a^2b^4 \times 2ab^{-3}$ **c** $6a^2b^3 \times 5a^{-4}b^{-5}$

  d $12a^2b^4 \div 6ab$ **e** $24a^{-3}b^4 \div 3a^2b^{-3}$

8 Simplify these expressions.

  a $\dfrac{6a^4b^3}{2ab}$ **b** $\dfrac{2a^2bc^2 \times 6abc^3}{4ab^2c}$ **c** $\dfrac{3abc \times 4a^3b^2c \times 6c^2}{9a^2bc}$

  9 Use the general rule for dividing powers of the same number, $\dfrac{a^x}{a^y} = a^{x-y}$, to prove that any number raised to the power zero is 1.

Indices of the form $\frac{1}{n}$

Consider the problem $7^x \times 7^x = 7$. This can be written as:

$$7^{(x + x)} = 7$$

$$7^{2x} = 7^1 \Rightarrow 2x = 1 \Rightarrow x = \tfrac{1}{2}$$

If we now substitute $x = \frac{1}{2}$ back into the original equation, we see that:

$$7^{\frac{1}{2}} \times 7^{\frac{1}{2}} = 7$$

This makes $7^{\frac{1}{2}}$ the same as $\sqrt{7}$.

You can similarly show that $7^{\frac{1}{3}}$ is the same as $\sqrt[3]{7}$. And that, generally,

$$x^{\frac{1}{n}} = \sqrt[n]{x} \text{ (nth root of } x)$$

For example,

$$49^{\frac{1}{2}} = \sqrt{49} = 7 \qquad 8^{\frac{1}{3}} = \sqrt[3]{8} = 2 \qquad 10\,000^{\frac{1}{4}} = \sqrt[4]{10\,000} = 10 \qquad 36^{-\frac{1}{2}} = \frac{1}{\sqrt{36}} = \frac{1}{6}$$

EXERCISE 10D

Evaluate the following.

1 $25^{\frac{1}{2}}$ **2** $100^{\frac{1}{2}}$ **3** $64^{\frac{1}{2}}$ **4** $81^{\frac{1}{2}}$ **5** $625^{\frac{1}{2}}$

6 $27^{\frac{1}{3}}$ **7** $64^{\frac{1}{3}}$ **8** $1000^{\frac{1}{3}}$ **9** $125^{\frac{1}{3}}$ **10** $512^{\frac{1}{3}}$

11 $144^{\frac{1}{2}}$ **12** $400^{\frac{1}{2}}$ **13** $625^{\frac{1}{4}}$ **14** $81^{\frac{1}{4}}$ **15** $100\,000^{\frac{1}{5}}$

16 $729^{\frac{1}{6}}$ **17** $32^{\frac{1}{5}}$ **18** $1024^{\frac{1}{10}}$ **19** $1296^{\frac{1}{4}}$ **20** $216^{\frac{1}{3}}$

21 $16^{-\frac{1}{2}}$ **22** $8^{-\frac{1}{3}}$ **23** $81^{-\frac{1}{4}}$ **24** $3125^{-\frac{1}{5}}$ **25** $1\,000\,000^{-\frac{1}{6}}$

26 $\left(\dfrac{25}{36}\right)^{\frac{1}{2}}$ **27** $\left(\dfrac{100}{36}\right)^{\frac{1}{2}}$ **28** $\left(\dfrac{64}{81}\right)^{\frac{1}{2}}$ **29** $\left(\dfrac{81}{25}\right)^{\frac{1}{2}}$ **30** $\left(\dfrac{25}{64}\right)^{\frac{1}{2}}$

31 $\left(\dfrac{27}{125}\right)^{\frac{1}{3}}$ **32** $\left(\dfrac{8}{512}\right)^{\frac{1}{3}}$ **33** $\left(\dfrac{1000}{64}\right)^{\frac{1}{3}}$ **34** $\left(\dfrac{64}{125}\right)^{\frac{1}{3}}$ **35** $\left(\dfrac{512}{343}\right)^{\frac{1}{3}}$

 36 Use the general rule for raising a power to another power to prove that $x^{\frac{1}{n}}$ is equivalent to $\sqrt[n]{x}$

Indices of the form $\frac{a}{b}$

Here are two examples of this form.

$$t^{\frac{2}{3}} = t^{\frac{1}{3}} \times t^{\frac{1}{3}} = (\sqrt[3]{t})^2 \qquad 81^{\frac{3}{4}} = (\sqrt[4]{81})^3 = 3^3 = 27$$

EXAMPLE 2

Evaluate the following. **a** $16^{-\frac{1}{4}}$ **b** $32^{-\frac{4}{5}}$

When dealing with negative indices do not make the mistake of thinking that the answer will be negative. Do problems like these in three steps.

Step 1: take the root of the base number given by the denominator of the fraction.

Step 2: raise the result to the power given by the numerator of the fraction.

Step 3: take the reciprocal (divide into 1) of the answer, which is what the negative power tells you to do.

a Step 1: $\sqrt[4]{16} = 2$.   Step 2: $2^1 = 2$.   Step 3: reciprocal of 2 is $\frac{1}{2}$

b Step 1: $\sqrt[5]{32} = 2$.   Step 2: $2^4 = 16$.   Step 3: reciprocal of 16 is $\frac{1}{16}$

EXERCISE 10E

1 Evaluate the following.

   a $32^{\frac{4}{5}}$ **b** $125^{\frac{2}{3}}$ **c** $1296^{\frac{3}{4}}$ **d** $243^{\frac{4}{5}}$

2 Rewrite the following in index form.

   a $\sqrt[3]{t^2}$ **b** $\sqrt[4]{m^3}$ **c** $\sqrt[5]{k^2}$ **d** $\sqrt{x^3}$

3 Evaluate the following.

   a $8^{\frac{2}{3}}$ **b** $27^{\frac{2}{3}}$ **c** $16^{\frac{3}{2}}$ **d** $625^{\frac{5}{4}}$

4 Evaluate the following.

   a $25^{-\frac{1}{2}}$ **b** $36^{-\frac{1}{2}}$ **c** $16^{-\frac{1}{4}}$ **d** $81^{-\frac{1}{4}}$

   e $16^{-\frac{1}{2}}$ **f** $8^{-\frac{1}{3}}$ **g** $32^{-\frac{1}{5}}$ **h** $27^{-\frac{1}{3}}$

5 Evaluate the following.

   a $25^{-\frac{3}{2}}$ **b** $36^{-\frac{3}{2}}$ **c** $16^{-\frac{3}{4}}$ **d** $81^{-\frac{3}{4}}$

   e $64^{-\frac{4}{3}}$ **f** $8^{-\frac{2}{3}}$ **g** $32^{-\frac{2}{5}}$ **h** $27^{-\frac{2}{3}}$

6 Evaluate the following.

   a $100^{-\frac{5}{2}}$ **b** $144^{-\frac{1}{2}}$ **c** $125^{-\frac{2}{3}}$ **d** $9^{-\frac{3}{2}}$

   e $4^{-\frac{5}{2}}$ **f** $64^{-\frac{5}{6}}$ **g** $27^{-\frac{4}{3}}$ **h** $169^{-\frac{1}{2}}$

Standard form

This section will introduce you to:

- standard form and show you how to calculate with standard form

Key words

powers
standard
form

Arithmetic of powers of 10

Multiplying

You have already done some arithmetic with multiples of 10 in Chapter 1. We will now look at **powers** of 10.

How many zeros does a million have? What is a million as a power of 10? This table shows some of the pattern of the powers of 10.

Number	0.001	0.01	0.1	1	10	100	1000	10 000	100 000
Powers	10^{-3}	10^{-2}	10^{-1}	10^0	10^1	10^2	10^3	10^4	10^5

What pattern is there in the top row? What pattern is there to the powers in the bottom row?

To multiply by any power of 10, we simply move the digits according to these two rules.

- When the index is *positive*, move the digits to the *left* by the same number of places as the value of the index.

- When the index is *negative*, move the digits to the *right* by the same number of places as the value of the index.

For example,

$$12.356 \times 10^2 = 1235.6 \qquad 3.45 \times 10^1 = 34.5$$

$$753.4 \times 10^{-2} = 7.534 \qquad 6789 \times 10^{-1} = 678.9$$

In certain cases, we have to insert the "hidden" zeros. For example,

$$75 \times 10^4 = 750\,000 \qquad 2.04 \times 10^5 = 204\,000$$

$$6.78 \times 10^{-3} = 0.006\,78 \qquad 0.897 \times 10^{-4} = 0.000\,0897$$

Dividing

To divide by any power of 10, we simply move the digits according to these two rules.

- When the index is *positive*, move the digits to the *right* by the same number of places as the value of the index.

- When the index is *negative*, move the digits to the *left* by the same number of places as the value of the index.

For example,

$712.35 \div 10^2 = 7.1235$ $\qquad$ $38.45 \div 10^1 = 3.845$

$3.463 \div 10^{-2} = 346.3$ $\qquad$ $6.789 \div 10^{-1} = 67.89$

In certain cases, we have to insert the "hidden" zeros. For example,

$75 \div 10^4 = 0.0075$ $\qquad$ $2.04 \div 10^5 = 0.000\,0204$

$6.78 \div 10^{-3} = 6780$ $\qquad$ $0.08 \div 10^{-4} = 800$

When doing the next exercise, remember:

$$10\,000 = 10 \times 10 \times 10 \times 10 = 10^4 \qquad 1 \qquad\qquad = 10^0$$
$$1000 = 10 \times 10 \times 10 \quad = 10^3 \qquad 0.1 = 1 \div 10 \qquad = 10^{-1}$$
$$100 = 10 \times 10 \qquad = 10^2 \qquad 0.01 = 1 \div 100 \quad = 10^{-2}$$
$$10 = 10 \qquad\qquad = 10^1 \qquad 0.001 = 1 \div 1000 = 10^{-3}$$

EXERCISE 10F

1 Write down the value of each of the following.

    a 3.1×10 **b** 3.1×100 **c** 3.1×1000 **d** $3.1 \times 10\,000$

2 Write down the value of each of the following.

    a 6.5×10 **b** 6.5×10^2 **c** 6.5×10^3 **d** 6.5×10^4

3 Write down the value of each of the following.

    a $3.1 \div 10$ **b** $3.1 \div 100$ **c** $3.1 \div 1000$ **d** $3.1 \div 10\,000$

4 Write down the value of each of the following.

    a $6.5 \div 10$ **b** $6.5 \div 10^2$ **c** $6.5 \div 10^3$ **d** $6.5 \div 10^4$

5 Evaluate the following.

    a 2.5×100 **b** 3.45×10 **c** 4.67×1000 **d** 34.6×10

    e 20.789×10 **f** 56.78×1000 **g** 2.46×10^2 **h** 0.076×10

    i 0.999×10^6 **j** 234.56×10^2 **k** 98.7654×10^3 **l** 43.23×10^6

    m $0.003\,4578 \times 10^5$ **n** 0.0006×10^7 **o** $0.005\,67 \times 10^4$ **p** 56.0045×10^4

6 Evaluate the following.

    a $2.5 \div 100$ **b** $3.45 \div 10$ **c** $4.67 \div 1000$ **d** $34.6 \div 10$

    e $20.789 \div 100$ **f** $56.78 \div 1000$ **g** $2.46 \div 10^2$ **h** $0.076 \div 10$

    i $0.999 \div 10^6$ **j** $234.56 \div 10^2$ **k** $98.7654 \div 10^3$ **l** $43.23 \div 10^6$

    m $0.003\,4578 \div 10^5$ **n** $0.0006 \div 10^7$ **o** $0.005\,67 \div 10^4$ **p** $56.0045 \div 10^4$

7 Without using a calculator, work out the following.

a 2.3×10^2 b 5.789×10^5 c 4.79×10^3 d 5.7×10^7

e 2.16×10^2 f 1.05×10^4 g 3.2×10^{-4} h 9.87×10^3

8 Which of these statements is true about the numbers in question **7**?

a The first part is always a number between 1 and 10.

b There is always a multiplication sign in the middle of the expression.

c There is always a power of 10 at the end.

d Calculator displays sometimes show numbers in this form.

Standard form

Standard form is also known as standard index form or SI form. On calculators, it is usually called scientific notation.

Standard form is a way of writing very large and very small numbers using powers of 10. In this form, a number is given a value between 1 and 10 multiplied by a power of 10. That is,

$a \times 10^n$ where $1 \leqslant a < 10$, and n is a whole number

Follow through these examples to see how numbers are written in standard form.

$$52 = \quad 5.2 \times 10 \quad = \mathbf{5.2 \times 10^1}$$
$$73 = \quad 7.3 \times 10 \quad = \mathbf{7.3 \times 10^1}$$
$$625 = \quad 6.25 \times 100 \quad = \mathbf{6.25 \times 10^2} \qquad \text{The numbers in bold are in standard form.}$$
$$389 = \quad 3.89 \times 100 \quad = \mathbf{3.89 \times 10^2}$$
$$3147 = 3.147 \times 1000 = \mathbf{3.147 \times 10^3}$$

When writing a number in this way, two rules must always be followed.

- The first part must be a number between 1 and 10 (1 is allowed but 10 isn't).

- The second part must be a whole number (negative or positive) power of 10. Note that we would *not normally* write the power 1.

Standard form on a calculator

A number such as 123 000 000 000 is obviously difficult to key into a calculator. Instead, you enter it in standard form (assuming you are using a scientific calculator):

$$123\ 000\ 000\ 000 = 1.23 \times 10^{11}$$

The key strokes to enter this into your calculator will be

1 **•** **2** **3** **EXP** **1** **1**   (On some calculators EXP is EE.)

Your calculator display should now show

1.23 $^{\boxed{11}}$ or   1.23 $\boxed{11}$

Be careful when you get an answer like this on your calculator. It needs to be written properly in standard form with × 10, not copied exactly as shown on the calculator display.

Standard form of numbers less than 1

These numbers are written in standard form. Make sure that you understand how they are formed.

a $0.4 = 4 \times 10^{-1}$

b $0.05 = 5 \times 10^{-2}$

c $0.007 = 7 \times 10^{-3}$

d $0.123 = 1.23 \times 10^{-1}$

e $0.007\,65 = 7.65 \times 10^{-3}$

f $0.9804 = 9.804 \times 10^{-1}$

g $0.0098 = 9.8 \times 10^{-3}$

h $0.000\,0078 = 7.8 \times 10^{-6}$

On a calculator you would enter 1.23×10^{-6}, for example, as

1 **•** **2** **3** **EXP** **+/−** **6**

or **1** **•** **2** **3** **EXP** **6** **+/−**

How you enter such numbers will depend on your type of calculator. Try some of the numbers **a** to **h** (above) to see what happens.

EXERCISE 10G

1 Write down the value of each of the following.

     a 3.1×0.1 **b** 3.1×0.01 **c** 3.1×0.001 **d** 3.1×0.0001

2 Write down the value of each of the following.

     a 6.5×10^{-1} **b** 6.5×10^{-2} **c** 6.5×10^{-3} **d** 6.5×10^{-4}

3 a What is the largest number you can enter into your calculator?

     b What is the smallest number you can enter into your calculator?

4 Work out the value of each of the following.

     a $3.1 \div 0.1$ **b** $3.1 \div 0.01$ **c** $3.1 \div 0.001$ **d** $3.1 \div 0.0001$

5 Work out the value of each of the following.

     a $6.5 \div 10^{-1}$ **b** $6.5 \div 10^{-2}$ **c** $6.5 \div 10^{-3}$ **d** $6.5 \div 10^{-4}$

6 Write these numbers out in full.

a 2.5×10^2 b 3.45×10 c 4.67×10^{-3} d 3.46×10

e 2.0789×10^{-2} f 5.678×10^3 g 2.46×10^2 h 7.6×10^3

i 8.97×10^5 j 8.65×10^{-3} k 6×10^7 l 5.67×10^{-4}

 7 Write these numbers in standard form.

a 250 b 0.345 c 46 700

d 3 400 000 000 e 20 780 000 000 f 0.000 5678

g 2460 h 0.076 i 0.000 76

j 0.999 k 234.56 l 98.7654

m 0.0006 n 0.005 67 o 56.0045

In questions **8** to **10**, write the numbers given in each question in standard form.

 8 One year, 27 797 runners completed the New York marathon.

 9 The largest number of dominoes ever toppled by one person is 303 621, although 30 people set up and toppled 4 002 136.

 10 The asteroid Phaethon comes within 12 980 000 miles of the sun, whilst the asteroid Pholus, at its furthest point, is a distance of 2997 million miles from the earth. The closest an asteroid ever came to Earth recently was 93 000 miles from the planet.

Calculating with standard form

Calculations involving very large or very small numbers can be done more easily using standard form. In these examples, we work out the area of a pixel on a computer screen, and how long it takes light to reach the Earth from a distant star.

EXAMPLE 3

A pixel on a computer screen is 2×10^{-2} cm long by 7×10^{-3} cm wide.

What is the area of the pixel?

The area is given by length times width:

Area $= 2 \times 10^{-2}$ cm $\times 7 \times 10^{-3}$ cm

$= (2 \times 7) \times (10^{-2} \times 10^{-3})$ cm$^2 = 14 \times 10^{-5}$ cm^2

Note that you multiply the numbers and add the powers of 10. (You should not need to use a calculator to do this calculation.) The answer is not in standard form as the first part is not between 1 and 10, so we have to change it to standard form.

Area $= 14 \times 10^{-5}$ cm$^2 = 1.4 \times 10^{-4}$ cm^2

221

EXAMPLE 4

The star Betelgeuse is 1.8×10^{15} miles from Earth. Light travels at 1.86×10^5 miles per second.

a How many seconds does it take light to travel from Betelgeuse to Earth? Give your answer in standard form.

b How many years does it take light to travel from Betelgeuse to Earth?

a Time = distance ÷ speed = 1.8×10^{15} miles ÷ 1.86×10^5 miles per second

$= (1.8 \div 1.86) \times (10^{15} \div 10^5)$ seconds

$= 0.967\,741\,935 \times 10^{10}$ seconds

Note that you divide the numbers and subtract the powers of 10. To change the answer to standard form, first round it off, which gives

$0.97 \times 10^{10} = 9.7 \times 10^9$ seconds

b To convert from seconds to years, you have to divide first by 3600 to get to hours, then by 24 to get to days, and finally by 365 to get to years.

$9.7 \times 10^9 \div (3600 \times 24 \times 365) = 307.6$ years

EXERCISE 10H

1 These numbers are not in standard form. Write them in standard form.

a 56.7×10^2 **b** 0.06×10^4 **c** 34.6×10^{-2}

d 0.07×10^{-2} **e** 56×10 **f** $2 \times 3 \times 10^5$

g $2 \times 10^2 \times 35$ **h** 160×10^{-2} **i** 23 million

j 0.0003×10^{-2} **k** 25.6×10^5 **l** $16 \times 10^2 \times 3 \times 10^{-1}$

m $2 \times 10^4 \times 56 \times 10^{-4}$ **n** $18 \times 10^2 \div 3 \times 10^3$ **o** $56 \times 10^3 \div 2 \times 10^{-2}$

2 Work out the following. Give your answers in standard form.

a $2 \times 10^4 \times 5.4 \times 10^3$ **b** $1.6 \times 10^2 \times 3 \times 10^4$ **c** $2 \times 10^4 \times 6 \times 10^4$

d $2 \times 10^{-4} \times 5.4 \times 10^3$ **e** $1.6 \times 10^{-2} \times 4 \times 10^4$ **f** $2 \times 10^4 \times 6 \times 10^{-4}$

g $7.2 \times 10^{-3} \times 4 \times 10^2$ **h** $(5 \times 10^3)^2$ **i** $(2 \times 10^{-2})^3$

3 Work out the following. Give your answers in standard form, rounding off to an appropriate degree of accuracy where necessary.

a $2.1 \times 10^4 \times 5.4 \times 10^3$ **b** $1.6 \times 10^3 \times 3.8 \times 10^3$ **c** $2.4 \times 10^4 \times 6.6 \times 10^4$

d $7.3 \times 10^{-6} \times 5.4 \times 10^3$ **e** $(3.1 \times 10^4)^2$ **f** $(6.8 \times 10^{-4})^2$

g $5.7 \times 10 \times 3.7 \times 10$ **h** $1.9 \times 10^{-2} \times 1.9 \times 10^9$ **i** $5.9 \times 10^3 \times 2.5 \times 10^{-2}$

j $5.2 \times 10^3 \times 2.2 \times 10^2 \times 3.1 \times 10^3$ **k** $1.8 \times 10^2 \times 3.6 \times 10^3 \times 2.4 \times 10^{-2}$

4 Work out the following. Give your answers in standard form.

a $5.4 \times 10^4 \div 2 \times 10^3$ **b** $4.8 \times 10^2 \div 3 \times 10^4$ **c** $1.2 \times 10^4 \div 6 \times 10^4$

d $2 \times 10^{-4} \div 5 \times 10^3$ **e** $1.8 \times 10^4 \div 9 \times 10^{-2}$ **f** $\sqrt{(36 \times 10^{-4})}$

g $5.4 \times 10^{-3} \div 2.7 \times 10^2$ **h** $1.8 \times 10^6 \div 3.6 \times 10^3$ **i** $5.6 \times 10^3 \div 2.8 \times 10^2$

5 Work out the following. Give your answers in standard form, rounding off to an appropriate degree of accuracy where necessary.

a $2.7 \times 10^4 \div 5 \times 10^2$ **b** $2.3 \times 10^4 \div 8 \times 10^6$ **c** $3.2 \times 10^{-1} \div 2.8 \times 10^{-1}$

d $2.6 \times 10^{-6} \div 4.1 \times 10^3$ **e** $\sqrt{(8 \times 10^4)}$ **f** $\sqrt{(30 \times 10^{-4})}$

g $5.3 \times 10^3 \times 2.3 \times 10^2 \div 2.5 \times 10^3$ **h** $1.8 \times 10^2 \times 3.1 \times 10^3 \div 6.5 \times 10^{-2}$

6 A typical adult has about 20 000 000 000 000 red corpuscles. Each red corpuscle weighs about 0.000 000 000 1 gram. Write both of these numbers in standard form and work out the total mass of red corpuscles in a typical adult.

7 If a man puts 1 grain of rice on the first square of a chess board, 2 on the second square, 4 on the third, 8 on the fourth and so on,

a how many grains of rice will he put on the 64th square of the board?

b how many grains of rice will there be altogether?

Give your answers in standard form.

8 The surface area of the Earth is approximately 2×10^8 square miles. The surface area of the earth covered by water is approximately 1.4×10^8 square miles.

a Calculate the surface area of the Earth not covered by water. Give your answer in standard form.

b What percentage of the Earth's surface is not covered by water?

9 The moon is a sphere with a radius of 1.080×10^3 miles. The formula for working out the surface area of a sphere is

Surface area = $4\pi r^2$

Calculate the surface area of the moon.

10 Evaluate $\dfrac{E}{M}$ when $E = 1.5 \times 10^3$ and $M = 3 \times 10^{-2}$, giving your answer in standard form.

11 Work out the value of $\dfrac{3.2 \times 10^7}{1.4 \times 10^2}$ giving your answer in standard form, correct to two significant figures.

12 In 2005, British Airways carried 23 million passengers. Of these, 70% passed through Heathrow Airport. On average, each passenger carried 19.7 kg of luggage. Calculate the total weight of the luggage carried by these passengers.

13 Many people withdraw money from their banks by using hole-in-the-wall machines. Each day there are eight million withdrawals from 32 000 machines. What is the average number of withdrawals per machine?

14 The mass of Saturn is 5.686×10^{26} tonnes. The mass of the Earth is 6.04×10^{21} tonnes. How many times heavier is Saturn than the Earth? Give your answer in standard form to a suitable degree of accuracy.

This section will explain about:

- reciprocals, and terminating and recurring decimals

Key words

rational
    number
reciprocal
recurring
    decimal
terminating
    decimal

Rational decimal numbers

A fraction, also known as a **rational number**, can be expressed as a decimal which is either a **terminating decimal** or a **recurring decimal**.

A terminating decimal contains a finite number of digits (decimal places). For example, changing $\frac{3}{16}$ into a decimal gives 0.1875 exactly.

A recurring decimal contains a digit or a block of digits that repeats. For example, changing $\frac{5}{9}$ into a decimal gives 0.5555 ..., while changing $\frac{14}{27}$ into a decimal gives 0.518 518 5 ... with the recurring block 518.

Recurring decimals are indicated by a dot placed over the first and last digits in the recurring block. For example, 0.5555 ... becomes $0.\dot{5}$, 0.518 518 5 ... becomes $0.\dot{5}1\dot{8}$, and 0.583 33 becomes $0.58\dot{3}$.

Converting decimals into fractions

Terminating decimals

When converting a terminating decimal, the numerator of the fraction is formed from the decimal, and its denominator is given by 10, 100 or 1000, depending on the number of decimal places. Because the terminating decimal ends at a specific decimal place, we know the place value at which the numerator ends. For example,

$$0.7 = \frac{7}{10}$$

$$0.045 = \frac{45}{1000} = \frac{9}{200}$$

$$2.34 = 2\frac{34}{100} = 2\frac{17}{50}$$

$$0.625 = \frac{625}{1000} = \frac{5}{8}$$

Recurring decimals

If a fraction does not give a terminating decimal, it will give a recurring decimal. You already know that $\frac{1}{3} = 0.333 ... = 0.\dot{3}$. This means that the 3s go on forever and the decimal never ends. To check whether a fraction is a recurring decimal, you usually have to use a calculator to divide the numerator by the denominator. Use a calculator to check the following recurring decimals. (Note that calculators round off the last digit so it may not always be a true recurring decimal in the display.)

$$\frac{2}{11} = 0.181818 \ldots = 0.\dot{1}\dot{8}$$

$$\frac{4}{15} = 0.2666\ldots = 0.2\dot{6}$$

$$\frac{8}{13} = 0.6153846153846 \ldots = 0.\dot{6}1538\dot{4}$$

To convert a recurring decimal to a fraction, you have to multiply the decimal by a suitable power of 10, and then perform a subtraction. These examples demonstrate the method.

EXAMPLE 5

Convert $0.\dot{7}$ to a fraction.

Let x be the fraction. Then

$$x = 0.777\,777\,777 \ldots \quad (1)$$

Multiply (1) by 10 $\qquad 10x = 7.777\,777\,777 \ldots \quad (2)$

Subtract (2) − (1) $\qquad 9x = 7$

$$\Rightarrow x = \frac{7}{9}$$

EXAMPLE 6

Convert $0.\dot{5}6\dot{4}$ to a fraction.

Let x be the fraction. Then

$$x = 0.564\,564\,564 \ldots \quad (1)$$

Multiply (1) by 1000 $\qquad 1000x = 564.564\,564\,564 \ldots \quad (2)$

Subtract (2) − (1) $\qquad 999x = 564$

$$\Rightarrow x = \frac{564}{999} = \frac{188}{333}$$

As a general rule multiply by 10 if one digit recurs, multiply by 100 if two digits recur, multiply by 1000 if three digits recur, and so on.

Reciprocals

The **reciprocal** of a number is the number divided into 1. So the reciprocal of 2 is $1 \div 2 = \frac{1}{2}$ or 0.5.

Reciprocals of fractions are quite easy to find as you just have to turn the fraction upside down. For example, the reciprocal of $\frac{2}{3}$ is $\frac{3}{2}$.

EXERCISE 10I

C

1 Work out each of these fractions as a decimal. Give them as terminating decimals or recurring decimals as appropriate.

a $\frac{1}{2}$ **b** $\frac{1}{3}$ **c** $\frac{1}{4}$ **d** $\frac{1}{5}$ **e** $\frac{1}{6}$

f $\frac{1}{7}$ **g** $\frac{1}{8}$ **h** $\frac{1}{9}$ **i** $\frac{1}{10}$ **j** $\frac{1}{13}$

2 There are several patterns to be found in recurring decimals. For example,

$\frac{1}{7}$ = 0.142 857 142 857 142 857 142 857...

$\frac{2}{7}$ = 0.285 714 285 714 285 714 285 714...

$\frac{3}{7}$ = 0.428 571 428 571 428 571 428 571...

and so on.

a Write down the decimals for $\frac{4}{7}, \frac{5}{7}, \frac{6}{7}$ to 24 decimal places.

b What do you notice?

3 Work out the ninths as recurring decimals, that is $\frac{1}{9}, \frac{2}{9}, \frac{3}{9}$ and so on, up to $\frac{8}{9}$.

Describe any patterns that you notice.

4 Work out the elevenths as recurring decimals, that is $\frac{1}{11}, \frac{2}{11}, \frac{3}{11}$ and so on, up to $\frac{10}{11}$.

Describe any patterns that you notice.

5 Write each of these fractions as a decimal. Use this to write the list in order of size, smallest first.

$\frac{4}{9}$ $\frac{5}{11}$ $\frac{3}{7}$ $\frac{9}{22}$ $\frac{16}{37}$ $\frac{6}{13}$

6 Write each of the following as a fraction with a denominator of 120. Use this to put them in order of size, smallest first.

$\frac{19}{60}$ $\frac{7}{24}$ $\frac{3}{10}$ $\frac{2}{5}$ $\frac{5}{12}$

7 Convert each of these terminating decimals to a fraction.

a 0.125   **b** 0.34   **c** 0.725   **d** 0.3125

e 0.89   **f** 0.05   **g** 2.35   **h** 0.218 75

8 Use a calculator to work out the reciprocals of the following values.

a 12   **b** 16   **c** 20   **d** 25   **e** 50

9 Write down the reciprocals of the following fractions.

a $\frac{3}{4}$ **b** $\frac{5}{6}$ **c** $\frac{2}{5}$ **d** $\frac{7}{10}$

e $\frac{11}{20}$ **f** $\frac{4}{15}$

10 a Work out the fractions and their reciprocals from question **9** as decimals. Write them as terminating decimals or recurring decimals as appropriate.

b Is it always true that a fraction that gives a terminating decimal has a reciprocal that gives a recurring decimal?

11 Multiply together the fractions and their reciprocals from question **9**. What results do you get every time?

12 $x = 0.242\,424\,\ldots$

a What is $100x$?

b By subtracting the original value from your answer to part **a**, work out the value of $99x$.

c What is x as a fraction?

13 Convert each of these recurring decimals to a fraction.

 a $0.\dot{8}$ **b** $0.\dot{3}\dot{4}$ **c** $0.4\dot{5}$ **d** $0.5\dot{6}\dot{7}$

 e $0.\dot{4}$ **f** $0.0\dot{4}$ **g** $0.1\dot{4}$ **h** $0.04\dot{5}$

 i $2.\dot{7}$ **j** $7.\dot{6}\dot{3}$ **k** $3.\dot{3}$ **l** $2.0\dot{6}$

14 a $\frac{1}{7}$ is a recurring decimal. $\left(\frac{1}{7}\right)^2 = \frac{1}{49}$ is also a recurring decimal.

 Is it true that when you square any fraction that is a recurring decimal, you get another fraction that is also a recurring decimal? Try this with at least four numerical examples before you make a decision.

b $\frac{1}{4}$ is a terminating decimal. $\left(\frac{1}{4}\right)^2 = \frac{1}{16}$ is also a terminating decimal.

 Is it true that when you square any fraction that is a terminating decimal, you get another fraction that is also a terminating decimal? Try this with at least four numerical examples before you make a decision.

c What type of fraction do you get when you multiply a fraction that gives a recurring decimal by another fraction that gives a terminating decimal? Try this with at least four numerical examples before you make a decision.

15 a Convert the recurring decimal $0.\dot{9}$ to a fraction.

b Prove that $0.4\dot{9}$ is equal to 0.5.

10.4 Surds

In this section you will learn how to:
● calculate and manipulate surds

Key words
rationalise
surds

It is useful at higher levels of mathematics to be able to work with **surds**, which are roots of numbers written as, for example,

$$\sqrt{2} \quad \sqrt{5} \quad \sqrt{15} \quad \sqrt{9} \quad \sqrt{3} \quad \sqrt{10}$$

Four general rules governing surds (which you can verify yourself by taking numerical examples) are:

$$\sqrt{a} \times \sqrt{b} = \sqrt{ab} \qquad\qquad C\sqrt{a} \times D\sqrt{b} = CD\sqrt{ab}$$

$$\sqrt{a} \div \sqrt{b} = \sqrt{\frac{a}{b}} \qquad\qquad C\sqrt{a} \div D\sqrt{b} = \frac{C}{D}\sqrt{\frac{a}{b}}$$

For example,

$$\sqrt{2} \times \sqrt{2} = \sqrt{4} = 2 \qquad\qquad \sqrt{2} \times \sqrt{10} = \sqrt{20} = \sqrt{(4 \times 5)} = \sqrt{4} \times \sqrt{5} = 2\sqrt{5}$$

$$\sqrt{2} \times \sqrt{3} = \sqrt{6} \qquad\qquad\quad \sqrt{6} \times \sqrt{15} = \sqrt{90} = \sqrt{9} \times \sqrt{10} = 3\sqrt{10}$$

$$\sqrt{2} \times \sqrt{8} = \sqrt{16} = 4 \qquad\qquad 3\sqrt{5} \times 4\sqrt{3} = 12\sqrt{15}$$

EXERCISE 10J

1 Simplify each of the following. Leave your answers in surd form.

a $\sqrt{2} \times \sqrt{3}$	**b** $\sqrt{5} \times \sqrt{3}$	**c** $\sqrt{2} \times \sqrt{2}$	**d** $\sqrt{2} \times \sqrt{8}$
e $\sqrt{5} \times \sqrt{8}$	**f** $\sqrt{3} \times \sqrt{3}$	**g** $\sqrt{6} \times \sqrt{2}$	**h** $\sqrt{7} \times \sqrt{3}$
i $\sqrt{2} \times \sqrt{7}$	**j** $\sqrt{2} \times \sqrt{18}$	**k** $\sqrt{6} \times \sqrt{6}$	**l** $\sqrt{5} \times \sqrt{6}$

2 Simplify each of the following. Leave your answers in surd form.

a $\sqrt{12} \div \sqrt{3}$	**b** $\sqrt{15} \div \sqrt{3}$	**c** $\sqrt{12} \div \sqrt{2}$	**d** $\sqrt{24} \div \sqrt{8}$
e $\sqrt{40} \div \sqrt{8}$	**f** $\sqrt{3} \div \sqrt{3}$	**g** $\sqrt{6} \div \sqrt{2}$	**h** $\sqrt{21} \div \sqrt{3}$
i $\sqrt{28} \div \sqrt{7}$	**j** $\sqrt{48} \div \sqrt{8}$	**k** $\sqrt{6} \div \sqrt{6}$	**l** $\sqrt{54} \div \sqrt{6}$

3 Simplify each of the following. Leave your answers in surd form.

a $\sqrt{2} \times \sqrt{3} \times \sqrt{2}$	**b** $\sqrt{5} \times \sqrt{3} \times \sqrt{15}$	**c** $\sqrt{2} \times \sqrt{2} \times \sqrt{8}$	**d** $\sqrt{2} \times \sqrt{8} \times \sqrt{3}$
e $\sqrt{5} \times \sqrt{8} \times \sqrt{8}$	**f** $\sqrt{3} \times \sqrt{3} \times \sqrt{3}$	**g** $\sqrt{6} \times \sqrt{2} \times \sqrt{48}$	**h** $\sqrt{7} \times \sqrt{3} \times \sqrt{3}$
i $\sqrt{2} \times \sqrt{7} \times \sqrt{2}$	**j** $\sqrt{2} \times \sqrt{18} \times \sqrt{5}$	**k** $\sqrt{6} \times \sqrt{6} \times \sqrt{3}$	**l** $\sqrt{5} \times \sqrt{6} \times \sqrt{30}$

A

4 Simplify each of the following. Leave your answers in surd form.

   a $\sqrt{2} \times \sqrt{3} \div \sqrt{2}$ **b** $\sqrt{5} \times \sqrt{3} \div \sqrt{15}$ **c** $\sqrt{32} \times \sqrt{2} \div \sqrt{8}$ **d** $\sqrt{2} \times \sqrt{8} \div \sqrt{8}$

   e $\sqrt{5} \times \sqrt{8} \div \sqrt{8}$ **f** $\sqrt{3} \times \sqrt{3} \div \sqrt{3}$ **g** $\sqrt{8} \times \sqrt{12} \div \sqrt{48}$ **h** $\sqrt{7} \times \sqrt{3} \div \sqrt{3}$

   i $\sqrt{2} \times \sqrt{7} \div \sqrt{2}$ **j** $\sqrt{2} \times \sqrt{18} \div \sqrt{3}$ **k** $\sqrt{6} \times \sqrt{6} \div \sqrt{3}$ **l** $\sqrt{5} \times \sqrt{6} \div \sqrt{30}$

5 Simplify each of these expressions.

   a $\sqrt{a} \times \sqrt{a}$ **b** $\sqrt{a} \div \sqrt{a}$ **c** $\sqrt{a} \times \sqrt{a} \div \sqrt{a}$

6 Simplify each of the following surds into the form $a\sqrt{b}$.

   a $\sqrt{18}$ **b** $\sqrt{24}$ **c** $\sqrt{12}$ **d** $\sqrt{50}$

   e $\sqrt{8}$ **f** $\sqrt{27}$ **g** $\sqrt{48}$ **h** $\sqrt{75}$

   i $\sqrt{45}$ **j** $\sqrt{63}$ **k** $\sqrt{32}$ **l** $\sqrt{200}$

   m $\sqrt{1000}$ **n** $\sqrt{250}$ **o** $\sqrt{98}$ **p** $\sqrt{243}$

7 Simplify each of these.

   a $2\sqrt{18} \times 3\sqrt{2}$ **b** $4\sqrt{24} \times 2\sqrt{5}$ **c** $3\sqrt{12} \times 3\sqrt{3}$ **d** $2\sqrt{8} \times 2\sqrt{8}$

   e $2\sqrt{27} \times 4\sqrt{8}$ **f** $2\sqrt{48} \times 3\sqrt{8}$ **g** $2\sqrt{45} \times 3\sqrt{3}$ **h** $2\sqrt{63} \times 2\sqrt{7}$

   i $2\sqrt{32} \times 4\sqrt{2}$ **j** $\sqrt{1000} \times \sqrt{10}$ **k** $\sqrt{250} \times \sqrt{10}$ **l** $2\sqrt{98} \times 2\sqrt{2}$

8 Simplify each of these.

   a $4\sqrt{2} \times 5\sqrt{3}$ **b** $2\sqrt{5} \times 3\sqrt{3}$ **c** $4\sqrt{2} \times 3\sqrt{2}$ **d** $2\sqrt{2} \times 2\sqrt{8}$

   e $2\sqrt{5} \times 3\sqrt{8}$ **f** $3\sqrt{3} \times 2\sqrt{3}$ **g** $2\sqrt{6} \times 5\sqrt{2}$ **h** $5\sqrt{7} \times 2\sqrt{3}$

   i $2\sqrt{2} \times 3\sqrt{7}$ **j** $2\sqrt{2} \times 3\sqrt{18}$ **k** $2\sqrt{6} \times 2\sqrt{6}$ **l** $4\sqrt{5} \times 3\sqrt{6}$

9 Simplify each of these.

   a $6\sqrt{12} \div 2\sqrt{3}$ **b** $3\sqrt{15} \div \sqrt{3}$ **c** $6\sqrt{12} \div \sqrt{2}$ **d** $4\sqrt{24} \div 2\sqrt{8}$

   e $12\sqrt{40} \div 3\sqrt{8}$ **f** $5\sqrt{3} \div \sqrt{3}$ **g** $14\sqrt{6} \div 2\sqrt{2}$ **h** $4\sqrt{21} \div 2\sqrt{3}$

   i $9\sqrt{28} \div 3\sqrt{7}$ **j** $12\sqrt{56} \div 6\sqrt{8}$ **k** $25\sqrt{6} \div 5\sqrt{6}$ **l** $32\sqrt{54} \div 4\sqrt{6}$

10 Simplify each of these.

   a $4\sqrt{2} \times \sqrt{3} \div 2\sqrt{2}$ **b** $4\sqrt{5} \times \sqrt{3} \div \sqrt{15}$ **c** $2\sqrt{32} \times 3\sqrt{2} \div 2\sqrt{8}$

   d $6\sqrt{2} \times 2\sqrt{8} \div 3\sqrt{8}$ **e** $3\sqrt{5} \times 4\sqrt{8} \div 2\sqrt{8}$ **f** $12\sqrt{3} \times 4\sqrt{3} \div 2\sqrt{3}$

   g $3\sqrt{8} \times 3\sqrt{12} \div 3\sqrt{48}$ **h** $4\sqrt{7} \times 2\sqrt{3} \div 8\sqrt{3}$ **i** $15\sqrt{2} \times 2\sqrt{7} \div 3\sqrt{2}$

   j $8\sqrt{2} \times 2\sqrt{18} \div 4\sqrt{3}$ **k** $5\sqrt{6} \times 5\sqrt{6} \div 5\sqrt{3}$ **l** $2\sqrt{5} \times 3\sqrt{6} \div \sqrt{30}$

11 Simplify each of these expressions.

   a $a\sqrt{b} \times c\sqrt{b}$ **b** $a\sqrt{b} \div c\sqrt{b}$ **c** $a\sqrt{b} \times c\sqrt{b} \div a\sqrt{b}$

12 Find the value of *a* that makes each of these surds true.

a $\sqrt{5} \times \sqrt{a} = 10$ **b** $\sqrt{6} \times \sqrt{a} = 12$ **c** $\sqrt{10} \times 2\sqrt{a} = 20$

d $2\sqrt{6} \times 3\sqrt{a} = 72$ **e** $2\sqrt{a} \times \sqrt{a} = 6$ **f** $3\sqrt{a} \times 3\sqrt{a} = 54$

13 Simplify the following.

a $\left(\dfrac{\sqrt{3}}{2}\right)^2$ **b** $\left(\dfrac{5}{\sqrt{3}}\right)^2$ **c** $\left(\dfrac{\sqrt{5}}{4}\right)^2$

d $\left(\dfrac{6}{\sqrt{3}}\right)^2$ **e** $\left(\dfrac{\sqrt{8}}{2}\right)^2$

14 The following rules are *not* true. Try some numerical examples to show this.

a $\sqrt{(a + b)} = \sqrt{a} + \sqrt{b}$ **b** $\sqrt{(a - b)} = \sqrt{a} - \sqrt{b}$

Calculating with surds

The following two examples show how surds can be used in solving problems.

EXAMPLE 7

In the right-angled triangle ABC, the side BC is $\sqrt{6}$ cm and the side AC is $\sqrt{18}$ cm.

Calculate the length of AB. Leave your answer in surd form.

Using Pythagoras' theorem

$$AC^2 + BC^2 = AB^2$$

$$(\sqrt{18})^2 + (\sqrt{6})^2 = 18 + 6 = 24$$

$$\Rightarrow AB = \sqrt{24} \text{ cm}$$

$$= 2\sqrt{6} \text{ cm}$$

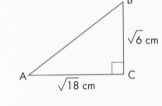

EXAMPLE 8

Calculate the area of a square with a side of $2 + \sqrt{3}$ cm. Give your answer in the form $a + b\sqrt{3}$.

Area $= (2 + \sqrt{3})^2$ cm^2

$= (2 + \sqrt{3})(2 + \sqrt{3})$ cm^2

$= 4 + 2\sqrt{3} + 2\sqrt{3} + 3$ cm^2

$= 7 + 4\sqrt{3}$ cm^2

Rationalising the denominator

It is not good mathematical practice to leave a surd on the bottom of an expression. To get rid of it, we make the denominator into a whole number, which we do by multiplying by the appropriate square root. This means that we must also multiply the top of the expression by the same root. The following example shows you what to do.

EXAMPLE 9

Rationalise the denominator of   **a** $\dfrac{1}{\sqrt{3}}$ and   **b** $\dfrac{2\sqrt{3}}{\sqrt{8}}$.

a Multiply the top and the bottom by $\sqrt{3}$:

$$\frac{1 \times \sqrt{3}}{\sqrt{3} \times \sqrt{3}} = \frac{\sqrt{3}}{3}$$

b Multiply the top and the bottom by $\sqrt{8}$:

$$\frac{2\sqrt{3} \times \sqrt{8}}{\sqrt{8} \times \sqrt{8}} = \frac{2\sqrt{24}}{8} = \frac{4\sqrt{6}}{8} = \frac{\sqrt{6}}{2}$$

EXERCISE 10K

1 Show that:

    a $(2 + \sqrt{3})(1 + \sqrt{3}) = 5 + 3\sqrt{3}$

    b $(1 + \sqrt{2})(2 + \sqrt{3}) = 2 + 2\sqrt{2} + \sqrt{3} + \sqrt{6}$

    c $(4 - \sqrt{3})(4 + \sqrt{3}) = 13$

2 Expand and simplify where possible.

    a $\sqrt{3}(2 - \sqrt{3})$ **b** $\sqrt{2}(3 - 4\sqrt{2})$ **c** $\sqrt{5}(2\sqrt{5} + 4)$

    d $3\sqrt{7}(4 - 2\sqrt{7})$ **e** $3\sqrt{2}(5 - 2\sqrt{8})$ **f** $\sqrt{3}(\sqrt{27} - 1)$

3 Expand and simplify where possible.

    a $(1 + \sqrt{3})(3 - \sqrt{3})$ **b** $(2 + \sqrt{5})(3 - \sqrt{5})$ **c** $(1 - \sqrt{2})(3 + 2\sqrt{2})$

    d $(3 - 2\sqrt{7})(4 + 3\sqrt{7})$ **e** $(2 - 3\sqrt{5})(2 + 3\sqrt{5})$ **f** $(\sqrt{3} + \sqrt{2})(\sqrt{3} + \sqrt{8})$

    g $(2 + \sqrt{5})^2$ **h** $(1 - \sqrt{2})^2$ **i** $(3 + \sqrt{2})^2$

4 Work out the missing lengths in each of these triangles, giving the answer in as simple a form as possible.

a

$\sqrt{8}$ cm x

$\sqrt{10}$ cm

b

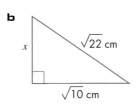

c

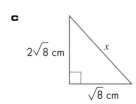

5 Calculate the area of each of these rectangles, simplifying your answers where possible.

a

$1 + \sqrt{3}$ cm

$2 - \sqrt{3}$ cm

b

$2 + \sqrt{10}$ cm

$\sqrt{5}$ cm

c

$2\sqrt{3}$ cm

$1 + \sqrt{27}$ cm

6 Rationalise the denominators of these expressions.

a $\dfrac{1}{\sqrt{3}}$

b $\dfrac{1}{\sqrt{2}}$

c $\dfrac{1}{\sqrt{5}}$

d $\dfrac{1}{2\sqrt{3}}$

e $\dfrac{3}{\sqrt{3}}$

f $\dfrac{5}{\sqrt{2}}$

g $\dfrac{3\sqrt{2}}{\sqrt{8}}$

h $\dfrac{5\sqrt{3}}{\sqrt{6}}$

i $\dfrac{\sqrt{7}}{\sqrt{3}}$

j $\dfrac{1 + \sqrt{2}}{\sqrt{2}}$

k $\dfrac{2 - \sqrt{3}}{\sqrt{3}}$

l $\dfrac{5 + 2\sqrt{3}}{\sqrt{3}}$

7 **a** Expand and simplify the following.

i $(2 + \sqrt{3})(2 - \sqrt{3})$

ii $(1 - \sqrt{5})(1 + \sqrt{5})$

iii $(\sqrt{3} - 1)(\sqrt{3} + 1)$

iv $(3\sqrt{2} + 1)(3\sqrt{2} - 1)$

v $(2 - 4\sqrt{3})(2 + 4\sqrt{3})$

b What happens in the answers to part **a**? Why?

c Rationalise the denominators of the following.

i $\dfrac{5}{1 - \sqrt{5}}$

ii $\dfrac{2 + \sqrt{3}}{\sqrt{3} - 1}$

1 A spaceship travelled for 6×10^2 hours at a speed of 8×10^4 km/h.

    a Calculate the distance travelled by the spaceship. Give your answer in standard form.

One month an aircraft travelled 2×10^5 km. The next month the aircraft travelled 3×10^4 km.

    b Calculate the total distance travelled by the aircraft in the two months. Give your answer as an ordinary number.

Edexcel, Question 10, Paper 5 Higher, June 2003

2 **a** **i** Write 40 000 000 in standard form.

       ii Write 3×10^{-5} as an ordinary number.

    b Work out the value of

       $3 \times 10^{-5} \times 40\,000\,000$

     Give your answer in standard form.

Edexcel, Question 4, Paper 5 Higher, November 2004

3 $x = \sqrt{\dfrac{p+q}{pq}}$

    $p = 4 \times 10^8$ $q = 3 \times 10^6$

Find the value of x. Give your answer in standard form correct to 2 significant figures.

Edexcel, Question 3, Paper 13B Higher, March 2005

4 **a** Simplify

    i $t^4 \times t^3$ **ii** $\dfrac{m}{m^6}$ **iii** $(3k^2m^2) \times (4k^3m)$

5 Simplify   **a** $\dfrac{8x^2y \times 3xy^3}{6x^2y^2}$ **b** $(2m^4p^2)^3$

6 Express the recurring decimal 0.5333333… as a fraction. Give your answer in its simplest form.

7 Find values of a and b such that

    $(3 + \sqrt5)(2 - \sqrt5) = a + b\sqrt5$

8 The area of this rectangle is 40 cm²

Find the value of x. Give your answer in the form $a\sqrt b$ where a and b are integers

$4\sqrt2$ cm

x cm

9 **a** Prove that $0.\dot7\dot2 = \dfrac{8}{11}$

    b Hence, or otherwise, express $0.3\dot7\dot2$ as a fraction.

10 **a** **i** Show that $\sqrt{32} = 4\sqrt2$

      ii Expand and simplify $(\sqrt2 + \sqrt{12})^2$

    b Show clearly that this triangle is right-angled

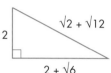

$\sqrt2 + \sqrt{12}$

2

$2 + \sqrt6$

11 Rationalise the denominator of $\dfrac{4 + \sqrt5}{\sqrt5}$

Simplify your answer fully.

WORKED EXAM QUESTION

a Expand and simplify as far as possible $(\sqrt2 + 3)(\sqrt2 - 1)$.

b Show clearly that $\dfrac{3}{\sqrt6} + \dfrac{\sqrt6}{3} = \dfrac{5}{\sqrt6}$

Solution

a $\sqrt2 \times \sqrt2 + \sqrt2 \times -1 + 3 \times \sqrt2 + 3 \times -1$

    $2 - \sqrt2 + 3\sqrt2 - 3 = -1 + 2\sqrt2$

                   Expand the brackets to get four terms.

                    Simplify the terms and collect together like terms.

b $\dfrac{3 \times 3 + \sqrt6 \times \sqrt6}{\sqrt6 \times 3}$

                    Combine the fractions together with the same common denominator.

  $\dfrac{9 + 6}{\sqrt6 \times 3} = \dfrac{15}{3\sqrt6} = \dfrac{5}{\sqrt6}$

                    Simplify the terms and collect together and cancel the common multiple of 3.

A scientist is doing some research on the production and consumption of oil in the world. She looks at 10 oil producing countries and, for each country, finds the most recent figures on the country's population, and its oil production and consumption, measured in barrels per day.

USA
Population: 295 734 134
Oil production: 7.8×10^6
Oil consumption: 19.65×10^6

With these figures she calculates for each country the oil produced per person *per year*, and the oil consumed per person *per year*, then finds the difference (all to 1 decimal place).

She then ranks the countries from 1 to 10 (highest difference to lowest difference), to see which countries are using less than they produce, and which countries are using more than they produce.

She also calculates each country's consumption as a percentage of its production (to the nearest 1%).

Help her complete the table and write a short paragraph on the results of the calculations.

Venezuela
Population: 25 375 281
Oil production: 2.6×10^6
Oil consumption: 500 000

Chile
Population: 15 980 912
Oil production: 18,500
Oil consumption: 240 000

Country	Oil produced, barrels per person per year	Oil consumed, barrels per person per year	Difference (produced – consumed)	Rank order	Consumption as a % of production
Algeria	13.5	2.3	11.2	3	17%
Australia					
Chile					
Indonesia					
Japan					
Nigeria					
Saudi Arabia					
UK					
USA					
Venezuela					

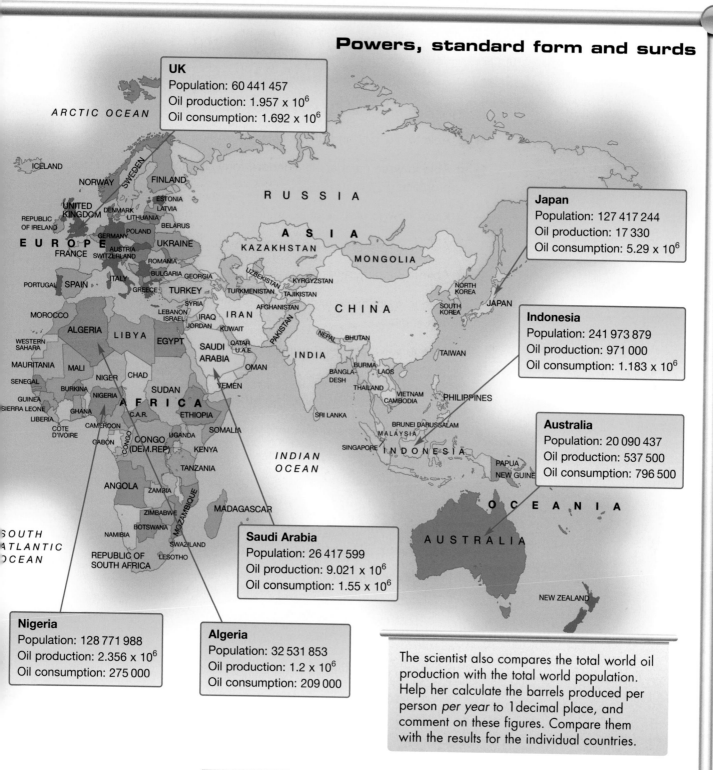

UK
Population: 60 441 457
Oil production: 1.957×10^6
Oil consumption: 1.692×10^6

Japan
Population: 127 417 244
Oil production: 17 330
Oil consumption: 5.29×10^6

Indonesia
Population: 241 973 879
Oil production: 971 000
Oil consumption: 1.183×10^6

Australia
Population: 20 090 437
Oil production: 537 500
Oil consumption: 796 500

Saudi Arabia
Population: 26 417 599
Oil production: 9.021×10^6
Oil consumption: 1.55×10^6

Nigeria
Population: 128 771 988
Oil production: 2.356×10^6
Oil consumption: 275 000

Algeria
Population: 32 531 853
Oil production: 1.2×10^6
Oil consumption: 209 000

The scientist also compares the total world oil production with the total world population. Help her calculate the barrels produced per person *per year* to 1 decimal place, and comment on these figures. Compare them with the results for the individual countries.

Year	World population	World oil production, barrels per day	World oil production, barrels per person per year
1984	4.77×10^9	5.45×10^7	4.2
1989	5.19×10^9	5.99×10^7	
1994	5.61×10^9	6.10×10^7	
1999	6.01×10^9	6.58×10^7	
2004	6.38×10^9	7.25×10^7	

GRADE YOURSELF

D Able to write and calculate numbers written in index form

C Able to multiply and divide numbers written in index form

B Able to write numbers in standard form and use these in various problems

A Know how to use the rules of indices for negative and fractional values

A Able to convert recurring decimals to fractions

A Able to simplify surds

A* Able to manipulate expressions containing surds and rationalise denominators

A* Able to solve problems using surds

What you should know now

- How to write numbers in standard form
- How to solve problems using numbers in standard form
- How to manipulate indices, both integer (positive and negative) and fractional
- How to compare fractions by converting them to decimals
- How to convert decimals into fractions
- What surds are and how to manipulate them

Chapter

11

Statistics 1

This chapter will show you ...

- how to calculate and use the mode, median, mean and range from frequency tables of discrete data
- how to decide which is the best average for different types of data
- how to recognise the modal class and calculate an estimate of the mean from frequency tables of grouped data
- how to draw frequency polygons and histograms
- how to calculate and use a moving average
- how to design questions for questionnaires and surveys

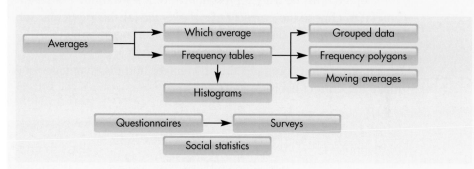

What you should already know

- How to work out the mean, mode, median and range of small sets of discrete data
- How to extract information from tables and diagrams

Quick check

1 The marks for 15 students in a maths test are

2, 3, 4, 5, 5, 6, 6, 6, 7, 7, 7, 7, 7, 8, 10

a What is the modal mark?

b What is the median mark?

c What is the range of the marks?

d What is the mean mark?

11.1 Averages

In this section you will learn how to:

- use averages
- solve more complex problems using averages
- identify the advantages and disadvantages of each type of average and learn which one to use in different situations

Key words

mean
measure of
location
median
mode

Average is a term we often use when describing or comparing sets of data. The average is also known as a **measure of location**. For example, we refer to the average rainfall in Britain, the average score of a batsman, an average weekly wage, the average mark in an examination. In each of these examples, we are representing the whole set of many values by just one single, typical value, which we call the average.

The idea of an average is extremely useful, because it enables us to compare one set of data with another set by comparing just two values – their averages.

There are several ways of expressing an average, but the most commonly used averages are the **mode**, the **median** and the **mean**.

An average must be truly representative of a set of data. So, when you have to find an average, it is crucial to choose the *correct type of average* for this particular set of data. If you use the wrong average, your results will be distorted and give misleading information.

This table, which compares the advantages and disadvantages of each type of average, will help you to make the correct decision.

	Mode	Median	Mean
Advantages	Very easy to find Not affected by extreme values Can be used for non-numerical data	Easy to find for ungrouped data Not affected by extreme values	Easy to find Uses all the values The total for a given number of values can be calculated from it
Disadvantages	Doesn't use all the values May not exist	Doesn't use all the values Often not understood	Extreme values can distort it Has to be calculated
Used for	Non-numerical data For finding the most likely value	Data with extreme values	Data whose values are spread in a balanced way

EXAMPLE 1

The ages of 20 people attending a conference are

23, 25, 26, 28, 28, 34, 34, 34, 37, 45, 47, 48, 52, 53, 56, 63, 67, 70, 73, 77

a Find **i** the mode, **ii** the median, **iii** the mean of the data.

b Which average best represents the age of the people at the conference.

a **i** The mode is 34, **ii** the median is 46, **iii** the mean is 920 ÷ 20 = 46

b The mean is distorted because of the few very old people at the conference. The median is also distorted by the larger values, so in this case the mode would be the most representative average.

EXERCISE 11A

1 Shopkeepers always want to keep the most popular items in stock. Which average do you think is often known as the shopkeeper's average?

2 A list contains seven even numbers. The largest number is 24. The smallest number is half the largest. The mode is 14 and the median is 16. Two of the numbers add up to 42. What are the seven numbers?

3 The marks of 25 students in an English examination are as follows.

55, 63, 24, 47, 60, 45, 50, 89, 39, 47, 38, 42, 69, 73, 38, 47, 53, 64, 58, 71, 41, 48, 68, 64, 75

Find the median.

4 Decide which average you would use for each of the following. Give a reason for your answer.

a The average mark in an examination.

b The average pocket money for a group of 16-year-old students.

c The average shoe size for all the girls in Year 10.

d The average height for all the artistes on tour with a circus.

e The average hair colour for pupils in your school.

f The average weight of all newborn babies in a hospital's maternity ward.

5 A pack of matches consisted of 12 boxes. The contents of each box are as follows.

34   31   29   35   33   30   31   28   29   35   32   31

On the box it states that the average contents is 32 matches. Is this correct?

6 This table shows the annual salaries for a firm's employees.

Chairman	£43 000
Managing director	£37 000
Floor manager	£25 000
Skilled worker 1	£24 000
Skilled worker 2	£24 000
Machinist	£18 000
Computer engineer	£18 000
Secretary	£18 000
Office junior	£7 000

a What is **i** the modal salary, **ii** the median salary, and **iii** the mean salary?

b The management has suggested a pay rise for all of 6%. The shopfloor workers want a pay rise for all of £1500. What difference to the mean salary would each suggestion make?

7 Mr Brennan, a caring maths teacher, told each pupil their individual test mark and only gave the test statistics to the whole class. He gave the class the modal mark, the median mark and the mean mark.

a Which average would tell a pupil whether he/she were in the top half or the bottom half of the class?

b Which average tells the pupils nothing really?

c Which average allows a pupil really to gauge how well he/she has done compared with everyone else?

8 A list of 9 numbers has a mean of 7.6. What number must be added to the list to give a new mean of 8?

9 A dance group of 17 teenagers had a mean weight of 44.5 kg. To enter a competition there needs to be 18 people in the group with an average weight of 44.4 kg or less. What is the maximum weight that the eighteenth person could be?

10 The mean age of a group of eight walkers is 42. Joanne joins the group and the mean age changes to 40. How old is Joanne?

11.2 Frequency tables

In this section you will learn how to:
- calculate the mode and median from a frequency table
- calculate the mean from a frequency table

Key word
frequency table

When a lot of information has been gathered, it is often convenient to put it together in a **frequency table**. From this table, you can then find the values of the mode, median, mean and range of the data.

EXAMPLE 2

A survey was done on the number of people in each car leaving the Meadowhall Shopping Centre, in Sheffield. The results are summarised in the table.

Calculate **a** the mode, **b** the median, **c** the mean number of people in a car.

Number of people in each car	1	2	3	4	5	6
Frequency	45	198	121	76	52	13

a The modal number of people in a car is easy to spot. It is the number with the largest frequency (198). Hence, the modal number of people in a car is 2.

b The median number of people in a car is found by working out where the middle of the set of numbers is located. First, add up frequencies to get the total number of cars surveyed, which comes to 505. Next, calculate the middle position

$(505 + 1) \div 2 = 253$

You now need to add the frequencies across the table to find which group contains the 253rd item. The 243rd item is the end of the group with 2 in a car. Therefore, the 253rd item must be in the group with 3 in a car. Hence, the median number of people in a car is 3.

c The mean number of people in a car is found by calculating the total number of people, and then dividing this total by the number of cars surveyed.

Number in car	Frequency	Number in these cars
1	45	$1 \times 45 = 45$
2	198	$2 \times 198 = 396$
3	121	$3 \times 121 = 363$
4	76	$4 \times 76 = 304$
5	52	$5 \times 52 = 260$
6	13	$6 \times 13 = 78$
Totals	505	1446

Hence, the mean number of people in a car is $1446 \div 505 = 2.9$ (2 significant figures).

Using your calculator

The previous example can also be done by using the statistical mode which is available on some calculators. However, not all calculators are the same, so you will have to either read your instruction manual or experiment with the statistical keys on your calculator.

You may find one labelled

DATA or M+ or Σ+ or $\bar{x}$ where $\bar{x}$ is printed in blue.

Try the following key strokes.

1 × 4 5 DATA   2 × 1 9 8 DATA ...

1 × 4 5 DATA $\bar{x}$

EXERCISE 11B

1   Find **i** the mode, **ii** the median and **iii** the mean from each frequency table below.

   a   A survey of the shoe sizes of all the Y10 boys in a school gave these results.

Shoe size	4	5	6	7	8	9	10
Number of pupils	12	30	34	35	23	8	3

   b   This is a record of the number of babies born each week over one year in a small maternity unit.

Number of babies	0	1	2	3	4	5	6	7	8	9	10	11	12	13	14
Frequency	1	1	1	2	2	2	3	5	9	8	6	4	5	2	1

2   A survey of the number of children in each family of a school's intake gave these results.

Number of children	1	2	3	4	5
Frequency	214	328	97	26	3

   a   Assuming each child at the school is shown in the data, how many children are at the school?

   b   Calculate the mean number of children in a family.

   c   How many families have this mean number of children?

   d   How many families would consider themselves average from this survey?

3   A dentist kept records of how many teeth he extracted from his patients.

   In 1970 he extracted 598 teeth from 271 patients.

   In 1980 he extracted 332 teeth from 196 patients.

   In 1990 he extracted 374 teeth from 288 patients.

   a   Calculate the average number of teeth taken from each patient in each year.

   b   Explain why you think the average number of teeth extracted falls each year.

4   The teachers in a school were asked to indicate the average number of hours they spent each day marking. The table summarises their replies.

Number of hours spent marking	1	2	3	4	5	6
Number of teachers	10	13	12	8	6	1

   a   How many teachers are at the school?

   b   What is the modal number of hours spent marking?

   c   What is the mean number of hours spent marking?

5 Two friends often played golf together. They recorded their scores for each hole over five games to determine who was more consistent and who was the better player. The results are summarised in the table.

No. of shots to hole ball	1	2	3	4	5	6	7	8	9
Roger	0	0	0	14	37	27	12	0	0
Brian	5	12	15	18	14	8	8	8	2

a What is the modal score for each player?

b What is the range of scores for each player?

c What is the median score for each player?

d What is the mean score for each player?

e Which player is the more consistent and explain why?

f Who would you say is the better player and state why?

6 The number of league goals scored by a football team over a season is given in the table.

Number of goals scored	0	1	2	3	4	5	6	7
Number of matches	3	8	10	11	4	2	1	1

a How many games were played that season?

b What is the range of goals scored?

c What is the modal number of goals scored?

d What is the median number of goals scored?

e What is the mean number of goals scored?

f Which average do you think the team's supporters would say is the average number of goals scored by the team that season?

g If the team also scored 20 goals in ten cup matches that season, what was the mean number of goals the team scored throughout the whole season?

7 The table shows the number of passengers in each of 100 taxis leaving London Airport one day.

No. of passengers in a taxi	1	2	3	4
No. of taxis	x	40	y	26

a Find the value of $x + y$.

b If the mean number of passengers per taxi is 2.66, show that $x + 3y = 82$.

c Find the values of x and y by solving appropriate equations.

d State the median of the number of passengers per taxi.

Grouped data

In this section you will learn how to:
- identify the modal group
- calculate and estimate the mean from a grouped table

Key words

continuous data
discrete data
estimated mean
groups
modal group

Sometimes the information we are given is grouped in some way, as in the table in Example 3, which shows the range of weekly pocket money given to Y10 students in a particular class.

EXAMPLE 3

From the data in the table

a write down the **modal group**

b calculate an estimate of the mean weekly pocket money.

Pocket money, p, (£)	$0 < p \leqslant 1$	$1 < p \leqslant 2$	$2 < p \leqslant 3$	$3 < p \leqslant 4$	$4 < p \leqslant 5$
No. of students	2	5	5	9	15

a The modal group is still easy to pick out, since it is simply the one with the largest frequency. Here the modal group is £4 to £5.

b The mean can only be estimated, since you do not have all the information. To estimate the mean, you simply assume that each person in each group has the midway amount, then you can proceed to build up the table as before.

Note how you find the midway value. The two end values are added together and then divided by two.

Pocket money, p, (£)	Frequency (f)	Midway (m)	$f \times m$
$0 < p \leqslant 1$	2	0.50	1.00
$1 < p \leqslant 2$	5	1.50	7.50
$2 < p \leqslant 3$	5	2.50	12.50
$3 < p \leqslant 4$	9	3.50	31.50
$4 < p \leqslant 5$	15	4.50	67.50
Totals	36		120

The **estimated mean** will be £120 ÷ 36 = £3.33 (rounded off).

Note the notation used for the groups.

$0 < p \leqslant 1$ means any amount above 0p up to and including £1.

$1 < p \leqslant 2$ means any amount above £1 up to and including £2.

If you had written 0.01 – 1.00, 1.01 – 2.00, etc. for the **groups**, then the midway values would have been 0.505, 1.505, etc. Although technically correct, this makes the calculation of the mean harder and does not have a significant effect on the final answer, which is an estimate anyway.

This issue only arises because money is **discrete data**, which is data that consists of separate numbers, such as goals scored, marks in a test, number of children and shoe sizes. Normally grouped tables use **continuous data** which is data which can have an infinite number of different values, such as height, weight, time, area and capacity. It is always rounded-off information.

Whatever the type of data, remember to find the midway value by adding the two end values of the group and dividing by 2.

EXERCISE 11C

1 For each table of values, find the following.

    i the modal group   **ii** an estimate for the mean

a

x	$0 < x \leqslant 10$	$10 < x \leqslant 20$	$20 < x \leqslant 30$	$30 < x \leqslant 40$	$40 < x \leqslant 50$
Frequency	4	6	11	17	9

b

y	$0 < y \leqslant 100$	$100 < y \leqslant 200$	$200 < y \leqslant 300$	$300 < y \leqslant 400$	$400 < y \leqslant 500$	$500 < y \leqslant 600$
Frequency	95	56	32	21	9	3

c

z	$0 < z \leqslant 5$	$5 < z \leqslant 10$	$10 < z \leqslant 15$	$15 < z \leqslant 20$
Frequency	16	27	19	13

HINTS AND TIPS

When you copy the tables, draw them vertically as in Example 3.

c

Weeks	1–3	4–6	7–9	10–12	13–15
Frequency	5	8	14	10	7

2 Jason brought 100 pebbles back from the beach and weighed them all to the nearest gram. His results are summarised in this table.

Weight, w (grams)	$40 < w \leqslant 60$	$60 < w \leqslant 80$	$80 < w \leqslant 100$	$100 < w \leqslant 120$	$120 < w \leqslant 140$	$140 < w \leqslant 160$
Frequency	5	9	22	27	26	11

Find the following.

  a the modal weight of the pebbles

  b an estimate of the total weight of all the pebbles

  c an estimate of the mean weight of the pebbles

3 One hundred light bulbs were tested by their manufacturer to see whether the average life span of the manufacturer's bulbs was over 200 hours. The table summarises the results.

Life span, h (hours)	$150 < h \leqslant 175$	$175 < h \leqslant 200$	$200 < h \leqslant 225$	$225 < h \leqslant 250$	$250 < h \leqslant 275$
Frequency	24	45	18	10	3

a What is the modal length of time a bulb lasts?

b What percentage of bulbs last longer than 200 hours?

c Estimate the mean life span of the light bulbs.

d Do you think the test shows that the average life span is over 200 hours? Fully explain your answer.

4 The table shows the distances run by an athlete who is training for a marathon.

Distance, d, miles	$0 < d \leqslant 5$	$5 < d \leqslant 10$	$10 < d \leqslant 15$	$15 < d \leqslant 20$	$20 < d \leqslant 25$
Frequency	3	8	13	5	2

a It is recommended that an athlete's daily average mileage should be at least one third of the distance of the race being trained for. A marathon is 26.2 miles. Is this athlete doing enough training?

b The athlete records the times of some runs and calculates that her average pace for all runs is $6\frac{1}{2}$ minutes to a mile. Explain why she is wrong to expect a finishing time of $26.2 \times 6\frac{1}{2}$ minutes $\approx$ 170 minutes for the marathon.

c The athlete claims that the difference between her shortest and longest run is 21 miles. Could this be correct? Explain your answer.

5 The owners of a boutique did a survey to find the average age of people using the boutique. The table summarises the results.

Age (years)	14–18	19–20	21–26	27–35	36–50
Frequency	26	24	19	16	11

What do you think is the average age of the people using the boutique?

6 Three supermarkets each claimed to have the lowest average price increase over the year. The table summarises their average price increases.

Price increase (p)	1–5	6–10	11–15	16–20	21–25	26–30	31–35
Soundbuy	4	10	14	23	19	8	2
Springfields	5	11	12	19	25	9	6
Setco	3	8	15	31	21	7	3

Using their average price increases, make a comparison of the supermarkets and write a report on which supermarket, in your opinion, has the lowest price increases over the year. Don't forget to justify your answers.

11.4 Frequency diagrams

In this section you will learn how to:

- draw frequency polygons for discrete and continuous data
- draw histograms for continuous data with equal intervals

Key words

continuous data
discrete data
frequency polygon
histogram

Frequency polygons

To help people understand it, statistical information is often presented in pictorial or diagrammatic form. For example, you should have seen pie charts, bar charts and stem-and-leaf diagrams. Another method of showing data is by **frequency polygons**.

Frequency polygons can be used to represent both ungrouped data and grouped data, as shown in Example 4 and Example 5 respectively. They are useful to show the shapes of distributions, and can be used to compare distributions.

EXAMPLE 4

No. of children	0	1	2	3	4	5
Frequency	12	23	36	28	16	11

This is the frequency polygon for the *ungrouped* data in the table.

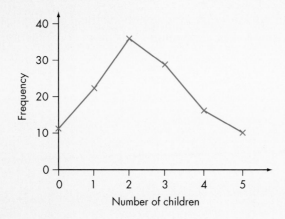

- You simply plot the coordinates from each ordered pair in the table.
- You complete the polygon by joining up the plotted points with straight lines.

EXAMPLE 5

Weight, w (kilograms)	$0 < w \leq 5$	$5 < w \leq 10$	$10 < w \leq 15$	$15 < w \leq 20$	$20 < w \leq 25$	$25 < w \leq 30$
Frequency	4	13	25	32	17	9

This is the frequency polygon for the grouped data in the table.

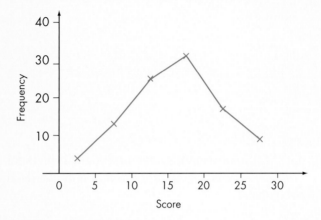

- You use the midway value of each group, just as in estimating the mean.
- You plot the ordered pairs of midway values with frequency, namely,

  (2.5, 4), (7.5, 13), (12.5, 25), (17.5, 32), (22.5, 17), (27.5, 9)

- You do not know what happens above and below the groups in the table, so do not draw lines before (2.5, 4) or after (27.5, 9). The diagram shows the shape of the distribution.

Bar charts and histograms

You should already be familiar with the bar chart in which the vertical axis represents frequency, and the horizontal axis represents the type of data. (Sometimes it is more convenient to have the axes the other way.)

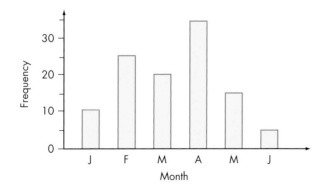

A **histogram** looks similar to a bar chart, but there are four fundamental differences.

- There are no gaps between the bars.

- The horizontal axis has a continuous scale since it represents **continuous** data, such as time, weight or length.

- The area of each bar represents the class or group frequency of the bar.

- The vertical axis is labelled "Frequency density", where

$$\text{Frequency density} = \frac{\text{Frequency of class interval}}{\text{Width of class interval}}$$

When the data is not continuous, a simple bar chart is used. For example, you would use a bar chart to represent the runs scored in a test match or the goals scored by a hockey team.

Look at the histogram below, which has been drawn from this table of times taken by people to walk to work.

Time, t (min)	$0 < t \leqslant 4$	$4 < t \leqslant 8$	$8 < t \leqslant 12$	$12 < t \leqslant 16$
Frequency	8	12	10	7
Frequency density	2	3	2.5	1.75

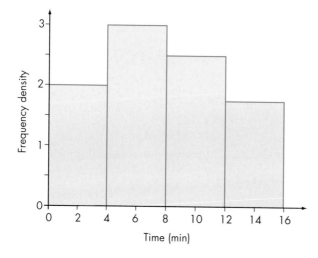

Notice that each histogram bar starts at the *least possible* time and finishes at the *greatest possible* time for its group.

Using your calculator

Histograms can also be drawn on graphics calculators or by using computer software packages. If you have access to either of these, try to use them.

EXERCISE 11D

1 The table shows how many students were absent from one particular class throughout the year.

Students absent	1	2	3	4	5
Frequency	48	32	12	3	1

a Draw a frequency polygon to illustrate the data.

b Calculate the mean number of absences each lesson.

2 The table shows the number of goals scored by a hockey team in one season.

Goals	1	2	3	4	5
Frequency	3	9	7	5	2

a Draw the frequency polygon for this data.

b Calculate the mean number of goals scored per game in the season.

3 The frequency polygon shows the amount of money spent in a corner shop by the first 40 customers on one day.

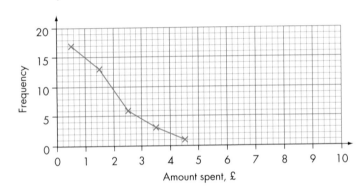

a i Use the frequency polygon to complete the table for the amounts spent by the first 40 customers

Amount spent, m, £	$0 < m \leqslant 1$	$1 < m \leqslant 2$	$2 < m \leqslant 3$	$3 < m \leqslant 4$	$4 < m \leqslant 5$
Frequency					

ii Work out the mean amount of money spent by these 40 customers.

b Mid morning the shopkeeper records the amount spent by another 40 customers. The table below shows the data.

Amount spent, m, £	$0 < m \leqslant 2$	$2 < m \leqslant 4$	$4 < m \leqslant 6$	$6 < m \leqslant 8$	$8 < m \leqslant 10$
Frequency	3	5	18	10	4

i On a copy of the graph above, draw the frequency polygon to show this data?

ii Calculate the mean amount spent by the 40 mid-morning customers..

c Comment on the differences between the frequency polygons and the average amounts spent by the different sets of customers.

4 The table shows the range of heights of the girls in Y11 at a London school.

Height, h (cm)	$120 < h \leqslant 130$	$130 < h \leqslant 140$	$140 < h \leqslant 150$	$150 < h \leqslant 160$	$160 < h \leqslant 170$
Frequency	15	37	25	13	5

a Draw a frequency polygon for this data.
b Draw a histogram for this data

c Estimate the mean height of the girls.

5 A doctor was concerned at the length of time her patients had to wait to see her when they came to the morning surgery. The survey she did gave her these results.

Time, m (minutes)	$0 < m \leqslant 10$	$10 < m \leqslant 20$	$20 < m \leqslant 30$	$30 < m \leqslant 40$	$40 < m \leqslant 50$	$50 < m \leqslant 60$
Monday	5	8	17	9	7	4
Tuesday	9	8	16	3	2	1
Wednesday	7	6	18	2	1	1

a Draw a frequency polygon for each day on the same pair of axes.

b What is the average amount of time spent waiting each day?

c Why might the average time for each day be different?

11.5 Histograms with bars of unequal width

In this section you will learn how to:
- draw and read histograms where the bars are of unequal width
- find the median, quartiles and interquartile range from a histogram

Key words

class interval
interquartile range
lower quartile
median
upper quartile

Sometimes the data in a frequency distribution are grouped into classes whose intervals are different. In this case, the resulting histogram has bars of unequal width.

The key fact that you should always remember is that the *area* of a bar in a histogram represents the class *frequency* of the bar. So, in the case of an unequal-width histogram, the height to draw each bar is found by dividing its class frequency by its class interval width (bar width), which is the difference between the lower and upper bounds for each interval. Conversely, given a histogram, any of its class frequencies can be found by multiplying the height of the corresponding bar by its width.

It is for this reason that the scale on the vertical axes of histograms is nearly always labelled "Frequency density", where

$$\text{Frequency density} = \frac{\text{Frequency of class interval}}{\text{Width of class interval}}$$

EXAMPLE 6

The heights of a group of girls were measured. The results were classified as shown in the table.

Height, h (cm)	$151 \leqslant h < 153$	$153 \leqslant h < 154$	$154 \leqslant h < 155$	$155 \leqslant h < 159$	$159 \leqslant h < 160$
Frequency	64	43	47	96	12

It is convenient to write the table vertically and add two columns, class width and frequency density.

The class width is found by subtracting the lower class boundary from the upper class boundary. The frequency density is found by dividing the frequency by the class width.

Height, h (cm)	Frequency	Class width	Frequency density
$151 \leqslant h < 153$	64	2	32
$153 \leqslant h < 154$	43	1	43
$154 \leqslant h < 155$	47	1	47
$155 \leqslant h < 159$	96	4	24
$159 \leqslant h < 160$	12	1	12

The histogram can now be drawn. The horizontal scale should be marked off as normal from a value below the lowest value in the table to a value above the largest value in the table. In this case, mark the scale from 150 cm to 160 cm. The vertical scale is always frequency density and is marked up to at least the largest frequency density in the table. In this case, 50 is a sensible value.

Each bar is drawn between the lower **class interval** and the upper class interval horizontally, and up to the frequency density vertically.

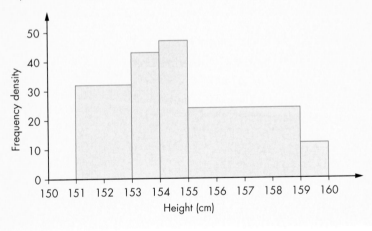

EXAMPLE 7

This histogram shows the distribution of heights of daffodils in a greenhouse.

a Complete a frequency table for the heights of the daffodils, and show the cumulative frequency.

b Find the **median** height.

c Find the **interquartile range** of the heights.

d Estimate the mean of the distribution.

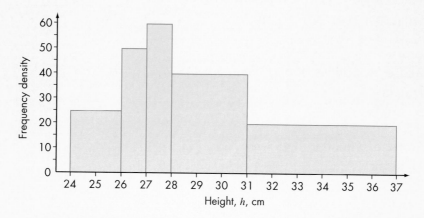

a The frequency table will have groups of $24 \leqslant h < 26$, $26 \leqslant h < 27$, etc. These are read from the height axis. The frequencies will be found by multiplying the width of each bar by the frequency density. Remember that the value on the vertical axis is not the frequency.

Height, h (cm)	$24 \leqslant h < 26$	$26 \leqslant h < 27$	$27 \leqslant h < 28$	$28 \leqslant h < 31$	$31 \leqslant h < 37$
Frequency	50	50	60	120	120
Cumulative frequency	50	100	160	280	400

b There are 400 values so the median will be the 200th value. Counting up the frequencies from the beginning we get the third row of the table above.

The median occurs in the $28 \leqslant h < 31$ group. There are 160 values before this group and 120 in it. To get to the 200th value we need to go 40 more values into this group. 40 out of 120 is one-third. One third of the way through this group is the value 29 cm. Hence the median is 29 cm.

c The interquartile range is the difference between the **upper quartile** and the **lower quartile**, the quarter and three-quarter values respectively. In this case, the lower quartile is the 100th value (found by dividing 400, the total number of values, by 4) and the upper quartile is the 300th value. So, in the same way that you found the median, you can find the lower (100th value) and upper (300th value) quartiles. The 100th value is at 27 cm and the 300th value is at 32 cm. The interquartile range is 32 cm − 27 cm = 5 cm.

d To estimate the mean, use the table to get the midway values of the groups and multiply these by the frequencies. The sum of these divided by 400 will give the estimated mean. So, the mean is

$$(25 \times 50 + 26.5 \times 50 + 27.5 \times 60 + 29.5 \times 120 + 34 \times 120) \div 400$$
$$= 11\,845 \div 400 = 29.6 \text{ cm (3 significant figures)}$$

1 Draw histograms for these grouped frequency distributions.

a

Temperature, t (°C)	$8 \leqslant t < 10$	$10 \leqslant t < 12$	$12 \leqslant t < 15$	$15 \leqslant t < 17$	$17 \leqslant t < 20$	$20 \leqslant t < 24$
Frequency	5	13	18	4	3	6

b

Wage, w (£1000)	$6 \leqslant w < 10$	$10 \leqslant w < 12$	$12 \leqslant w < 16$	$16 \leqslant w < 24$
Frequency	16	54	60	24

c

Age, a (nearest year)	$11 \leqslant a < 14$	$14 \leqslant a < 16$	$16 \leqslant a < 17$	$17 \leqslant a < 20$
Frequency	51	36	12	20

d

Pressure, p (mm)	$745 \leqslant p < 755$	$755 \leqslant p < 760$	$760 \leqslant p < 765$	$765 \leqslant p < 775$
Frequency	4	6	14	10

e

Time, t (min)	$0 \leqslant t < 8$	$8 \leqslant t < 12$	$12 \leqslant t < 16$	$16 \leqslant t < 20$
Frequency	72	84	54	36

2 The following information was gathered about the weekly pocket money given to 14 year olds.

Pocket money, p (£)	$0 \leqslant p < 2$	$2 \leqslant p < 4$	$4 \leqslant p < 5$	$5 \leqslant p < 8$	$8 \leqslant p < 10$
Girls	8	15	22	12	4
Boys	6	11	25	15	6

a Represent the information about the boys on a histogram.

b Represent both sets of data with a frequency polygon, using the same pair of axes.

c What is the mean amount of pocket money given to each sex? Comment on your answer.

3 The sales of the Star newspaper over 65 years are recorded in this table.

Years	1930–50	1951–70	1971–80	1981–90	1991–95	1995–2000
Copies	62 000	68 000	71 000	75 000	63 000	52 000

Illustrate this information on a histogram. Take the class boundaries as 1930, 1950, 1970, 1980, 1990, 1995, 2000.

4 The London trains were always late, so one month a survey was undertaken to find how many trains were late, and by how many minutes (to the nearest minute). The results are illustrated by this histogram.

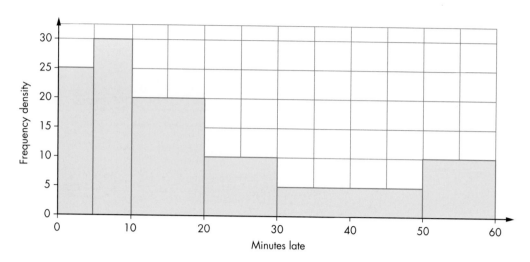

a How many trains were in the survey?

b How many trains were delayed for longer than 15 minutes?

5 For each of the frequency distributions illustrated in the histograms

   i write down the grouped frequency table,

  ii state the modal group,

 iii estimate the median,

  iv find the lower and upper quartiles and the interquartile range,

   v estimate the mean of the distribution.

a

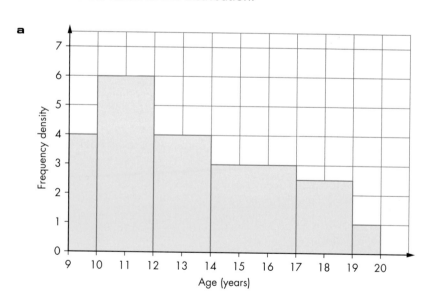

b

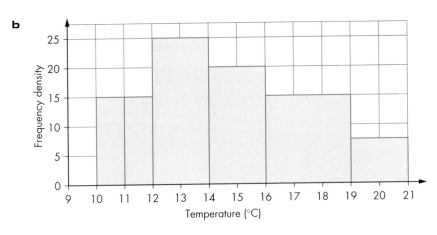

c

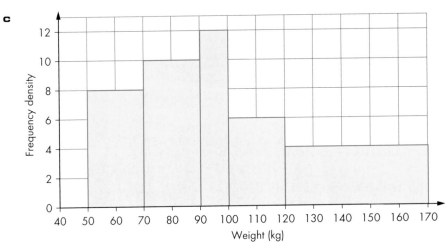

6 All the patients in a hospital were asked how long it was since they last saw a doctor. The results are shown in the table.

Hours, h	$0 \leq h < 2$	$2 \leq h < 4$	$4 \leq h < 6$	$6 \leq h < 10$	$10 \leq h < 16$	$16 \leq h < 24$
Frequency	8	12	20	30	20	10

a Find the median time since a patient last saw a doctor.

b Estimate the mean time since a patient last saw a doctor.

c Find the interquartile range of the times.

7 One summer, Albert monitored the weight of the tomatoes grown on each of his plants. His results are summarised in this table.

Weight, w (kg)	$6 \leq w < 10$	$10 \leq w < 12$	$12 \leq w < 16$	$16 \leq w < 20$	$20 \leq w < 25$
Frequency	8	15	28	16	10

a Draw a histogram for this distribution.

b Estimate the median weight of tomatoes the plants produced.

c Estimate the mean weight of tomatoes the plants produced.

d How many plants produced more than 15 kg?

8 A survey was carried out to find the speeds of cars passing a particular point on the M1. The histogram illustrates the results of the survey.

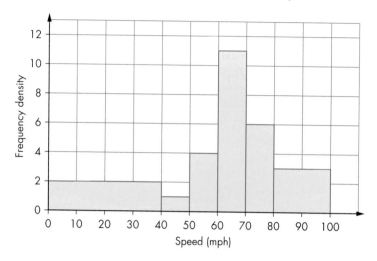

a Copy and complete this table.

Speed, v (mph)	$0 < v \leqslant 40$	$40 < v \leqslant 50$	$50 < v \leqslant 60$	$60 < v \leqslant 70$	$70 < v \leqslant 80$	$80 < v \leqslant 100$
Frequency		10	40	110		

b Find the number of cars included in the survey.

c Work out an estimate of the median speed of the cars on this part of the M1.

d Work out an estimate of the mean speed of the cars on this part of the M1.

11.6 Moving averages

In this section you will learn how to:
• calculate a moving average and use it to predict future trends

Key words
moving
    average
seasonal
    trend
trend line

A **moving average** gives a clear indication of the trend of a set of data. It smoothes out, for example, **seasonal trends** such as monthly variations or daily differences.

EXAMPLE 8

A van rental firm has a record of how many vans were hired in each month of a year. This data is shown in the table. Using a four-point moving average, predict the number of vans the firm will rent out during the following January.

Months	Jan	Feb	Mar	Apr	May	Jun	Jul	Aug	Sep	Oct	Nov	Dec
Vans	9	22	37	14	18	24	42	17	20	27	48	20

First, plot the raw data. The resulting line graph shows a normal variation of business for the hire firm, but does not reveal the general trend of business. Is the firm's business improving, declining or remaining the same?

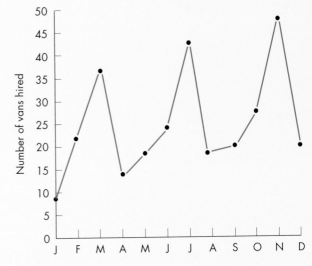

You can show the general trend by first calculating the mean for each four-month span, month on month. This is the four-point moving average.

Mean for Jan, Feb, Mar and April
$(9 + 22 + 37 + 14) ÷ 4 = 20.5$

Mean for Feb, Mar, Apr and May
$(22 + 37 + 14 + 18) ÷ 4 = 22.75$

Mean for Mar, Apr, May and Jun $(37 + 14 + 18 + 24) ÷ 4 = 23.25$

And so on, giving 24.5, 25.25, 25.75, 26.5, 28, 28.75 as the remaining averages.

Then plot, on the first graph, each mean value at the midpoint of the corresponding four-month span. This produces a much smoother graph, which, in this case, shows a slight upward trend. In other words, business is improving.

Draw a line of best fit (the **trend line**) through the data and read off the predicted value of the next four-point moving average. This is about 30.

Let the value for the next January be x, then $(27 + 48 + 20 + x) ÷ 4 = 30$

$\Rightarrow 95 + x = 120$

$\Rightarrow \quad x = 25$

So we can predict that the firm will rent out 25 vans the following January.

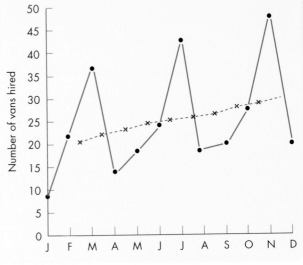

In Example 8, we used an interval of four months to construct a moving average but there is nothing special about this interval. It could well have been five or six months, except that you would then have needed data for more months to give sufficient mean values to show a trend. The number of months, weeks or even years used for moving averages depends on the likely variations of the data. You would not expect to use less than three or more than 12 items of data at a time.

EXERCISE 11F

1 The table shows the daily sales of milk at a local corner shop for a month.

Sun	Mon	Tue	Wed	Thu	Fri	Sat
12	8	6	9	4	11	15
11	7	7	6	3	15	14
14	9	7	7	5	12	15
11	12	8	7	4	14	19

Make a table showing the moving average using a seven-day span, and draw a graph to show the trend of milk sales over the month.

2 The table shows the amounts collected for a charity by the students at Pope Pius School in the ten weeks leading up to Christmas.

Week	1	2	3	4	5	6	7	8	9	10
Amount (£)	42	45	44	47	33	40	45	51	42	45

   a Plot a line graph of the amounts collected and a four-week moving average.

   b Comment on the trend shown.

3 The table shows the quarterly electricity bill over a four-year period.

	2002	2003	2004	2005
First quarter	£123.39	£119.95	£127.39	£132.59
Second quarter	£108.56	£113.16	£117.76	£119.76
Third quarter	£87.98	£77.98	£102.58	£114.08
Fourth quarter	£112.47	£127.07	£126.27	£130.87

   a Plot the line graph of the electricity bills shown in the table, and on the same axes plot a four-quarter moving average.

   b Comment on the price of electricity over the four years.

   c Use the trend line of the moving averages to predict the bill for the first quarter of 2006.

4 The table shows the telephone bills for a family over four years.

	2002	2003	2004	2005
First quarter	£82	£87	£98	£88
Second quarter	£87	£88	£95	£91
Third quarter	£67	£72	£87	£78
Fourth quarter	£84	£81	£97	£87

   a Plot a line graph showing the amounts paid each month.

   b Plot a four-quarter moving average.

   c Comment on the trend shown and give a possible reason for it.

   d Use the trend line of the moving averages to predict the bill for the first quarter of 2006.

5 A factory making computer components has the following sales figures (in hundreds) for electric fans.

	Jan	Feb	Mar	Apr	May	Jun	Jul	Aug	Sep	Oct	Nov	Dec
2004	12	13	12	14	13	3	15	12	14	13	14	12
2005	13	14	12	14	13	14	13	13	15	15	15	14

a Plot a line graph of the sales, and a three-month moving average.

b Comment on the trend in the sales.

c Use the trend line of the moving averages to predict the number of electric fan sales in January 2006.

6 The table shows the total sales of video recorders and DVD players from 1999 to 2005 from an electrical store in the USA.

	1999	2000	2001	2002	2003	2004	2005
Video (thousands)	3.4	3.8	3.9	3.2	2.8	2.5	2.3
DVD (thousands)	0.2	0.8	0.9	1.5	1.9	2.8	3.7

a Plot a line graph showing the sales for each product over these years.

b On the same diagram, plot the three-year moving average of each product.

c Comment on the trends seen in the sales of video recorders and DVDs.

d Use the trend line of the moving averages to predict the number of video recorders and DVD players sold in 2006.

11.7 Surveys

In this section you will learn how to:
- conduct surveys
- ask good questions in order to collect reliable and valid data

Key words
data collection sheet
hypothesis
leading question
survey

A **survey** is an organised way of asking a lot of people a few, well-constructed questions, or of making a lot of observations in an experiment, in order to reach a conclusion about something.

Surveys are used to test out people's opinions or to test a **hypothesis**.

Simple data collection sheet

If you just need to collect some data to analyse, you will have to design a simple **data collection sheet**. This section will show you how to design a clear, easy-to-fill-in data collection sheet.

For example, if you want to find out Y10 students' preferences for the end-of-term trip from four options you could ask:

Where do you want to go for the Y10 trip at the end of term – Blackpool, Alton Towers, The Great Western Show or London?

You would put this question, on the same day, to a lot of Y10 students, and enter their answers straight onto a data collection sheet, as below.

Place	Tally	Frequency
Blackpool	ЖЖ ЖЖ ЖЖ ЖЖ III	23
Alton Towers	ЖЖ ЖЖ ЖЖ ЖЖ ЖЖ ЖЖ ЖЖ ЖЖ ЖЖ I	46
The Great Western Show	ЖЖ ЖЖ IIII	14
London	ЖЖ ЖЖ ЖЖ ЖЖ II	22

Notice how plenty of space is available for the tally marks, and how the tallies are gated in groups of five to make counting easier when the survey is complete.

This is a good, simple data collection sheet because:

• only one question (*Where do you want to go?*) has to be asked

• all the four possible venues are listed

• the answer from each interviewee can be easily and quickly tallied, then on to the next interviewee.

Notice, too, that since the question listed specific places, they must appear on the data collection sheet. You would lose many marks in an examination if you just asked the open question: *Where do you want to go?*

Data sometimes needs to be collected to obtain responses for two different categories. The data collection sheet is then in the form of a two-way table.

EXAMPLE 9

The head of a school carries out a survey to find out how much time students in different year groups spend on their homework during a particular week. He asks a sample of 60 students and fills in a two-way table with headings as follows.

	0–5 hours	0–10 hours	10–20 hours	More than 20 hours
Year 7				

This is not a good table as the headings overlap. A student who does 10 hours work a week could tick either of two columns. Response sections should not overlap, so that there is only one possible place to put a tick.

A better table would be:

	0 up to 5 hours	More than 5 and up to 10 hours	More than 10 and up to 15 hours	More than 15 hours
Year 7	ⲖⲖ‖	ⲖⲖ		
Year 8	ⲖⲖ	ⲖⲖ‖		
Year 9	‖‖	ⲖⲖ‖	‖	
Year 10	‖‖	ⲖⲖ	‖‖	‖
Year 11	‖	‖‖‖	‖‖‖	‖

This gives a clearer picture of the amount of homework done in each year group.

Using your computer

Once the data has been collected for your survey, it can be put into a computer database. This allows the data to be stored and amended or updated at a later date if necessary.

From the database, suitable statistical diagrams can easily be drawn using software, and averages calculated. The results can then be published in, for example, the school magazine.

EXERCISE 11G

1 "People like the supermarket to open on Sundays."

   a To see whether this statement is true, design a data collection sheet which will allow you to capture data while standing outside a supermarket.

   b Does it matter on which day you collect data outside the supermarket?

2 The school tuck shop wants to know which types of chocolate it should get in to sell – plain, milk, fruit and nut, wholenut or white chocolate.

   a Design a data collection sheet which you could use to ask pupils in your school which of these chocolate types are their favourite.

HINTS AND TIPS

Include space for tallies.

   b Invent the first 30 entries on the chart.

3 When you throw two dice together, what number are you most likely to get?

  a Design a data collection sheet on which you can record the data from an experiment in which two dice are thrown together and note the sum of the two numbers shown on the dice.

  b Carry out this experiment for at least 100 throws.

  c Which sums are most likely to occur?

  d Illustrate your results on a frequency polygon.

4 Who uses the buses the most in the mornings? Is it pensioners, mums, schoolchildren, the unemployed or some other group? Design a data collection sheet to be used in a survey of bus passengers.

5 Design two-way tables to show

  a how students in different year groups travel to school in the morning

  b the type of programme which different age groups prefer to watch on TV

  c the favourite sport of boys and girls

  d how much time students in different year groups spend on the computer in the evening.

  Invent about 40 entries for each one.

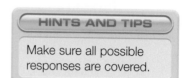

HINTS AND TIPS

Make sure all possible responses are covered.

Questionnaires

This section will show you how to put together a clear, easy-to-use questionnaire.

When you are putting together a questionnaire, you must think very carefully about the sorts of question you are going to ask. Here are five rules that you should *always* follow.

• Never ask a **leading question** designed to get a particular response.

• Never ask a personal, irrelevant question.

• Keep each question as simple as possible.

• Include questions that will get a response from whomever is asked.

• Make sure the responses do not overlap and keep the number of choices to a reasonable number (six at the most).

The following questions are badly constructed and should *never* appear in any questionnaire.

What is your age? This is personal. Many people will not want to answer. It is always better to give a range of ages.

☐ Under 15   ☐ 16–20   ☐ 21–30   ☐ 31–40   ☐ Over 40

Slaughtering animals for food is cruel to the poor defenceless animals. Don't you agree? This is a **leading question**, designed to get a "yes" response. It is better to ask an impersonal question.

Are you a vegetarian?   ☐ Yes   ☐ No

Do you go to discos when abroad? This can be answered only by people who have been abroad. It is better to ask a starter question, with a follow-up question.

Have you been abroad for a holiday?   ☐ Yes   ☐ No

If yes, did you go to a disco whilst you were away?   ☐ Yes   ☐ No

When you first get up in a morning and decide to have some sort of breakfast that might be made by somebody else, do you feel obliged to eat it all or not? This is a too-complicated question. It is better to ask a series of shorter questions.

What time do you get up for school?   ☐ Before 7   ☐ Between 7 and 8   ☐ After 8

Do you have breakfast every day?   ☐ Yes   ☐ No

If No, on how many school days do you have breakfast?   ☐ 0   ☐ 1   ☐ 2   ☐ 3   ☐ 4   ☐ 5

A questionnaire is usually put together to test a hypothesis or a statement. For example, a questionnaire might be constructed to test this statement.

> *People buy cheaper milk from the supermarket as they don't mind not getting it on their doorstep. They'd rather go out to buy it.*

A questionnaire designed to test whether this statement is true or not should include these questions:

Do you have milk delivered to your doorstep?

Do you buy cheaper milk from the supermarket?

Would you buy your milk only from the supermarket?

Once these questions have been answered, the responses can be looked at to see whether the majority of people hold views that agree with the statement.

EXERCISE 11H

1 These are questions from a questionnaire on healthy eating.

a | Fast food is bad for you. Don't you agree?
☐ Strongly agree   ☐ Agree   ☐ Don't know

Give two criticisms of the question.

b | Do you eat fast food?   ☐ Yes   ☐ No

If yes, how many times on average do you eat fast food a week?

☐ Once or less   ☐ 2 or 3 times   ☐ 4 or 5 times   ☐ More than 5 times

Give two reasons why these are good questions.

2 This is a question from a survey on pocket money.

How much pocket money do you get each week?

☐ £0–£2   ☐ £0–£5   ☐ £5–£10   ☐ £10 or more

a Give a reason why this is not a good question.

b Rewrite the question to make it good question.

3 Design a questionnaire to test this statement.

People under 16 do not know what is meant by all the jargon used in the business news on TV, but the over-twenties do.

4 Design a questionnaire to test this statement.

The under-twenties feel quite at ease with computers, while the over-forties would rather not bother with them. The 20–40s are all able to use computers effectively.

5 Design a questionnaire to test this hypothesis.

The older you get, the less sleep you need.

6 A head teacher wants to find out if her pupils think they have too much, too little or just the right amount of homework. She also wants to know the parents' views about homework.

Design a questionnaire that could be used to find the data that the head teacher needs to look at.

Social statistics

In this section you will learn about:

- learn about social statistics
- be introduced to some of the more common social statistics in daily use

Key words

margin of error
national census
polls
Retail Price Index
social statistics
time series

Many situations occur in daily life where statistical techniques are used to produce data. The results of surveys appear in newspapers every day. There are many on-line **polls** and phone-ins to vote in reality TV shows, for example.

Results for these polls are usually given as a percentage with a **margin of error**, which is a measure of how accurate the information is.

Here are some common social statistics in daily use.

General Index of Retail Prices

This is also know as the **Retail Price Index** (RPI). It measures how much the daily cost of living increases (or decreases). One year is chosen as the base year and given an index number, usually 100. The costs of subsequent years are compared to this and given a number proportional to the base year, say 103, etc.

Note the numbers do not represent actual values but just compare current prices to the base year.

Time series

Like the RPI, a **time series** measures changes in a quantity over time. Unlike the RPI the actual values of the quantity are used. This might measure how the exchange rate between the pound and the dollar changes over time.

National Census

A **national census** is a survey of all people and households in a country. Data about age, gender, religion, employment status, etc. is collected to enable governments to plan where to allocate resources in the future. In Britain, a national census is taken every 10 years. The last census was in 2001.

EXERCISE 11I

1 In 2000, the cost of a litre of petrol was 68p. Using 2000 as a base year, the price index of petrol for the next 5 years is shown in this table.

Year	2000	2001	2002	2003	2004	2005
Index	100	103	108	109	112	120
Price	78p					

Work out the price of petrol in each subsequent year. Give your answers to 1 decimal place.

2 The graph shows the exchange rate for the dollar against the pound for each month in 2005.

a What was the exchange rate in January?

b Between which two months did the exchange rate fall the most ?

c Explain why you could not use the graph to predict the exchange rate in January 2006.

Exchange rate of the dollar against the pound, 2005

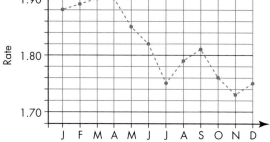

3 The following is taken from the UK government statistics website.

> In mid-2004 the UK was home to 59.8 million people, of which 50.1 million lived in England. The average age was 38.6 years, an increase on 1971 when it was 34.1 years. In mid-2004 approximately one in five people in the UK were aged under 16 and one in six people were aged 65 or over.

Use this extract to answer these questions.

a How many of the population of the UK *do not* live in England?

b By how much has the average age increased since 1971?

c Approximately how many of the population are under 16?

d Approximately how many of the population are over 65?

4 The General Index of Retail Prices started in January 1987 when it was given a base number of 100. In January 2006 the index number was 194.1.

If the "standard weekly shopping basket" cost £38.50 in January 1987, how much would it be in January 2006?

5 This time series shows car production in Britain from November 2004 to November 2005.

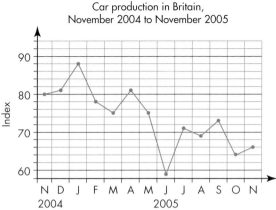

Car production in Britain, November 2004 to November 2005

a Why was there a sharp drop in production in July?

b The average production over the first three months shown was 172 thousand cars.

  i Work out an approximate number for the average production over the last three months shown.

  ii The base month for the index is January 2000 when the index was 100. What was the approximate production in January 2000?

11.9 Sampling

In this section you will learn how to:
- understand different methods of sampling
- collect unbiased reliable data

Key words

population
random
sample
stratified
unbiased

Statisticians often have to carry out surveys to collect information and test hypotheses about the **population** of a wide variety of things. (In statistics, population does not only mean a group of people, it also means a group of objects or events.)

It is seldom possible to survey a whole population, mainly because such a survey would cost too much and take a long time. Also there are populations for which it would be physically impossible to survey every member. For example, if you wanted to find the average length of eels in the North Sea, it would be impossible to find and measure every eel. So a statistician chooses a small part of the population to survey and assumes that the results for this **sample** are representative of the whole population.

Therefore, to ensure the accuracy of a survey, two questions have to be considered.

- Will the sample be representative of the whole population and thereby eliminate bias?

- How large should the sample be to give results which are valid for the whole population?

You will use many of these ideas in your Handling Data coursework.

Sampling methods

There are two main types of sample: **random** and **stratified**.

In a random sample, every member of the population has an equal chance of being chosen. For example, it may be the first 100 people met in a survey, or 100 names picked from a hat, or 100 names taken at random from the electoral register or a telephone directory.

In a stratified sample, the population is first divided into categories and the number of members in each category determined. The sample is then made up of members from these categories in the same proportions as they are in the population. The required sample in each category is chosen by random sampling.

EXAMPLE 10

A school's pupil numbers are given in the table. The head teacher wants to take a stratified sample of 100 pupils for a survey.

a Calculate the number of boys and girls in each year that should be interviewed.

b Explain how the pupils could then be chosen to give a random sample.

School year	Boys	Girls	Total
7	52	68	120
8	46	51	97
9	62	59	121
10	47	61	108
11	39	55	94
Total number in school			540

a To get the correct number in each category, say, boys in year 7, the calculation is done as follows.

$$\frac{52}{540} \times 100 = 9.6 \text{ (1 decimal place)}$$

After all calculations are done, you should get the values in this table.

School Year	Boys	Girls
7	9.6	12.6
8	8.5	9.4
9	11.5	10.9
10	8.7	11.3
11	7.2	10.2

Obviously you cannot have a decimal point of a pupil, so round off all values and make sure that the total is 100. This gives the final table.

School year	Boys	Girls	Total
7	10	13	23
8	8	9	17
9	12	11	23
10	9	11	20
11	7	10	17

b Within each category, choose pupils to survey at random. For example, all the year 7 girls could have their names put into a hat and 13 names drawn out or they could be listed alphabetically and a random number generator used to pick out 13 names from 68.

Sample size

Before the sampling of a population can begin, it is necessary to determine how much data needs to be collected to ensure that the sample is representative of the population. This is called the sample size.

Two factors determine sample size:

- the desired precision with which the sample represents the population

- the amount of money available to meet the cost of collecting the sample data.

The greater the precision desired, the larger the sample size needs to be. But the larger the sample size, the higher the cost will be. Therefore, the benefit of achieving high accuracy in a sample will always have to be set against the cost of achieving it.

There are statistical procedures for determining the most suitable sample size, but these are beyond the scope of the GCSE syllabus.

The next example addresses some of the problems associated with obtaining an **unbiased** sample.

EXAMPLE 11

You are going to conduct a survey among an audience of 30 000 people at a rock concert. How would you choose the sample?

1 You would not want to question all of them, so you might settle for a sample size of 2%, which is 600 people.

2 Assuming that there will be as many men at the concert as women, you would need the sample to contain the same proportion of each, namely, 300 men and 300 women.

3 Assuming that about 20% of the audience will be aged under 20, you would also need the sample to contain 120 people aged under 20 (20% of 600) and 480 people aged 20 and over (600 − 120 or 80% of 600).

4 You would also need to select people from different parts of the auditorium in equal proportions so as to get a balanced view. Say this breaks down into three equal groups of people, taken respectively from the front, the back and the middle of the auditorium. So, you would further need the sample to consist of 200 people at the front, 200 at the back and 200 in the middle.

5 If you now assume that one researcher can survey 40 concert-goers, you would arrive at this sampling strategy

   600 ÷ 40 = 15 researchers to conduct the survey

   15 ÷ 3 = 5 researchers in each part of the auditorium

Each researcher would need to question four men aged under 20, 16 men aged 20 and over, four women aged under 20 and 16 women aged 20 and over.

EXERCISE 11J

1 Comment on the reliability of the following ways of finding a sample.

    a Find out about smoking by asking 50 people in a non-smoking part of a restaurant.

    b Find out how many homes have DVD players by asking 100 people outside a DVD hire shop.

    c Find the most popular make of car by counting 100 cars in a city car park.

    d Find a year representative on a school's council by picking a name out of a hat.

    e Decide whether the potatoes have cooked properly by testing one with a fork.

2 Comment on the way the following samples have been taken. For those that are not satisfactory, suggest a better way to find a more reliable sample.

    a Joseph had a discussion with his dad about pocket money. To get some information, he asked 15 of his friends how much pocket money they each received.

    b Douglas wanted to find out what proportion of his school went abroad for holidays, so he asked the first 20 people he came across in the school yard.

    c A teacher wanted to know which lesson his pupils enjoyed most. So he asked them all.

    d It has been suggested that more females go to church than males. So Ruth did a survey in her church that Sunday and counted the number of females there.

    e A group of local people asked for a crossing on a busy road. The council conducted a survey by asking a randomly selected 100 people in the neighbourhood.

3 For a school project you have been asked to do a presentation of the social activities of the pupils in your school. You decide to interview a sample of pupils. Explain how you will choose the pupils you wish to interview if you want your results to be

    a reliable,   **b** unbiased,   **c** representative,   **d** random.

4 A fast-food pizza chain attempted to estimate the number of people who eat pizzas in a certain town. One evening they telephoned 50 people living in the town and asked: "Have you eaten a pizza in the last month?" Eleven people said "Yes". The pizza chain stated that 22% of the town's population eat pizzas. Give three criticisms of this method of estimation.

5 **a** Adam is writing a questionnaire for a survey about the Meadowhall shopping centre in Sheffield. He is told that fewer local people visit Meadowhall than people from further away. He is also told that the local people spend less money per visit. Write two questions which would help him to test these ideas. Each question should include at least three options for a response. People are asked to choose one of these options.

    b For another survey, Adam investigates how much is spent at the chocolate machines by students at his school. The number of students in each year group is shown in the table. Explain, with calculations, how Adam should obtain a stratified random sample of 100 students for his survey.

Year group	7	8	9	10	11
Numbers of students	143	132	156	131	108

6 Claire made a survey of pupils in her school. She wanted to find out their opinions on the eating facilities in the school. The size of each year group in the school is shown in the table.

Year group	Boys	Girls	Total
8	96	78	174
9	84	86	170
10	84	91	175
11	82	85	167
6th form	83	117	200
			886

Claire took a sample of 90 pupils.

a Explain why she should not have sampled equal numbers of boys and girls in the sixth form.

b Calculate the number of pupils she should have sampled in the sixth form.

Using the Internet

Through the Internet you have access to a vast amount of data on many topics, which you can use to carry out statistical investigations. This data will enable you to draw statistical diagrams, answer a variety of questions and test all manner of hypotheses.

Here are some examples of hypotheses you can test.

Football teams are most likely to win when they are playing at home.

Boys do better than girls at GCSE mathematics.

The number 3 gets drawn more often than the number 49 in the National Lottery.

The literacy rate in a country is linked to that country's average income.

People in the north of England have larger families than people who live in the south.

The following websites are a useful source of data for some of the above.

www.statistics.gov.uk

www.lufc.co.uk

www.national-lottery.co.uk

www.cia.gov/cia/publications/factbook/

1 The number of matches in 20 matchboxes is shown in the table.

No. of matches (m)	Frequency
42	2
43	5
44	11
45	1
46	1

Calculate the mean number of matches in the 20 boxes.

2 50 people were asked how long they had to wait for a tram. The table shows the results.

a Which class interval contains the median time?

Time taken, t (min)	Frequency
$0 < t \leqslant 5$	17
$5 < t \leqslant 10$	22
$10 < t \leqslant 15$	9
$15 < t \leqslant 20$	2

b Draw a frequency diagram to represent the data.

3 In a Junior School there are 30 students who take the Maths and Science KS2 tests. Their National Curriculum levels in these subjects are shown in the two-way table.

		Level in Maths					
		1	2	3	4	5	6
Level in Science	1	0	3	1	0	0	0
	2	0	1	2	1	0	0
	3	0	0	3	3	1	0
	4	0	0	1	4	1	0
	5	0	0	1	1	5	1
	6	0	0	0	0	0	1

a What is the modal level for Maths?

b What is the median level for Maths?
Show clearly how you obtained your answer.

c What is the mean level for Science?
Show clearly how you obtained your answer.

d The teacher claims that the students are better at Maths than at Science. How can you tell from the table that this is true?

4 The table shows the times taken for a train journey for 20 days.

Time taken, t (min)	Frequency
$18 < t \leqslant 20$	4
$20 < t \leqslant 22$	6
$22 < t \leqslant 24$	5
$24 < t \leqslant 26$	3
$26 < t \leqslant 28$	2

Calculate an estimate of the mean journey time

5 Some students at Highfliers School took a mathematics examination. The unfinished table and histogram show some information about their marks.

Mark (x%)	Frequency
$0 < x \leqslant 40$	10
$40 < x \leqslant 60$	40
$60 < x \leqslant 75$	45
$75 < x \leqslant 85$	60
$85 < x \leqslant 95$	
$95 < x \leqslant 100$	25

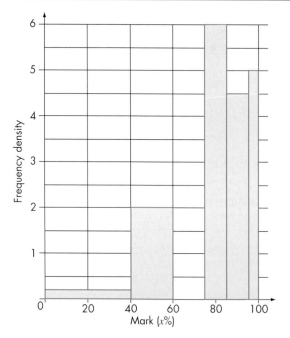

a Use the information in the table to copy and complete the histogram.

b Use the information in the histogram to find the missing frequency from the table.

Edexcel, Question 6, Paper 13A Higher, March 2004

6 Jack and Jill are doing a survey on fast food.

a This is one of Jack's questions.

> Burgers are bad for you and make you fat.
>
> Yes ☐   No ☐

Give two reasons why this is not a good question.

b This is one of Jill's questions.

> How many times, on average, do you visit a fast food outlet in a week?
>
> Never ☐   1 or 2 times ☐
>
> 3 or 4 times ☐   More than 4 times ☐

Give two reasons why this is good question.

7 A shop sells DVD players. The table shows the number of DVD players sold in every three-month period from January 2003 to June 2004.

Year	Months	Number of DVD players sold
2003	Jan–Mar	58
	Apr–Jun	64
	Jul–Sep	86
	Oct–Dec	104
2004	Jan–Mar	65
	Apr–Jun	70

a Calculate the set of four-point moving averages for this data.

b What do your moving averages in part **a** tell you about the trend in the sale of DVD players?

Edexcel, Question 4, Paper 10B Higher, March 2005

8 **a** Explain what is meant by

    i a random sample,   **ii** a stratified sample.

The table shows some information about the members of a golf club.

Age range	Male	Female	Total
Under 18	29	10	39
18 to 30	82	21	103
31 to 50	147	45	192
Over 50	91	29	120
Total number of members			454

The club secretary carries out a survey of the members.

He chooses a sample, stratified both by age range and by gender, of 90 of the 454 members.

b Work out an estimate of the number of male members, in the age range 31 to 50, he would have to sample.

Edexcel, Question 8, Paper 18 Higher, June 2003

9 A vet does a weekly check on the water animals at a zoo. There are 3 walruses, 146 penguins and 22 seals. The vet is required to see 10% of the animals and to see each type.

a What is this kind of sampling procedure called?

b How many of each type of animal should the vet see?

10 The masses of 50 marrows are measured.

Mass, m, (grams)	Frequency
$500 < m \leqslant 600$	4
$600 < m \leqslant 800$	8
$800 < m \leqslant 850$	11
$850 < m \leqslant 1000$	12
$1000 < m \leqslant 1250$	15

a Draw a histogram to show this information

b Use, your histogram, or otherwise, to estimate the median mass of the marrows.

11 The histogram shows the number of students at 320 different Junior schools in Wales.

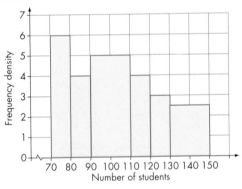

a Find the median number of students at the schools.

b Find the interquartile range of the number of students at the schools.

12 **a** This histogram shows the cricket scores of 100 Yorkshire League players.

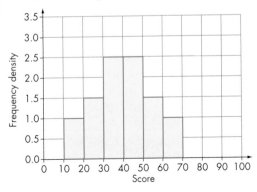

    i What is the median score?

    ii What is the interquartile range?

b This histogram is incomplete. It shows some of the cricket scores for 100 Lancashire League players. The median score is the same as for the Yorkshire players. The upper quartile for the Lancashire players is 50.

   i What is the lower quartile for the Lancashire players?
   ii Complete a possible histogram.

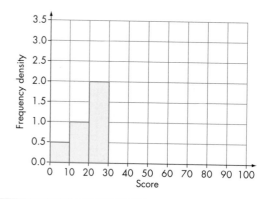

WORKED EXAM QUESTION

The distances travelled by 100 cars using 10 litres of petrol is shown in the histogram and table.

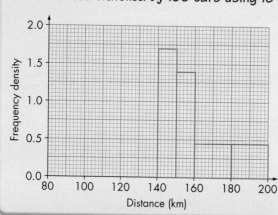

a Complete the histogram and the table.
b Estimate the number of cars that travel between 155 km and 185 km using 10 litres of petrol.

Distance (km)	80–110	110–130	130–140	140–150	150–160	160–200
Frequency	9	22	20			

Solution

a Set up the table with columns for class width and frequency density and fill in the given information, reading frequency densities from the graph (be careful with scales).

Now fill in the rest of the information using f.d. = $\dfrac{\text{frequency}}{\text{class width}}$ and
frequency = f.d. × class width.
These values are shown in red.
Complete the graph.

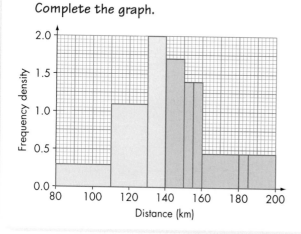

Distance (km)	Frequency	Class width	Frequency density
80–110	9	30	0.3
110–130	22	20	1.1
130–140	20	10	2
140–150	17	10	1.7
150–160	14	10	1.4
160–200	18	40	0.45

b Draw lines at 155 and 185. The number of cars is represented by the area between these lines. In the 150–160 bar the area is $\frac{1}{2}$ of the total. In the 160–200 bar the area is $\frac{5}{8}$ of the total.

Number of cars = $\frac{1}{2} \times 14 + \frac{5}{8} \times 18 = 18.25 \approx 18$ cars

Mr Davies is a dairy farmer. Every month he records the thousands of litres of milk produced by his cows.

For his business plan he compares the amount of milk he produces in 2004 with 2005.

Monthly milk production in thousands of litres		
Month	2004	2005
Jan	51	62
Feb	53	65
Mar	55	62
Apr	56	67
May	64	72
Jun	72	83
Jul	70	81
Aug	75	86
Sep	64	75
Oct	64	73
Nov	62	70
Dec	58	68

Mr Davies calculates three-month moving averages for 2004 and 2005. He plots line graphs showing the moving averages for these two years.

Help him to complete the moving averages table, and the line graphs. Comment on the trends shown.

3-month moving average for milk production in thousands of litres												
	Jan	Feb	Mar	Apr	May	Jun	Jul	Aug	Sep	Oct	Nov	Dec
2004		53	54.7									
2005	61.7	63										

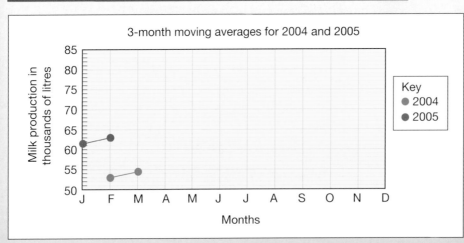

3-month moving averages for 2004 and 2005

Milk production in thousands of litres

Key
● 2004
● 2005

Months

For his business plan Mr Davies compares the amount of milk he produces in 2005, with the graphs showing the hours of sunshine and amount of rain that year.

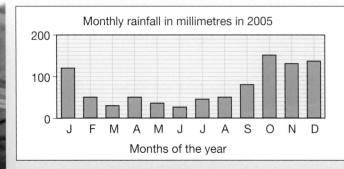

Monthly rainfall in millimetres in 2005

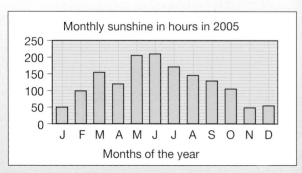

Monthly sunshine in hours in 2005

Draw two scatter graphs; one showing his monthly milk production and monthly rainfall, the other showing his monthly milk production and the monthly sunshine.

Comment on the correlation shown by these graphs.

D Able to find the mean from a frequency table of discrete data

D Able to draw a frequency polygon for discrete data

C Able to find an estimate of the mean from a grouped table of continuous data

C Able to draw a frequency polygon for continuous data

C Able to design questionnaires and surveys

B Able to use a moving average to predict future values

A Able to draw histograms from frequency tables with unequal class intervals

A Able to calculate the numbers to be surveyed for a stratified sample

A* Able to find the median, quartiles and the interquartile range from a histogram

What you should know now

- Which average to use in different situations
- How to find the modal class and an estimated mean for continuous data
- How to draw frequency polygons and histograms for discrete and continuous data
- How to design questionnaires and surveys

Algebra 2

This chapter will show you ...

- how to expand two linear brackets to obtain a quadratic expression
- how to factorise a quadratic expression
- how to solve quadratic equations by factorisation, the quadratic formula and completing the square

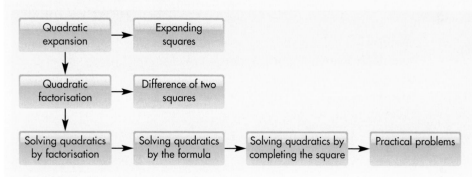

What you should already know

- The basic language of algebra
- How to collect together like terms
- How to multiply together two algebraic expressions
- How to solve simple linear equations

Quick check

1 Simplify the following.

   a $-2x - x$ **b** $3x - x$ **c** $-5x + 2x$

   d $2m \times 3m$ **e** $3x \times -2x$ **f** $-4p \times 3p$

2 Solve these equations.

   a $x + 6 = 0$ **b** $2x + 1 = 0$ **c** $3x - 2 = 0$

Expanding brackets

This section will show you how to:

- expand two linear brackets to obtain a quadratic expression

Quadratic expansion

A **quadratic expression** is one in which the highest power of the variables is 2. For example,

$$y^2 \qquad 3t^2 + 5t \qquad 5m^2 + 3m + 8$$

An expression such as $(3y + 2)(4y - 5)$ can be expanded to give a quadratic expression.

This multiplying out of such pairs of brackets is usually called **quadratic expansion**.

The rule for expanding expressions such as $(t + 5)(3t - 4)$ is similar to that for expanding single brackets: multiply everything in one bracket by everything in the other bracket.

There are several methods for doing this. Examples 1 to 3 show the three main methods, "expansion", "FOIL" and "the box method".

EXAMPLE 1

In the expansion method split up the first bracket and make each of its terms multiply the second bracket. We then simplify the outcome.

Expand $(x + 3)(x + 4)$.

$$(x + 3)(x + 4) = x(x + 4) + 3(x + 4)$$
$$= x^2 + 4x + 3x + 12$$
$$= x^2 + 7x + 12$$

EXAMPLE 2

FOIL stands for First, Outer, Inner and Last. This is the order of multiplying the terms from each bracket.

Expand $(t + 5)(t - 2)$.

First terms give: $t \times t = t^2$. Outer terms give: $t \times -2 = -2t$.

Inner terms give: $5 \times t = 5t$. Last terms give: $+5 \times -2 = -10$.

$$(t + 5)(t - 2) = t^2 - 2t + 5t - 10$$
$$= t^2 + 3t - 10$$

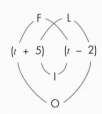

EXAMPLE 3

The box method is similar to that used to do long multiplication.

Expand $(k - 3)(k - 2)$.

$(k - 3)(k - 2) = k^2 - 2k - 3k + 6$

$\qquad\qquad = k^2 - 5k + 6$

×	k	−3
k	k^2	−3k
−2	−2k	+6

Warning: Be careful with the signs. This is the main place where marks are lost in examination questions involving the expansion of brackets.

EXERCISE 12A

Expand the following expressions.

1 $(x + 3)(x + 2)$ **2** $(t + 4)(t + 3)$ **3** $(w + 1)(w + 3)$

4 $(m + 5)(m + 1)$ **5** $(k + 3)(k + 5)$ **6** $(a + 4)(a + 1)$

7 $(x + 4)(x - 2)$ **8** $(t + 5)(t - 3)$ **9** $(w + 3)(w - 1)$

10 $(f + 2)(f - 3)$ **11** $(g + 1)(g - 4)$ **12** $(y + 4)(y - 3)$

13 $(x - 3)(x + 4)$ **14** $(p - 2)(p + 1)$ **15** $(k - 4)(k + 2)$

16 $(y - 2)(y + 5)$ **17** $(a - 1)(a + 3)$ **18** $(t - 3)(t + 4)$

HINTS AND TIPS

Use whichever method you prefer. There is no fixed method in GCSE examinations. Examiners give credit for all methods.

HINTS AND TIPS

A common error is to get minus signs wrong.
$-2x - 3x = -5x$ and
$-2 \times -3 = +6$

The expansions of the expressions below follow a pattern. Work out the first few and try to spot the pattern that will allow you immediately to write down the answers to the rest.

19 $(x + 3)(x - 3)$ **20** $(t + 5)(t - 5)$ **21** $(m + 4)(m - 4)$

22 $(t + 2)(t - 2)$ **23** $(y + 8)(y - 8)$ **24** $(p + 1)(p - 1)$

25 $(5 + x)(5 - x)$ **26** $(7 + g)(7 - g)$ **27** $(x - 6)(x + 6)$

All the algebraic terms in x^2 in Exercise 12A have a **coefficient** of 1 or –1. The next two examples show you what to do if you have to expand brackets containing terms in x^2 whose coefficients are not 1 or –1.

EXAMPLE 4

Expand $(2t + 3)(3t + 1)$.

$(2t + 3)(3t + 1) = 6t^2 + 2t + 9t + 3$

$\qquad\qquad = 6t^2 + 11t + 3$

×	2t	+3
3t	$6t^2$	+9t
+1	+2t	+3

EXAMPLE 5

Expand $(4x - 1)(3x - 5)$.

$(4x - 1)(3x - 5) = 4x(3x - 5) - (3x - 5)$ [**Note:** $(3x - 5)$ is the same as $1(3x - 5)$.]

$\qquad\qquad\qquad\quad = 12x^2 - 20x - 3x + 5$

$\qquad\qquad\qquad\quad = 12x^2 - 23x + 5$

EXERCISE 12B

Expand the following expressions.

1 $(2x + 3)(3x + 1)$ **2** $(3y + 2)(4y + 3)$

3 $(3t + 1)(2t + 5)$ **4** $(4t + 3)(2t - 1)$

5 $(5m + 2)(2m - 3)$ **6** $(4k + 3)(3k - 5)$

7 $(3p - 2)(2p + 5)$ **8** $(5w + 2)(2w + 3)$

9 $(2a - 3)(3a + 1)$ **10** $(4r - 3)(2r - 1)$

11 $(3g - 2)(5g - 2)$ **12** $(4d - 1)(3d + 2)$

13 $(5 + 2p)(3 + 4p)$ **14** $(2 + 3t)(1 + 2t)$ **15** $(4 + 3p)(2p + 1)$

16 $(6 + 5t)(1 - 2t)$ **17** $(4 + 3n)(3 - 2n)$ **18** $(2 + 3f)(2f - 3)$

19 $(3 - 2q)(4 + 5q)$ **20** $(1 - 3p)(3 + 2p)$ **21** $(4 - 2t)(3t + 1)$

> **HINTS AND TIPS**
>
> Always give answers in the form $\pm ax^2 \pm bx \pm c$ even if the quadratic coefficient is negative.

EXERCISE 12C

Try to spot the pattern in each of the following expressions so that you can immediately write down the expansion.

1 $(2x + 1)(2x - 1)$ **2** $(3t + 2)(3t - 2)$ **3** $(5y + 3)(5y - 3)$

4 $(4m + 3)(4m - 3)$ **5** $(2k - 3)(2k + 3)$ **6** $(4h - 1)(4h + 1)$

7 $(2 + 3x)(2 - 3x)$ **8** $(5 + 2t)(5 - 2t)$ **9** $(6 - 5y)(6 + 5y)$

10 $(a + b)(a - b)$ **11** $(3t + k)(3t - k)$ **12** $(2m - 3p)(2m + 3p)$

13 $(5k + g)(5k - g)$ **14** $(ab + cd)(ab - cd)$ **15** $(a^2 + b^2)(a^2 - b^2)$

Expanding squares

Whenever you see a **linear** bracket squared you must write the bracket down twice and then use whichever method you prefer to expand the brackets.

EXAMPLE 6

Expand $(x + 3)^2$.

$$(x + 3)^2 = (x + 3)(x + 3)$$
$$= x(x + 3) + 3(x + 3)$$
$$= x^2 + 3x + 3x + 9$$
$$= x^2 + 6x + 9$$

EXAMPLE 7

Expand $(3x - 2)^2$.

$$(3x - 2)^2 = (3x - 2)(3x - 2)$$
$$= 9x^2 - 6x - 6x + 4$$
$$= 9x^2 - 12x + 4$$

F   L

$(3x - 2)$ $(3x - 2)$

I

O

EXERCISE 12D

Expand the following squares.

HINTS AND TIPS

Remember *always* write down the bracket twice. Do not try to take any short cuts.

1 $(x + 5)^2$

2 $(m + 4)^2$

3 $(6 + t)^2$

4 $(3 + p)^2$

5 $(m - 3)^2$

6 $(t - 5)^2$

7 $(4 - m)^2$

8 $(7 - k)^2$

9 $(3x + 1)^2$

10 $(4t + 3)^2$

11 $(2 + 5y)^2$

12 $(3 + 2m)^2$

13 $(4t - 3)^2$

14 $(3x - 2)^2$

15 $(2 - 5t)^2$

16 $(6 - 5r)^2$

17 $(x + y)^2$

18 $(m - n)^2$

19 $(2t + y)^2$

20 $(m - 3n)^2$

21 $(x + 2)^2 - 4$

22 $(x - 5)^2 - 25$

23 $(x + 6)^2 - 36$

24 $(x - 2)^2 - 4$

- factorise a quadratic expression into two linear brackets

Key words

brackets
coefficient
difference of
    two squares
factorisation
identity
quadratic
    expression

Factorisation involves putting a **quadratic expression** back into its **brackets** (if possible). We start with the factorisation of quadratic expressions of the type

$$x^2 + ax + b$$

where a and b are integers.

Sometimes it is easy to put a quadratic expression back into its brackets, other times it seems hard. However, there are some simple rules that will help you to factorise.

- Each bracket will start with an x, and the signs in the quadratic expression show which signs to put after the xs.

- When the *second* sign in the expression is a *plus*, both bracket signs are the *same* as the *first* sign.

    $x^2 + ax + b = (x + ?)(x + ?)$ Since everything is positive.

    $x^2 - ax + b = (x - ?)(x - ?)$ Since −ve × −ve = +ve.

- When the *second* sign is a *minus*, the bracket signs are *different*.

    $x^2 + ax - b = (x + ?)(x - ?)$ Since +ve × −ve = −ve.

    $x^2 - ax - b = (x + ?)(x - ?)$

- Next, look at the *last* number, b, in the expression. When multiplied together, the two numbers in the brackets must give b.

- Finally, look at the *coefficient of x* number, a. The *sum* of the two numbers in the brackets will give a.

EXAMPLE 8

Factorise $x^2 - x - 6$.

Because of the signs we know the brackets must be $(x + ?)(x - ?)$.

Two numbers that have a product of -6 and a sum of -1 are -3 and $+2$.

So, $x^2 - x - 6 = (x + 2)(x - 3)$

EXAMPLE 9

Factorise $x^2 - 9x + 20$.

Because of the signs we know the brackets must be $(x - ?)(x - ?)$.

Two numbers that have a product of $+20$ and a sum of -9 are -4 and -5.

So, $x^2 - 9x + 20 = (x - 4)(x - 5)$

EXERCISE 12E

Factorise the following.

1 $x^2 + 5x + 6$

2 $t^2 + 5t + 4$

3 $m^2 + 7m + 10$

4 $k^2 + 10k + 24$

5 $p^2 + 14p + 24$

6 $r^2 + 9r + 18$

7 $w^2 + 11w + 18$

8 $x^2 + 7x + 12$

9 $a^2 + 8a + 12$

10 $k^2 + 10k + 21$

11 $f^2 + 22f + 21$

12 $b^2 + 20b + 96$

13 $t^2 - 5t + 6$

14 $d^2 - 5d + 4$

15 $g^2 - 7g + 10$

16 $x^2 - 15x + 36$

17 $c^2 - 18c + 32$

18 $t^2 - 13t + 36$

19 $y^2 - 16y + 48$

20 $j^2 - 14j + 48$

21 $p^2 - 8p + 15$

22 $y^2 + 5y - 6$

23 $t^2 + 2t - 8$

24 $x^2 + 3x - 10$

25 $m^2 - 4m - 12$

26 $r^2 - 6r - 7$

27 $n^2 - 3n - 18$

28 $m^2 - 7m - 44$

29 $w^2 - 2w - 24$

30 $t^2 - t - 90$

31 $h^2 - h - 72$

32 $t^2 - 2t - 63$

33 $d^2 + 2d + 1$

34 $y^2 + 20y + 100$

35 $t^2 - 8t + 16$

36 $m^2 - 18m + 81$

37 $x^2 - 24x + 144$

38 $d^2 - d - 12$

39 $t^2 - t - 20$

40 $q^2 - q - 56$

> **HINTS AND TIPS**
>
> First decide on the signs in the brackets, then look at the numbers.

Difference of two squares

In Exercise 12C, you found that $(a + b)(a - b) \equiv a^2 - b^2$. This type of expansion is known as an **identity** which is what the sign '$\equiv$' represents. It means it is true for all values of a and b. This expansion gives two perfect squares separated by a minus sign and is known as the **difference of two squares**. You should have found that all the expansions in Exercise 12C are the differences of two squares.

The exercise illustrates a system of factorisation that will *always* work for the difference of two squares such as these.

$$x^2 - 9 \qquad x^2 - 25 \qquad x^2 - 4 \qquad x^2 - 100$$

- Recognise the pattern of the expression as x^2 minus a square number n^2.

- Its factors are $(x + n)(x - n)$.

EXAMPLE 10

Factorise $x^2 - 36$.

- Recognise the difference of two squares x^2 and 6^2.
- So it factorises to $(x + 6)(x - 6)$.

Expanding the brackets shows that they do come from the original expression.

EXAMPLE 11

$9x^2 - 169$

- Recognise the difference of two squares $(3x)^2$ and 13^2.
- So it factorises to $(3x + 13)(3x - 13)$.

EXERCISE 12F

Each of these is the difference of two squares. Factorise them.

HINTS AND TIPS

Learn how to spot the difference of two squares as it occurs a lot in GCSE examinations.

B

1. $x^2 - 9$
2. $t^2 - 25$
3. $m^2 - 16$
4. $9 - x^2$
5. $49 - t^2$
6. $k^2 - 100$
7. $4 - y^2$
8. $x^2 - 64$
9. $t^2 - 81$

A

10. $x^2 - y^2$
11. $x^2 - 4y^2$
12. $x^2 - 9y^2$
13. $9x^2 - 1$
14. $16x^2 - 9$
15. $25x^2 - 64$
16. $4x^2 - 9y^2$
17. $9t^2 - 4w^2$
18. $16y^2 - 25x^2$

Factorising $ax^2 + bx + c$

We can adapt the method for factorising $x^2 + ax + b$ to take into account the factors of the **coefficient** of x^2.

EXAMPLE 12

Factorise $3x^2 + 8x + 4$.

- First we note that both signs are positive. So both bracket signs must be $(?x + ?)(?x + ?)$
- As 3 has only 3×1 as factors, the brackets must be $(3x + ?)(x + ?)$
- Next, we note that the factors of 4 are 4×1 and 2×2.
- We now have to find which pair of factors of 4 combine with 3×1 to give 8.

③ | 4 ②
① | 1 ②

We see that the combination 3×2 and 1×2 adds up to 8.

- So, the complete factorisation becomes $(3x + 2)(x + 2)$.

EXAMPLE 13

Factorise $6x^2 - 7x - 10$.

- First we note that both signs are negative. So both bracket signs must be $(?x + ?)(?x - ?)$
- As 6 has 6×1 and 3×2 as factors, the brackets could be $(6x \pm ?)(x \pm ?)$ or $(3x \pm ?)(2x \pm ?)$
- Next, we note that the factors of 10 are 5×2 and 1×10.
- We now have to find which pair of factors of 10 combine with the factors of 6 to give -7.

3 ⑥ | ± 1 ㉔
2 ① | ± 10 ⑤

We see that the combination 6×-2 and 1×5 adds up to -7.

- So, the complete factorisation becomes $(6x + 5)(x - 2)$.

Although this seems to be very complicated, it becomes quite easy with practice and experience.

EXERCISE 12G

Factorise the following expressions.

1 $2x^2 + 5x + 2$

2 $7x^2 + 8x + 1$

3 $4x^2 + 3x - 7$

4 $24t^2 + 19t + 2$

5 $15t^2 + 2t - 1$

6 $16x^2 - 8x + 1$

7 $6y^2 + 33y - 63$

8 $4y^2 + 8y - 96$

9 $8x^2 + 10x - 3$

10 $6t^2 + 13t + 5$

11 $3x^2 - 16x - 12$

12 $7x^2 - 37x + 10$

A

Solving quadratic equations by factorisation

This section will show you how to:
- solve a quadratic equation by factorisation

Key words
factors
solve

Solving the quadratic equation $x^2 + ax + b = 0$

To **solve** a quadratic equation such as $x^2 - 2x - 3 = 0$, you first have to be able to factorise it. Follow through Examples 14 to 16 below to see how this is done.

EXAMPLE 14

Solve $x^2 + 6x + 5 = 0$.

This factorises into $(x + 5)(x + 1) = 0$.

The only way this expression can ever equal 0 is if the value of one of the brackets is 0. Hence either $(x + 5) = 0$ or $(x + 1) = 0$

$\Rightarrow x + 5 = 0 \quad$ or $\quad x + 1 = 0$

$\Rightarrow x = -5 \quad\quad$ or $\quad x = -1$

So the solution is $x = -5$ or $x = -1$.

EXAMPLE 15

Solve $x^2 + 3x - 10 = 0$.

This factorises into $(x + 5)(x - 2) = 0$.

Hence $x + 5 = 0 \quad$ or $\quad x - 2 = 0$

$\Rightarrow x = -5 \quad\quad$ or $\quad x = 2$

So the solution is $x = -5$ or $x = 2$.

EXAMPLE 16

Solve $x^2 - 6x + 9 = 0$.

This factorises into $(x - 3)(x - 3) = 0$.

The equation has repeated roots. That is $(x - 3)^2 = 0$.

Hence, there is only one solution, $x = 3$.

EXERCISE 12H

Solve these equations.

1 $(x + 2)(x + 5) = 0$ **2** $(t + 3)(t + 1) = 0$ **3** $(a + 6)(a + 4) = 0$

4 $(x + 3)(x - 2) = 0$ **5** $(x + 1)(x - 3) = 0$ **6** $(t + 4)(t - 5) = 0$

7 $(x - 1)(x + 2) = 0$ **8** $(x - 2)(x + 5) = 0$ **9** $(a - 7)(a + 4) = 0$

10 $(x - 3)(x - 2) = 0$ **11** $(x - 1)(x - 5) = 0$ **12** $(a - 4)(a - 3) = 0$

First factorise, then solve these equations.

13 $x^2 + 5x + 4 = 0$ **14** $x^2 + 11x + 18 = 0$ **15** $x^2 - 6x + 8 = 0$

16 $x^2 - 8x + 15 = 0$ **17** $x^2 - 3x - 10 = 0$ **18** $x^2 - 2x - 15 = 0$

19 $t^2 + 4t - 12 = 0$ **20** $t^2 + 3t - 18 = 0$ **21** $x^2 - x - 2 = 0$

22 $x^2 + 4x + 4 = 0$ **23** $m^2 + 10m + 25 = 0$ **24** $t^2 - 8t + 16 = 0$

25 $t^2 + 8t + 12 = 0$ **26** $k^2 - 2k - 15 = 0$ **27** $a^2 - 14a + 49 = 0$

First rearrange these equations, then solve them.

28 $x^2 + 10x = -24$ **29** $x^2 - 18x = -32$

30 $x^2 + 2x = 24$ **31** $x^2 + 3x = 54$

32 $t^2 + 7t = 30$ **33** $x^2 - 7x = 44$

34 $t^2 - t = 72$ **35** $x^2 = 17x - 72$ **36** $x^2 + 1 = 2x$

> **HINTS AND TIPS**
>
> You cannot solve a quadratic equation unless it is in the form
> $x^2 + ax + b = 0$

Solving the general quadratic equation by factorisation

The general quadratic equation is of the form $ax^2 + bx + c = 0$ where a, b and c are positive or negative whole numbers. (It is easier to make sure that a is always positive). Before any quadratic equation can be solved it must be rearranged to this form.

The method is similar to that used to solve equations of the form $x^2 + ax + b = 0$. That is, we have to find two **factors** of $ax^2 + bx + c$ whose product is 0.

EXAMPLE 17

Solve these quadratic equations.　　**a** $12x^2 - 28x = -15$　　**b** $30x^2 - 5x - 5 = 0$

a First, rearrange the equation to the general form.

$$12x^2 - 28x + 15 = 0$$

This factorises into $(2x - 3)(6x - 5) = 0$.

The only way this product can equal 0 is if the value of one of the brackets is 0. Hence,

either $2x - 3 = 0$ 　or　 $6x - 5 = 0$

$\Rightarrow 2x = 3$ 　or　 $6x = 5$

$\Rightarrow x = \frac{3}{2}$ 　or　 $x = \frac{5}{6}$

So the solution is $x = 1\frac{1}{2}$ or $x = \frac{5}{6}$.

Note: It is almost always the case that if a solution is a fraction which is then changed into a rounded-off decimal number, the original equation cannot be evaluated exactly using that decimal number. So it is preferable to leave the solution in its fraction form. This is called the rational form (see page 224).

b This equation is already in the general form and it will factorise to $(15x + 5)(2x - 1) = 0$ or $(3x + 1)(10x - 5) = 0$.

Look again at the equation. There is a common factor of 5 which can be factorised out to give

$$5(6x^2 - x - 1 = 0).$$

This is much easier to factorise to $5(3x + 1)(2x - 1) = 0$, which can be solved to give $x = -\frac{1}{3}$ or $x = \frac{1}{2}$.

Sometimes the values of b and c are zero. (Note that if a is zero the equation is no longer a quadratic equation but a linear equation. These were covered in Chapter 5.)

EXAMPLE 18

Solve these quadratic equations.　　**a** $3x^2 - 4 = 0$　**b** $4x^2 - 25 = 0$　**c** $6x^2 - x = 0$

a Rearrange to get $3x^2 = 4$.

Divide both sides by 3: 　　　　　$x^2 = \frac{4}{3}$

Square root both sides: 　　　　$x = \pm\sqrt{\frac{4}{3}} = \pm\frac{2}{\sqrt{3}}$

Note: A square root can be positive or negative. The answer is in surd form (see Chapter 10).

b You can use the method of part **a** or you should recognise this as the difference of two squares (page 285). This can be factorised to $(2x - 5)(2x + 5) = 0$

Each bracket can be put equal to zero.

$2x - 5 = 0 \quad \Rightarrow \quad x = +\frac{5}{2}$

$2x + 5 = 0 \quad \Rightarrow \quad x = -\frac{5}{2}$ 　　　　So the solution is $x = \pm\frac{5}{2}$.

c There is a common factor of x, so factorise as $x(6x - 1) = 0$

There is only one bracket this time but each factor can be equal to zero, so $x = 0$ or $6x - 1 = 0$

Hence $x = 0$ or $\frac{1}{6}$.

EXERCISE 12I

Give your answers either in rational form or as mixed numbers.

1 Solve the following equations.

a $3x^2 + 8x - 3 = 0$

b $6x^2 - 5x - 4 = 0$

c $5x^2 - 9x - 2 = 0$

d $4t^2 - 4t - 35 = 0$

e $18t^2 + 9t + 1 = 0$

f $3t^2 - 14t + 8 = 0$

g $6x^2 + 15x - 9 = 0$

h $12x^2 - 16x - 35 = 0$

i $15t^2 + 4t - 35 = 0$

j $28x^2 - 85x + 63 = 0$

k $24x^2 - 19x + 2 = 0$

l $16t^2 - 1 = 0$

m $4x^2 + 9x = 0$

n $25t^2 - 49 = 0$

p $9m^2 - 24m - 9 = 0$

> **HINTS AND TIPS**
>
> Look out for the special cases where b or c is zero.

2 Rearrange into the general form then solve the following equations.

a $x^2 - x = 42$

b $8x(x + 1) = 30$

c $(x + 1)(x - 2) = 40$

d $13x^2 = 11 - 2x$

e $(x + 1)(x - 2) = 4$

f $10x^2 - x = 2$

g $8x^2 + 6x + 3 = 2x^2 + x + 2$

h $25x^2 = 10 - 45x$

i $8x - 16 - x^2 = 0$

j $(2x + 1)(5x + 2) = (2x - 2)(x - 2)$

k $5x + 5 = 30x^2 + 15x + 5$

l $2m^2 = 50$

m $6x^2 + 30 = 5 - 3x^2 - 30x$

n $4x^2 + 4x - 49 = 4x$

p $2t^2 - t = 15$

12.4 Solving a quadratic equation by the quadratic formula

This section will show you how to:

- solve a quadratic equation by using the quadratic formula

Key words

quadratic formula

soluble

solve

Many quadratic equations cannot be solved by factorisation because they do not have simple factors. Try to factorise, for example, $x^2 - 4x - 3 = 0$ or $3x^2 - 6x + 2 = 0$. You will find it is impossible.

One way to **solve** this type of equation is to use the **quadratic formula**. This formula can be used to solve *any* quadratic equation that is **soluble**. (Some are not, which the quadratic formula would immediately show. See section 12.6.)

The solution of the equation $ax^2 + bx + c = 0$ is given by:

$$x = \frac{-b \pm \sqrt{b^2 - 4ac}}{2a}$$

This is the quadratic formula. It is given on the formula sheet of GCSE exams but it is best to learn it.

The symbol ± states that the square root has a positive and a negative value, *both* of which must be used in solving for *x*.

EXAMPLE 19

Solve $5x^2 - 11x - 4 = 0$, correct to two decimal places.

Take the quadratic formula:

$$x = \frac{-b \pm \sqrt{b^2 - 4ac}}{2a}$$

and put $a = 5$, $b = -11$ and $c = -4$, which gives:

$$x = \frac{-(-11) \pm \sqrt{(-11)^2 - 4(5)(-4)}}{2(5)}$$

Note that the values for *a*, *b* and *c* have been put into the formula in brackets. This is to avoid mistakes in calculation. It is a very common mistake to get the sign of *b* wrong or to think that -11^2 is -121. Using brackets will help you do the calculation correctly.

$$x = \frac{11 \pm \sqrt{121 + 80}}{10} = \frac{11 \pm \sqrt{201}}{10}$$

$$\Rightarrow \quad x = 2.52 \text{ or } -0.32$$

Note: The calculation has been done in stages. With a calculator it is possible just to work out the answer, but make sure you can use your calculator properly. If not, break the calculation down. Remember the rule "if you try to do two things at once, you will probably get one of them wrong".

Examination tip: If you are asked to solve a quadratic equation to one or two decimal places, you can be sure that it can be solved only by the quadratic formula.

EXERCISE 12J

Solve the following equations using the quadratic formula.
Give your answers to 2 decimal places.

HINTS AND TIPS

Use brackets when substituting and do not try to work two things out at the same time.

1 $2x^2 + x - 8 = 0$

2 $3x^2 + 5x + 1 = 0$

3 $x^2 - x - 10 = 0$

4 $5x^2 + 2x - 1 = 0$

5 $7x^2 + 12x + 2 = 0$

6 $3x^2 + 11x + 9 = 0$

7 $4x^2 + 9x + 3 = 0$

8 $6x^2 + 22x + 19 = 0$

9 $x^2 + 3x - 6 = 0$

10 $3x^2 - 7x + 1 = 0$

11 $2x^2 + 11x + 4 = 0$

12 $4x^2 + 5x - 3 = 0$

13 $4x^2 - 9x + 4 = 0$

14 $7x^2 + 3x - 2 = 0$

15 $5x^2 - 10x + 1 = 0$

Solving a quadratic equation by completing the square

This section will show you how to:

- solve a quadratic equation by completing the square

Another method for solving quadratic equations is **completing the square**. This method can be used to give answers to a specified number of decimal places or to leave answers in **surd** form.

You will remember that:

$$(x + a)^2 = x^2 + 2ax + a^2$$

which gives:

$$x^2 + 2ax = (x + a)^2 - a^2$$

This is the basic principle behind completing the square.

EXAMPLE 20

Rewrite $x^2 + 4x - 7$ in the form $(x + a)^2 - b$. Hence solve the equation $x^2 + 4x - 7 = 0$, giving your answers to 2 decimal places.

We note that:

$$x^2 + 4x = (x + 2)^2 - 4$$

So, we have:

$$x^2 + 4x - 7 = (x + 2)^2 - 4 - 7 = (x + 2)^2 - 11$$

When $x^2 + 4x - 7 = 0$, we can rewrite the equations using completing the square, as $(x + 2)^2 - 11 = 0$.

Rearranging gives $(x + 2)^2 = 11$

Taking the **square root** of both sides gives

$$x + 2 = \pm\sqrt{11}$$
$$\Rightarrow x = -2 \pm \sqrt{11}$$

This answer is in surd form and could be left like this, but we are asked to evaluate it to $x = 1.32$ or -5.32 (to 2 decimal places)

EXAMPLE 21

Solve $x^2 - 6x - 1 = 0$ by completing the square. Leave your answer in the form $a \pm \sqrt{b}$.

$$x^2 - 6x = (x - 3)^2 - 9$$

So $x^2 - 6x - 1 = (x - 3)^2 - 9 - 1 = (x - 3)^2 - 10$

When $x^2 - 6x - 1 = 0$, then $(x - 3)^2 - 10 = 0$

$$\Rightarrow \quad (x - 3)^2 = 10$$

Taking the square root of both sides gives:

$$x - 3 = \pm\sqrt{10}$$

$$\Rightarrow x = 3 \pm\sqrt{10}$$

EXERCISE 12K

1 Write an equivalent expression in the form $(x \pm a)^2 - b$.

  a $x^2 + 4x$ **b** $x^2 + 14x$ **c** $x^2 - 6x$ **d** $x^2 + 6x$

  e $x^2 - 4x$ **f** $x^2 + 3x$ **g** $x^2 - 5x$ **h** $x^2 + x$

  i $x^2 + 10x$ **j** $x^2 + 7x$ **k** $x^2 - 2x$ **l** $x^2 + 2x$

2 Write an equivalent expression in the form $(x \pm a)^2 - b$.

Question **1** will help with **a** to **h**.

  a $x^2 + 4x - 1$ **b** $x^2 + 14x - 5$ **c** $x^2 - 6x + 3$ **d** $x^2 + 6x + 7$

  e $x^2 - 4x - 1$ **f** $x^2 + 3x + 3$ **g** $x^2 - 5x - 5$ **h** $x^2 + x - 1$

  i $x^2 + 8x - 6$ **j** $x^2 + 2x - 1$ **k** $x^2 - 2x - 7$ **l** $x^2 + 2x - 9$

3 Solve the following equations by completing the square. Leave your answers in surd form where appropriate. The answers to question **2** will help.

  a $x^2 + 4x - 1 = 0$ **b** $x^2 + 14x - 5 = 0$ **c** $x^2 - 6x + 3 = 0$

  d $x^2 + 6x + 7 = 0$ **e** $x^2 - 4x - 1 = 0$ **f** $x^2 + 3x + 3 = 0$

  g $x^2 - 5x - 5 = 0$ **h** $x^2 + x - 1 = 0$ **i** $x^2 + 8x - 6 = 0$

  j $x^2 + 2x - 1 = 0$ **k** $x^2 - 2x - 7 = 0$ **l** $x^2 + 2x - 9 = 0$

> **HINTS AND TIPS**
>
> When the coefficient of x is an odd number you will get fractional values.

4 Solve by completing the square. Give your answers to two decimal places.

  a $x^2 + 2x - 5 = 0$ **b** $x^2 - 4x - 7 = 0$ **c** $x^2 + 2x - 9 = 0$

5 Prove that the solutions to the equation $x^2 + bx + c = 0$ are

$$-\frac{b}{2} \pm \sqrt{\left(\frac{b^2}{4} - c\right)}$$

This section will show you why:

- some quadratic equations do not factorise and explain how to solve practical problems using quadratic equations

Key word
discriminant

Quadratic equations with no solution

The quantity $(b^2 - 4ac)$ in the quadratic formula is known as the **discriminant**.

When $b^2 > 4ac$, $(b^2 - 4ac)$ is positive. This has been the case in almost all of the quadratics you have solved so far and it means there are two solutions.

When $b^2 = 4ac$, $(b^2 - 4ac)$ is zero. This has been the case in some of the quadratics you have solved so far. It means there is only one solution (the repeated root).

When $b^2 < 4ac$, $(b^2 - 4ac)$ is negative. So its square root is that of a negative number.

Such a square root cannot be found (at GCSE level) and therefore there are no solutions. You will not be asked about this in examinations but if it happens then you will have made a mistake and should check your working.

EXAMPLE 22

Find the discriminant $b^2 - 4ac$ of the equation $x^2 + 3x + 5 = 0$ and explain what the result tells you.

$$b^2 - 4ac = (3)^2 - 4(1)(5) = 9 - 20 = -11.$$

This means there are no solutions for x.

EXERCISE 12L

Work out the discriminant $b^2 - 4ac$ of the following equations. In each case say how many solutions the equation has.

1. $3x^2 + 2x - 4 = 0$
2. $2x^2 - 7x - 2 = 0$
3. $5x^2 - 8x + 2 = 0$

4. $3x^2 + x - 7 = 0$
5. $16x^2 - 23x + 6 = 0$
6. $x^2 - 2x - 16 = 0$

7. $5x^2 + 5x + 3 = 0$
8. $4x^2 + 3x + 2 = 0$
9. $5x^2 - x - 2 = 0$

10. $x^2 + 6x - 1 = 0$
11. $17x^2 - x + 2 = 0$
12. $x^2 + 5x - 3 = 0$

A*

Using the quadratic formula without a calculator

In the non-calculator paper, you could be asked to solve a quadratic equation that does not factorise. The clue would be that you would be asked to leave your answer in root or surd form. You could use completing the square but this gets very messy if the coefficient of x^2 is not 1 and/or the coefficient of x is not an even number. In these cases the quadratic formula is easier to use.

EXAMPLE 23

Solve the equation $x^2 - 5x - 5 = 0$. Give your answer in the form $a \pm \sqrt{b}$.

Using the quadratic formula gives:

$$x = \frac{-(-5) \pm \sqrt{(-5)^2 - 4(1)(-5)}}{2(1)}$$

$$x = \frac{5 \pm \sqrt{45}}{2} = \frac{5}{2} \pm \frac{3\sqrt{5}}{2}$$

EXAMPLE 24

Solve the equation $2x^2 + 6x - 5 = 0$. Give your answer in surd form.

Using the quadratic formula gives:

$$x = \frac{-(6) \pm \sqrt{(6)^2 - 4(2)(-5)}}{2(2)}$$

$$x = \frac{-6 \pm \sqrt{76}}{4} = \frac{-6 \pm 2\sqrt{19}}{4} = \frac{-3 \pm \sqrt{19}}{2}$$

EXERCISE 12M

1 Solve the following equations by the quadratic formula.

Give your answers in the form $a \pm \sqrt{b}$.

a $x^2 - 2x - 4 = 0$

b $x^2 + 2x - 7 = 0$

c $x^2 + 4x - 44 = 0$

d $x^2 + 2x - 6 = 0$

e $x^2 - 8x + 2 = 0$

f $x^2 - 4x + 2 = 0$

> **HINTS AND TIPS**
>
> The form $a \pm \sqrt{b}$ and surd form are basically the same thing.
> You should try to simplify surds if possible.

2 Solve the following equations by the quadratic formula. Give your answers in surd form.

a $2x^2 + 4x - 5 = 0$

b $2x^2 + 4x - 7 = 0$

c $2x^2 + 6x - 5 = 0$

d $2x^2 - 5x - 8 = 0$

e $5x^2 + x - 3 = 0$

f $2x^2 + 3x - 3 = 0$

Problems solved by quadratic equations

You are likely to have to solve a problem which involves generating a quadratic equation and finding its solution.

EXAMPLE 25

Find the sides of the right-angled triangle shown in the diagram.

Applying the theorem of Pythagoras gives:

$$(x + 5)^2 + (x - 2)^2 = 13^2$$
$$(x^2 + 10x + 25) + (x^2 - 4x + 4) = 169$$
$$2x^2 + 6x + 29 = 169$$
$$2x^2 + 6x - 140 = 0$$

Divide by a factor of 2: $x^2 + 3x - 70 = 0$

This factorises to $(x + 10)(x - 7) = 0$

Giving $x = -10$ or 7. We reject the negative value as it would give negative lengths.

Hence the sides of the triangle are 5, 12 and 13.

Note: You may know the Pythagorean triple 5, 12, 13 and guessed the answer but you would be expected to show working. Most "real-life" problems will end up with a quadratic that factorises as the questions are complicated enough without expecting you to use the quadratic formula or completing the square.

EXAMPLE 26

Solve this equation. $2x - \dfrac{3}{x} = 5$

Multiply through by x to give: $2x^2 - 3 = 5x$

Rearrange into the general form: $2x^2 - 5x - 3 = 0$

This factorises to: $(2x + 1)(x - 3) = 0$

So $x = -\dfrac{1}{2}$ or $x = 3$.

EXAMPLE 27

A coach driver undertook a journey of 300 km. Her actual average speed turned out to be 10 km/h slower than expected. Therefore, she took 1 hour longer over the journey than expected. Find her actual average speed.

Let the driver's actual average speed be x km/h. So the estimated speed would have been $(x + 10)$ km/h.

Time taken $= \dfrac{\text{Distance travelled}}{\text{Speed}}$ At x km/h, she did the journey in $\dfrac{300}{x}$ hours.

At $(x + 10)$ km/h, she would have done the journey in $\dfrac{300}{x + 10}$ hours.

Since the journey took 1 hour longer than expected, then

$$\text{time taken} = \dfrac{300}{x + 10} + 1 = \dfrac{300 + x + 10}{x + 10} = \dfrac{310 + x}{x + 10}$$

So $\dfrac{300}{x} = \dfrac{310 + x}{x + 10} \Rightarrow 300(x + 10) = x(310 + x) \Rightarrow 300x + 3000 = 310x + x^2$

Rearranging into the general form gives: $x^2 + 10x - 3000 = 0$

This factorises into: $(x + 60)(x - 50) = 0 \Rightarrow x = -60$ or 50

The coach's average speed could not be -60 km/h, so it has to be 50 km/h.

EXERCISE 12N

1. The sides of a right-angled triangle are x, $(x + 2)$ and $(2x - 2)$. The hypotenuse is length $(2x - 2)$. Find the actual dimensions of the triangle.

2. The length of a rectangle is 5 m more than its width. Its area is 300 m². Find the actual dimensions of the rectangle.

3. The average weight of a group of people is 45.2 kg. A newcomer to the group weighs 51 kg, which increases the average weight by 0.2 kg. How many people are now in the group?

4. Solve the equation $x + \dfrac{3}{x} = 7$. Give your answers correct to 2 decimal places.

5. Solve the equation $2x + \dfrac{5}{x} = 11$.

6. A tennis court has an area of 224 m². If the length were decreased by 1 m and the width increased by 1 m, the area would be increased by 1 m². Find the dimensions of the court.

7. On a journey of 400 km, the driver of a train calculates that if he were to increase his average speed by 2 km/h, he would take 20 minutes less. Find his average speed.

8. The difference of the squares of two positive numbers, whose difference is 2, is 184. Find these two numbers.

9. The length of a carpet is 1 m more than its width. Its area is 9 m². Find the dimensions of the carpet to 2 decimal places.

10. The two shorter sides of a right-angled triangle differ by 2 cm. The area is 24 cm². Find the shortest side of the triangle.

11. Helen worked out that she could save 30 minutes on a 45 km journey if she travelled at an average speed which was 15 km/h faster than that at which she had planned to travel. Find the speed at which Helen had originally planned to travel.

12. Claire intended to spend £3.20 on balloons for her party. But each balloon cost her 2p more than she expected, so she had to buy 8 fewer balloons. Find the cost of each balloon.

13. The sum of a number and its reciprocal is 2.05. What are the two numbers?

14. A woman buys goods for £60x and sells them for £$(600 - 6x)$ at a loss of x%. Find x.

15. A train has a scheduled time for its journey. If the train averages 50 km/h, it arrives 12 minutes early. If the train averages 45 km/h, it arrives 20 minutes late. Find how long the train should take for the journey.

16. A rectangular garden measures 15 m by 11 m and is surrounded by a path of uniform width whose area is 41.25 m². Find the width of the path.

1 a Factorise $8p - 6$
  b Factorise $r^2 + 6r$
  c Simplify $s^2 \times s^4$

 **2 a** Expand $(x + 5)(x + 8)$
  b Factorise $x^2 - 5x - 14$

Edexcel, Question 1, Paper 13B Higher, March 2004

 3 a Factorise $x^5 - 4x^2$
  b i Factorise $x^2 - 3x - 10$
    ii Hence solve the equation $x^2 - 3x - 10 = 0$

4 a Factorise completely $2(x - 5)^2 + 4(x - 5)$
  b Simplify $\dfrac{5(x - 3)}{(x - 3)^2}$

5 a Expand and simplify $(a + b)(a - b)$
  b i Factorise $x^2 - 20x + 36$
    ii Hence solve the equation $x^2 - 20x + 36 = 0$

6 a Expand and simplify $(x + y)^2$
  b Hence or otherwise, find the value of
    $5.36^2 + 2 \times 5.36 \times 4.64 + 4.64^2$

 7 Solve $x^2 + 3x - 5 = 0$
  Give your solutions correct to 4 significant figures.

Edexcel, Question 5, Paper 13B Higher, January 2004

 8 Factorise fully $3x^2 - 12y^2$
    $a^2 - 25$

 9 a Factorise $3x^2 + 4x + 1$
  b Hence, or otherwise, write 341 as the product of two prime factors.

 10 Solve $x^2 + 6x = 4$
  Give your answer in the form $p \pm \sqrt{q}$, where p and q are integers.

Edexcel, Question 7, Paper 13A Higher, January 2005

11 a Find the values of a and b such that
    $x^2 + 8x - 3 = (x + a)^2 + b$
  b Hence, or otherwise, solve the equation
    $x^2 + 8x - 3 = 0$
  giving your answers in surd form.

12 a Factorise $2x^2 - 7x - 9$
  b Hence, or otherwise, solve the equation
    $2(y - 2)^2 - 7(y - 2) - 9 = 0$

 WORKED EXAM QUESTION

a You are given that
  $(2x + b)^2 + c = ax^2 - 4x - 5$
  Calculate the values a, b and c

b You are given $q = a(p + 3)^{-3}$. When $p = 7$, $q = 2$.
  Find p when $q = \frac{1}{4}$.

Solution

a $4x^2 + 4bx + b^2 + c = ax^2 - 4x - 5$
  $4x^2 = ax^2 \quad \Rightarrow \quad a = 4$
  $4bx = -4x \quad \Rightarrow \quad b = -1$
  $b^2 + c = -5 \quad \Rightarrow \quad c = -6$

> Expand and simplify the left-hand side.

> Equate the terms in x^2, x and the constant term. Solve the resulting equations.

b $2 = a(7 + 3)^{-3} \Rightarrow \quad 2 = \dfrac{a}{1000} \Rightarrow a = 2000$

  $\dfrac{1}{4} = 2000(p + 3)^{-3} \qquad \dfrac{1}{4} = \dfrac{2000}{(p + 3)^3}$

  $(p + 3)^3 = 8000 \quad p + 3 = 20 \quad p = 17$

> Substitute the given values into the equation and solve to get the value of a.

> Substitute these values into the equation and solve to get p.

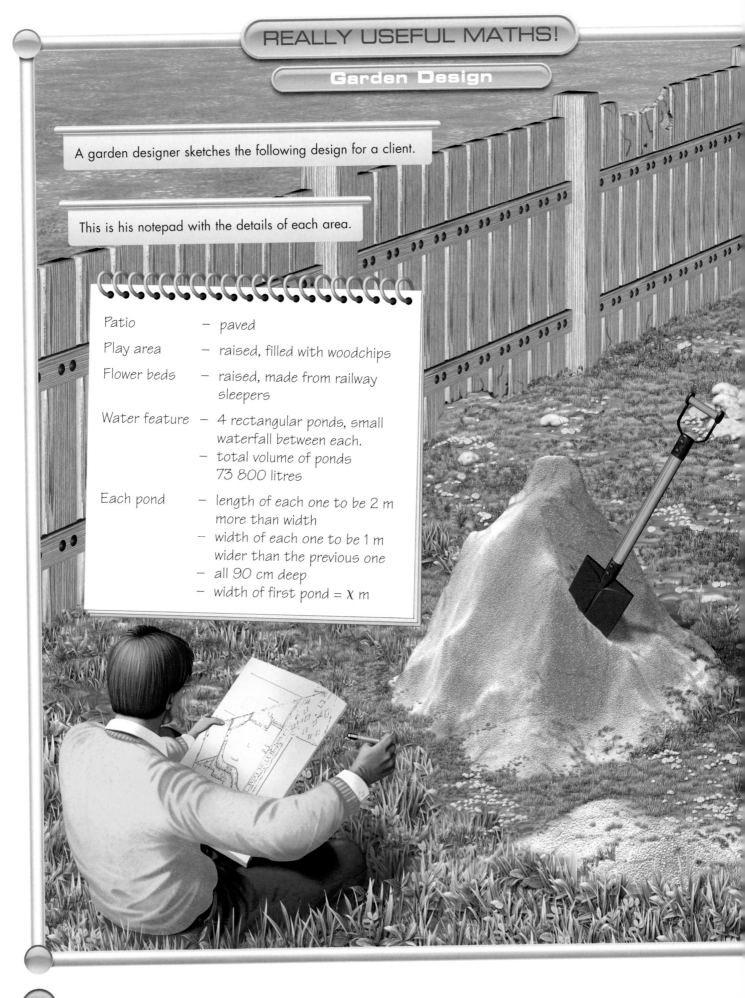

A garden designer sketches the following design for a client.

This is his notepad with the details of each area.

Patio	– paved
Play area	– raised, filled with woodchips
Flower beds	– raised, made from railway sleepers
Water feature	– 4 rectangular ponds, small waterfall between each.
	– total volume of ponds 73 800 litres
Each pond	– length of each one to be 2 m more than width
	– width of each one to be 1 m wider than the previous one
	– all 90 cm deep
	– width of first pond = x m

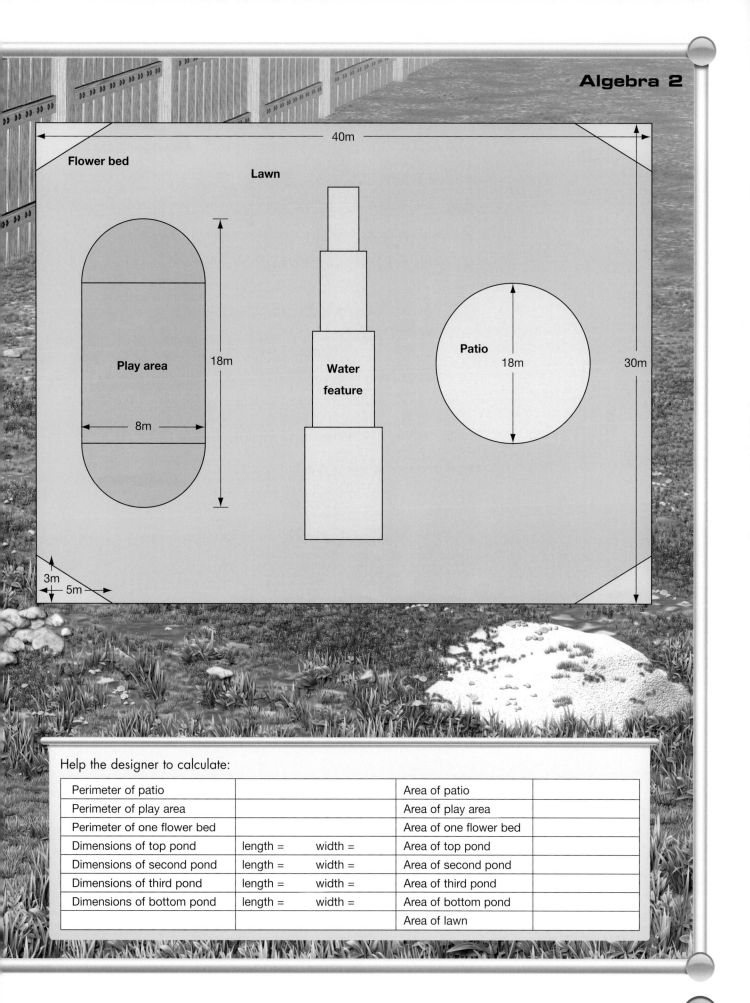

Help the designer to calculate:

Perimeter of patio			Area of patio	
Perimeter of play area			Area of play area	
Perimeter of one flower bed			Area of one flower bed	
Dimensions of top pond	length =	width =	Area of top pond	
Dimensions of second pond	length =	width =	Area of second pond	
Dimensions of third pond	length =	width =	Area of third pond	
Dimensions of bottom pond	length =	width =	Area of bottom pond	
			Area of lawn	

GRADE YOURSELF

C Able to expand a pair of linear brackets to get a quadratic expression

B Able to factorise a quadratic expression of the form $x^2 + ax + b$

B Able to solve a quadratic equation of the form $x^2 + ax + b = 0$

A Able to factorise a quadratic expression of the form $ax^2 + bx + c$

A Able to solve a quadratic equation of the form $ax^2 + bx + c = 0$ by factorisation

A Able to solve a quadratic equation of the form $ax^2 + bx + c = 0$ by the quadratic formula

A* Able to solve a quadratic equation using completing the square

A* Able to solve real-life problems that lead to a quadratic equation

What you should know now

- How to expand linear brackets
- How to solve quadratic equations by factorisation, the quadratic formula and completing the square
- How to set up practical problems using algebra to obtain a quadratic equation which can then be solved

Real-life graphs

This chapter will show you ...

- how to interpret distance–time and velocity–time graphs
- how to interpret other types of graph associated with real-life situations

Visual overview

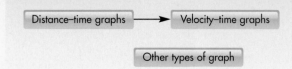

What you should already know

- How to plot coordinate points
- How to read scales

Quick check

1 Give the coordinates of points A, B and C.

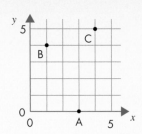

2 What are the values shown on the following scales?

a

b

Straight-line distance–time graphs

This section you will learn how to:
● interpret distance–time graphs

Key words
distance
gradient
speed
time

Units of speed

Sometimes when using **distance–time** graphs, you will need to change the given units of **speed**.

EXAMPLE 1

Change 15 metres per second to kilometres per hour.

15 m/s = 15 × 60 × 60 metres per hour = 54 000 m/h

54 000 m/h = 54 000 ÷ 1000 km/h = 54 km/h

EXAMPLE 2

Change 24 kilometres per hour to metres per minute.

24 km/h = 24 × 1000 m/h = 24 000 m/h

24 000 m/h = 24 000 ÷ 60 m/min = 400 m/min

EXERCISE 13A

1 Paul was travelling in his car to a meeting. He set off from home at 7:00 am, and stopped on the way for a break. This distance–time graph illustrates his journey.

a At what time did he:

 i stop for his break?

 ii set off after his break?

 iii get to his meeting place?

b At what average speed was he travelling:

 i over the first hour?

 ii over the second hour?

 iii for the last part of his journey?

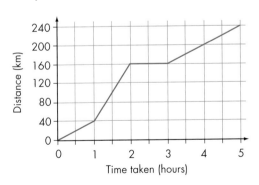

2 James was travelling to Cornwall on his holidays. This distance–time graph illustrates his journey.

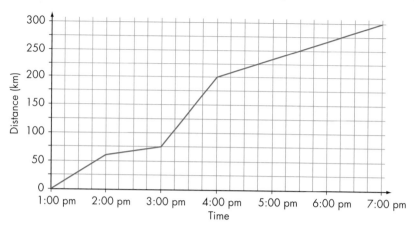

a His fastest speed was on the motorway.

   i How much motorway did he use?

   ii What was his average speed on the motorway?

b **i** When did he travel the slowest?

   ii What was his slowest average speed?

3 Richard and Paul had a 5000 m race. The distance covered is illustrated below.

a Paul ran a steady race. What is his average speed in:

   i metres per minute?

   ii km/h?

b Richard ran in spurts. What was his quickest average speed?

c Who won the race and by how much?

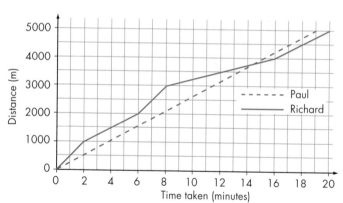

4 Three friends, Patrick, Araf and Sean, ran a 1000 metres race. The race is illustrated on the distance–time graph below.

a Describe the race of each friend.

b **i** What is the average speed of Araf in m/s?

   ii What is this speed in km/h?

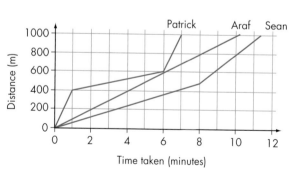

Gradient of straight-line distance–time graphs

The **gradient** of a straight line is a measure of its slope.

The gradient of this line can be found by constructing a right-angled triangle whose hypotenuse (sloping side) is on the line. Then:

$$\text{Gradient} = \frac{\text{Distance measured vertically}}{\text{Distance measured horizontally}} = \frac{6}{4} = 1.5$$

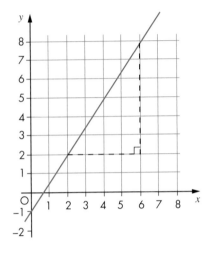

Look at the following examples of straight lines and their gradients.

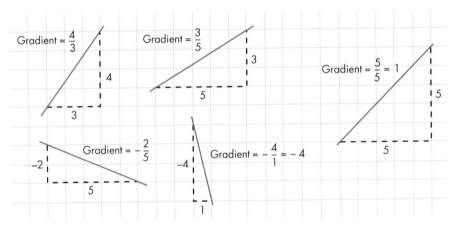

Note: Lines which slope downwards from left to right have *negative gradients*.

In the case of a straight-line graph between two quantities, its gradient is found using the *scales* on its axes, *not* the actual number of grid squares. The gradient usually represents a third quantity whose value we want to know. For example, look at the next graph.

The gradient on this distance–time graph represents average speed.

$$\text{Gradient} = \frac{500 \text{ km}}{2 \text{ h}} = 250 \text{ km/h}$$

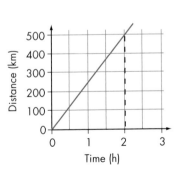

EXERCISE 13B

1 Calculate the gradient of each line, using the scales on the axes.

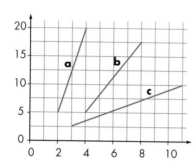

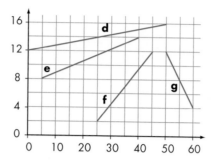

2 Calculate the average speed of the journey represented by each line in the following diagrams.

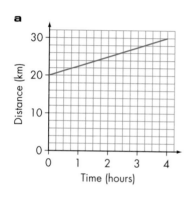

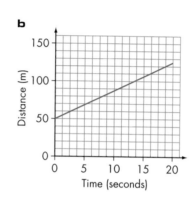

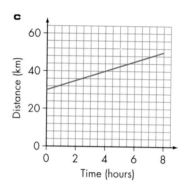

3 From each diagram below, calculate the speed between each stage of each journey.

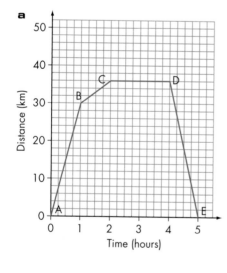

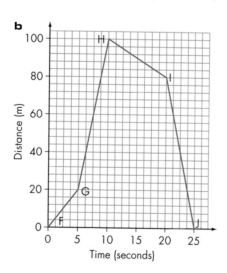

Straight-line velocity–time graphs

In this section you will learn how to:
- interpret velocity–time graphs

Velocity

In our calculations of speed, we have ignored the sign of the **gradient**. The sign of the gradient of a distance–time graph gives the *direction of travel*. Once we introduce the direction of travel into our calculations, then we must use the term **velocity** instead of speed.

Velocity at time t is the gradient of the distance–time graph at t, *including its sign*.

When the velocity of a moving object is plotted against time, the gradient of the **velocity–time** graph at any time t is equal to the **acceleration** of the object at that time.

Acceleration is rate of change of velocity, so when the gradient becomes negative, the object is slowing down. Negative acceleration is called *deceleration*.

The units of acceleration and deceleration are m/s^2 or $m\ s^{-2}$, and km/h^2 or $km\ h^{-2}$.

EXAMPLE 3

Below is the velocity–time graph of a particle over a 6-second period, drawn from measurements made during a scientific experiment. Describe what is happening at each stage of the 6 seconds.

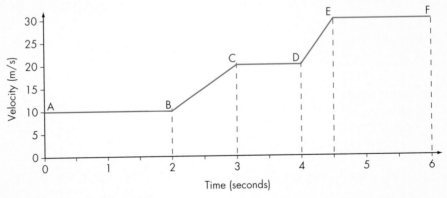

The graph shows a constant particle velocity of 10 m/s for the first 2 seconds (AB). Then the velocity increases uniformly from 10 m/s to 20 m/s over 1 second (BC). Then follows another period of constant velocity (20 m/s) over 1 second (CD), after which the velocity increases uniformly from 20 m/s to 30 m/s in 0.5 seconds (DE). During the final 1.5 seconds the velocity is constant at 30 m/s.

There are two periods of acceleration: BC and DE.

$$\text{Acceleration over BC} = \text{gradient of BC} = \frac{10\ m/s}{1\ s} = 10\ m/s^2$$

$$\text{Acceleration over DE} = \text{gradient of DE} = \frac{10\ m/s}{0.5\ s} = 20\ m/s^2$$

EXERCISE 13C

1 The diagram shows the velocity of a model car over 6 seconds.

Calculate the acceleration:

a over the first second

b after 5 seconds.

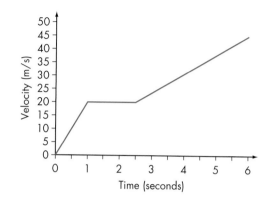

2 The diagram shows the velocity–time graph for a short tram journey between stops.

Find:

a the acceleration over the first 10 seconds

b the deceleration over the last 10 seconds.

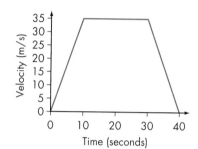

3 The diagram shows the velocity of a boat over an 18-hour period.

Calculate:

a the times at which the boat was travelling at a constant velocity

b the acceleration during each part of the journey.

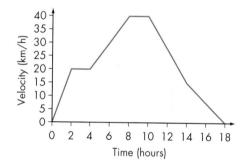

4 An aircraft flying at a constant height of 300 m dropped a load fitted to a parachute. During the times stated, the velocity of the parachute was as follows:

0–2 seconds	The load accelerated uniformly up to 20 m/s.
2–6 seconds	The parachute opened, which brought the velocity down uniformly to 2 m/s.
After 6 seconds	The load fell with a constant speed of 2 m/s.

Draw a velocity–time graph for the first 8 seconds.

5 Starting from rest (zero velocity), a particle travels as indicated below.

- Accelerates at a constant rate over 5 seconds to reach 15 m/s.
- Keeps this velocity for 10 seconds.
- Accelerates over the next 5 seconds to reach 25 m/s.
- Steadily slows down to reach rest (zero velocity) over the next 10 seconds.

a Draw the velocity–time graph.

b Calculate the acceleration over the first 5 seconds.

Other types of graph

In this section you will learn how to:

- identify and draw some of the more unusual types of real-life graphs

Some situations can lead to unusual graphs. For example, this graph represents the cost of postage of a first-class letter against its weight.

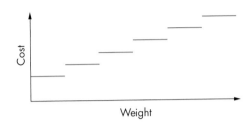

This next graph shows the change in the depth of water in a flat-bottomed flask, as it is filled from a tap delivering water at a steady rate. The graph shows that at first the depth of water increases quickly then slows down as the flask gets wider. As the flask gets narrower, the depth increases at a faster rate. Finally, when the water reaches the neck, which has a constant cross-section, the depth increases at a constant rate to the top of the neck.

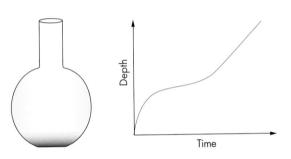

The application of graphs to describe the rate of change of depth as a container is filled with water is also covered in question **1** (Exercise 13D).

Two other examples of the use of graphs are set-out in Exercise 13D. They are the calculation of personal income tax (question **2**) and the calculation of mortgage repayments (question **3**).

Further practical applications of graphs, with special reference to finding the formulae or rules governing them, are featured on page 13 of the Year 11 book.

EXERCISE 13D

1 Draw a graph of the depth of water in each of these containers as it is filled steadily.

a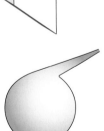

b

c

d

e

f

2 The following is a simplified model of how income tax is calculated for an individual.

The first £4000 earned is tax free. Any income over £4000 up to £30 000 is taxed at 25%. For example, a person who earns £10 000 per year would pay 25% of £6000 = £1500. Any income over £30 000 is taxed at 40%.

a Draw a graph to show the amount of tax paid by people who earn up to £40 000 per year.

(Take the horizontal axis as "Income" from £0 to £40 000. Take the vertical axis as "Tax paid" from £0 to £11 000.)

b For people who earn up to £40 000 per year, draw a graph of the percentage of income paid as tax against income.

(Take the horizontal axis as "Income" from £0 to £40 000. Take the vertical axis as "Percentage of income paid as tax" from 0% to 30%.)

3 In a repayment mortgage, a fixed amount is paid per month for a long period (usually 15 to 25 years). At first, most of the money is used to pay off the interest and only a small amount is paid off the sum borrowed. Over time, the amount due to interest reduces and more money is used to pay off the sum borrowed. The following is a simple model for a loan of £50 000 (the capital) borrowed over 15 years at a fixed annual rate of interest of 5%. The monthly amount to be paid is £400.

a Copy and complete the following calculations to show that it takes approximately 15 years to pay off the money borrowed plus interest.

Amount owing at end of year 1	=	50 000 + 5%	=	52 500
Repayments over year 1	=	12 × 400	=	4 800
Total owed at end of year 1			=	47 700
Amount owing at end of year 2	=	47 700 + 5%	=	50 085
Repayments over year 2	=	12 × 400	=	4 800
Total owed at end of year 2			=	45 285
Amount owing at end of year 3	=	45 285 + 5%	=	………
Repayments over year 3	=	12 × 400	=	4 800
Total owed at end of year 3			=	………

and so on

b Draw a graph of "Amount owing (£)" against "Time (years)".

(Take the horizontal axis as "Time" from 0 to 15 years.
Take the vertical axis as "Amount owing" from £0 to £50 000.)

Plot the first point as (0, 50 000), The second as (1, 47 700), and so on.

> **HINTS AND TIPS**
>
> This repeat calculation can easily be set up on a scientific calculator or a graphics calculator.

 **1** P, Q and R are three stations on a railway line.

PQ = 26 miles.
QR = 4 miles.

A passenger train leaves P at 12.00. It arrives at Q at 12.30.

Information about the journey from P to Q is shown on the travel graph below.

The passenger train stops at Q for 10 minutes.
It then returns to P at the same speed as on the journey from P to Q.

a On a copy of the grid, complete the travel graph for this train.

A goods train leaves R at 12.00.
It arrives at P at 13.00.

b On a copy of the grid, draw the travel graph for the goods train.

c Write down the distance from P where the goods train passes the passenger train.

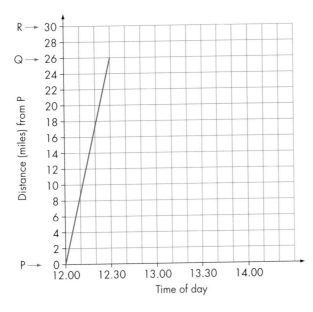

Edexcel, Question 5, Paper 4 Intermediate, November 2004

 2 A man left home at 12 noon to go for a cycle ride.
The travel graph represents part of the man's journey.
At 12.45 pm the man stopped for a rest.

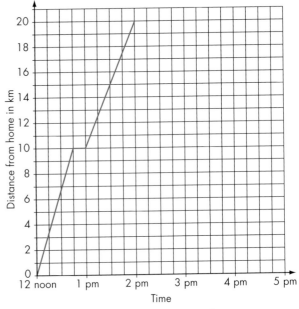

a For how many minutes did he rest?

b Find his distance from home at 1.30 pm.

The man stopped for another rest at 2 pm.
He rested for one hour.
Then he cycled home at a steady speed. It took him 2 hours.

c Copy and complete the travel graph.

Edexcel, Question 8, Paper 4 Intermediate, June 2005

 3 A train travels from Scotland to London in $4\frac{1}{4}$ hours.
The distance traveled is 289 miles. Find the average speed of the train in miles per hour.

 4 Cheryl drives a car 453 km from Cornwall to Scotland, using 30 litres of petrol. 396 km are on the motorway and 57 kilometres on normal roads. On normal roads the car averages 9.5 km to a litre of petrol. How many km per litre does the car average on the motorways?

 5 Daniel leaves his house at 07.00.

He drives 87 miles to work.
He drives at an average speed of 36 miles per hour.

At what time does Daniel arrive at work?

Edexcel, Question 16, Paper 4 Intermediate, November 2003

6 A pool takes 5 hours to fill. For the first $1\frac{1}{2}$ hours the pool is filled at the rate of 60 000 litres per hour. For the next 2 hours the pool is filled at the rate of 70 000 litres per hour. For the last $1\frac{1}{2}$ hours the pool is filled at 80 000 litres per hour.

a Show this information on a graph with a horizontal axis showing time from 0 to 6 hours and a vertical axis showing litres from 0 to 400 000.

b The pool takes 7 hours to empty at a steady rate. What is the average rate of flow when the pool is emptying?

7 Charlotte cycles up a country lane, setting off from home at 9 am. She cycles for 30 km at a steady speed of 20 km/hour. She stops at that point for a 30 minute rest, then sets off back home again, arriving at 11:45 am.

a Show this information on a travel graph with a horizontal axis showing time from 9 am to 12 pm and a vertical axis showing distance from home from 0 to 40 km.

b Calculate the average speed of the return journey in km per hour.

WORKED EXAM QUESTION

Jane cycles from A to B and then from B to C. Details of each stage of her journey are given below.

A to B   Distance 55 km
              Average speed 22 km per hour

B to C   Time taken 1 hour 30 minutes
              Average speed 30 km per hour

Calculate Jane's average speed over the whole of her journey from A to C.

Time = Distance ÷ Speed = 55 ÷ 22 = 2.5 hours
                         = 2 hours 30 minutes

> Calculate the time taken for the journey from A to B. Remember to convert the decimal to hours and minutes.

Distance = Speed × Time = 30 × 1.5 = 45 km

> Now calculate the distance of the journey from A to B. Remember to change the time from hours and minutes to a decimal.

Average speed = Total distance ÷ Total time
               = (55 + 45) ÷ (1.5 + 2.5) = 100 ÷ 4
               = 25 km/h

> Now calculate the total distance and total time. Remember to change the time from hours and minutes to a decimal.

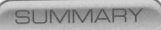

GRADE YOURSELF

D Able to draw and read information from a distance–time graph

C Able to calculate the gradient of a straight line and use this to find speed from a distance–time graph

B Able to interpret real-life graphs

A Able to interpret and draw more complex real-life graphs

What you should know now

- How to find the speed from a distance–time graph
- How to interpret real-life graphs

Similarity

1 Similar triangles

2 Areas and volumes of similar shapes

This chapter will show you ...

- what similar triangles are
- how to work out the scale factor between similar figures
- how to use the scale factor to work out lengths in similar figures
- how to use the scale factor to work out areas and volumes of similar shapes

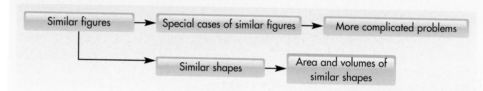

What you should already know

- The meaning of congruency
- How to calculate a ratio and cancel it down
- The square and cubes of integers
- How to solve equations of the form $\frac{x}{9} = \frac{2}{3}$

Quick check

1 Which of the following triangles is congruent to this triangle.

a **b** **c** **d** **e**

2 Solve the equations.

a $\frac{x}{12} = \frac{7}{3}$

b $\frac{x}{10} = \frac{21}{15}$

14.1 Similar triangles

In this section you will learn how to:

- show two triangles are similar
- work out the scale factor between similar triangles

Key word
similar

Triangles are **similar** if their corresponding angles are equal. Their corresponding sides are then in the same ratio.

EXAMPLE 1

The triangles ABC and PQR are similar. Find the length of the side PR.

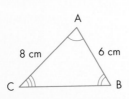
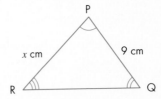

Take two pairs of corresponding sides, one pair of which must contain the unknown side. Form each pair into a fraction, so that x is on top. Since these fractions must be equal

$$\frac{PR}{AC} = \frac{PQ}{AB}$$

$$\frac{x}{8} = \frac{9}{6}$$

To find x.

$$x = \frac{9 \times 8}{6} \, cm \quad \Rightarrow \quad x = \frac{72}{6} = 12 \, cm$$

EXERCISE 14A

1 These diagrams are drawn to scale. What is the scale factor of the enlargement in each case?

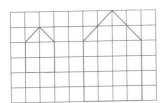
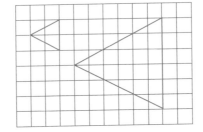

> **HINTS AND TIPS**
>
> If you need to revise scale of enlargement, look back at Section 8.5.

2 Are these pairs of shapes similar? If so, give the scale factor. If not, give a reason.

a

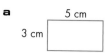

5 cm

3 cm

20 cm

12 cm

b

12 cm

5 cm

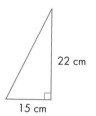

22 cm

15 cm

3 **a** Explain why these shapes are similar.

b Give the ratio of the sides.

c Which angle corresponds to angle C?

d Which side corresponds to side QP?

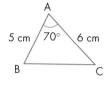

A
5 cm 70° 6 cm
B   C

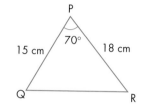

P
15 cm 70° 18 cm
Q   R

4 **a** Explain why these shapes are similar.

b Which angle corresponds to angle A?

c Which side corresponds to side AC?

B
6 cm
A 5 cm C

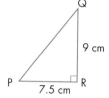

Q
9 cm
P 7.5 cm R

5 **a** Explain why triangle ABC is similar to triangle AQR.

b Which angle corresponds to the angle at B?

c Which side of triangle AQR corresponds to side AC of triangle ABC? Your answers to question **4** may help you.

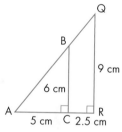

Q
B
9 cm
6 cm
A 5 cm C 2.5 cm R

6 In the diagrams **a** to **f**, each pair of shapes are similar but not drawn to scale. Find the lengths of the sides as requested.

a Find *x*.

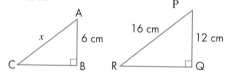

A
x 6 cm
C   B

P
16 cm 12 cm
R   Q

b Find PQ.

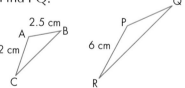

2.5 cm
A B
2 cm
C

P Q
6 cm
R

c Find *x* and *y*.

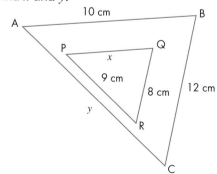

10 cm
A   B
P   Q
x
9 cm 8 cm 12 cm
y   R
C

d Find *x* and *y*.

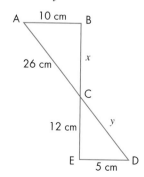

A 10 cm B
26 cm *x*
C
12 cm *y*
E 5 cm D

e Find AB and PQ.

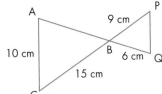

f Find QR.

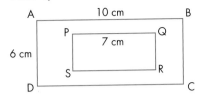

  7 a Explain why these two triangles are similar.

b What is the ratio of their sides?

c Use Pythagoras' theorem to calculate the length of side AC of triangle ABC.

d Write down the length of the side PR of triangle PQR.

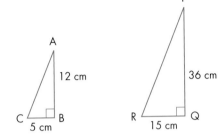

  8 A model railway is made to a scale of 1 : 40. If the model bridge is 12 cm high, how high would a real railway bridge be? Give your answer in metres.

Special cases of similar triangles

EXAMPLE 2

Find the sides marked x and y in these triangles (not drawn to scale).

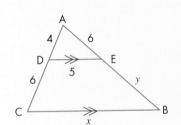

Triangles AED and ABC are similar. So using the corresponding sides CB, DE with AC, AD gives

$$\frac{x}{5} = \frac{10}{4}$$

$$\Rightarrow \quad x = \frac{10 \times 5}{4} = 12.5$$

Using the corresponding sides AE, AB with AD, AC gives

$$\frac{y+6}{6} = \frac{10}{4} \quad \Rightarrow \quad y + 6 = \frac{10 \times 6}{4} = 15$$

$$\Rightarrow \quad y = 15 - 6 = 9$$

EXAMPLE 3

Ahmed wants to work out the height of a tall building. He walks 100 paces from the building and sticks a pole, 2 metres long, vertically into the ground. He then walks another 10 paces on the same line and notices that when he looks from ground level, the top of the pole and the top of the building are in line. How tall is the building?

First, draw a diagram of the situation and label it.

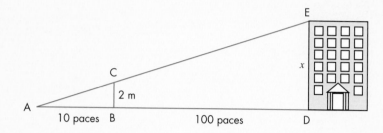

Using corresponding sides ED, CB with AD, AB gives

$$\frac{x}{2} = \frac{110}{10}$$

$$\Rightarrow \quad x = \frac{110 \times 2}{10} = 22 \text{ m}$$

Hence the building is 22 metres high.

EXERCISE 14B

1 In each of the cases below, state a pair of similar triangles and find the length marked x. Separate the similar triangles if it makes it easier for you.

a
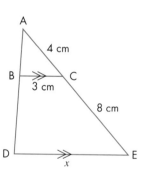

b
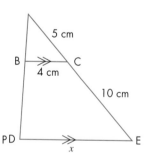

2 In the diagrams **a** to **e**, find the lengths of the sides as requested.

a Find x.
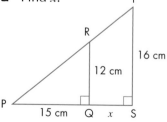

b Find CE.
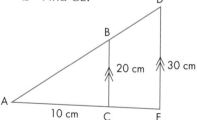

c Find *x* and *y*.

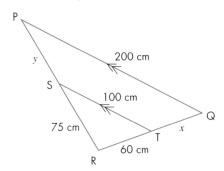

d Find *x* and *y*.

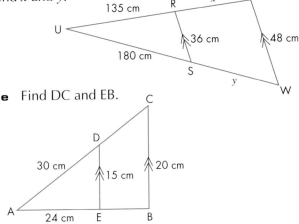

e Find DC and EB.

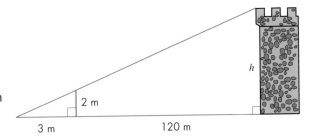

3 This diagram shows a method of working out the height of a tower.

A stick, 2 metres long, is placed vertically 120 metres from the base of a tower so that the top of the tower and the top of the stick is in line with a point on the ground 3 metres from the base of the stick. How high is the tower?

4 It is known that a factory chimney is 330 feet high. Patrick paces out distances as shown in the diagram, so that the top of the chimney and the top of the flag pole are in line with each other. How high is the flag pole?

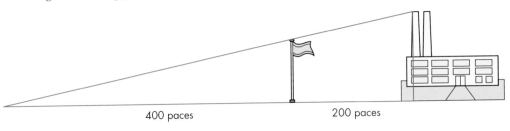

5 The shadow of a tree and the shadow of a golf flag coincide, as shown in the diagram. How high is the tree?

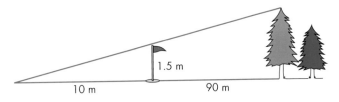

6 Find the height of a pole which casts a shadow of 1.5 metres when at the same time a man of height 165 cm casts a shadow of 75 cm.

7 Andrew, who is about 120 cm tall, notices that when he stands at the bottom of his garden, which is 20 metres away from his house, his dad, who is about 180 cm tall, looks as big as the house when he is about 2.5 metres away from Andrew. How high is the house?

More complicated problems

The information given in a similar triangle situation can be more complicated than anything you have so far met, and you will need to have good algebraic skills to deal with it. Example 4 is typical of the more complicated problem you may be asked to solve, so follow it through carefully.

EXAMPLE 4

Find the value of x in this triangle.

You know that triangle ABC is similar to triangle ADE.

Splitting up the triangles may help you to see what will be needed.

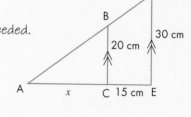

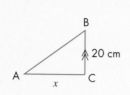
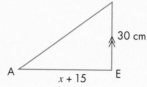

So your equation will be

$$\frac{x + 15}{x} = \frac{30}{20}$$

Cross multiplying (moving each of the two bottom terms to the opposite side and multiplying) gives

$$20x + 300 = 30x$$

$$\Rightarrow \quad 300 = 10x \quad \Rightarrow \quad x = 30 \text{ cm}$$

EXERCISE 14C

Find the lengths x or x and y in the diagrams **1** to **6**.

  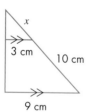
  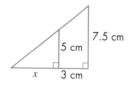

  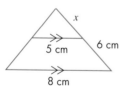
  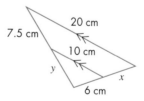

  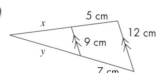
  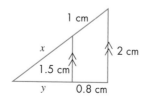

Areas and volumes of similar shapes

This section will show you how to:

- do problems involving the area and volume of similar shapes

Key words

area ratio
area scale factor
length ratio
linear scale
    factor
volume ratio
volume scale
    factor

There are relationships between the lengths, areas and volumes of similar shapes.

You saw on pages 182–184 that when a plane shape is enlarged by a given scale factor to form a new, similar shape, the corresponding lengths of the original shape and the new shape are all in the same ratio, which is equal to the scale factor. This scale factor of the lengths is called the **length ratio** or **linear scale factor**.

Two similar shapes also have an **area ratio**, which is equal to the ratio of the squares of their corresponding lengths. The area ratio, or **area scale factor**, is the square of the length ratio.

Likewise, two 3-D shapes are similar if their corresponding lengths are in the same ratio. Their **volume ratio** is equal to the ratio of the cubes of their corresponding lengths. The volume ratio, or **volume scale factor**, is the cube of the length ratio.

Generally, the relationship between similar shapes can be expressed as

Length ratio	$x : y$
Area ratio	$x^2 : y^2$
Volume ratio	$x^3 : y^3$

EXAMPLE 5

A model yacht is made to a scale of $\frac{1}{20}$ of the size of the real yacht. The area of the sail of the model is 150 cm^2. What is the area of the sail of the real yacht?

At first sight, it may appear that you do not have enough information to solve this problem, but it can be done as follows.

Linear scale factor	$= 1 : 20$
Area scale factor	$= 1 : 400$ (square of the linear scale factor)
Area of real sail	$= 400 \times$ area of model sail
	$= 400 \times 150$ cm^2
	$= 60\,000$ cm$^2 = 6$ m^2

EXAMPLE 6

A bottle has a base radius of 4 cm, a height of 15 cm and a capacity of 650 cm^3. A similar bottle has a base radius of 3 cm.

  a What is the length ratio?

  b What is the volume ratio?

  c What is the volume of the smaller bottle?

  a The length ratio is given by the ratio of the two radii, that is 4 : 3.

  b The volume ratio is therefore $4^3 : 3^3 = 64 : 27$.

  c Let v be the volume of the smaller bottle. Then the volume ratio is

$$\frac{\text{Volume of smaller bottle}}{\text{Volume of larger bottle}} = \frac{v}{650} = \frac{27}{64}$$

$$\Rightarrow v = \frac{27 \times 650}{64} = 274 \text{ cm}^3 \text{ (3 significant figures)}$$

EXAMPLE 7

The cost of a paint can, height 20 cm, is £2.00 and its label has an area of 24 cm^2.

  a If the cost is based on the amount of paint in the can, what is the cost of a similar can, 30 cm high?

  b Assuming the labels are similar, what will be the area of the label on the larger can?

  a The cost of the paint is proportional to the volume of the can.

      Length ratio $= 20 : 30 = 2 : 3$

      Volume ratio $= 2^3 : 3^3 = 8 : 27$

    Let P be the cost of the larger can. Then the cost ratio is

$$\frac{\text{Cost of larger can}}{\text{Cost of smaller can}} = \frac{P}{2}$$

    Therefore,

$$\frac{P}{2} = \frac{27}{8}$$

$$\Rightarrow P = \frac{27 \times 2}{8} = £6.75$$

  b Area ratio $= 2^2 : 3^2 = 4 : 9$

    Let A be the area of the larger label. Then the area ratio is

$$\frac{\text{Larger label area}}{\text{Smaller label area}} = \frac{A}{24}$$

    Therefore,

$$\frac{A}{24} = \frac{9}{4}$$

$$\Rightarrow A = \frac{9 \times 24}{4} = 54 \text{ cm}^2$$

EXERCISE 14D

1 The length ratio between two similar solids is 2 : 5.

    a What is the area ratio between the solids?

    b What is the volume ratio between the solids?

2 The length ratio between two similar solids is 4 : 7.

    a What is the area ratio between the solids?

    b What is the volume ratio between the solids?

3 Copy and complete this table.

Linear scale factor	Linear ratio	Linear fraction	Area scale factor	Volume scale factor
2	1 : 2	$\frac{2}{1}$		
3				
$\frac{1}{4}$	4 : 1	$\frac{1}{4}$		
				$\frac{1}{64}$
			25	
				$\frac{1}{1000}$
	1 : 7			
	5 : 1			
			$\frac{1}{4}$	

4 Some years ago, a famous beer advertisement showed a bar attendant taking an ordinary pint glass and filling it with beer underneath the counter. When the glass reappeared, it was full of beer and its width and height were twice those of the original glass. The slogan on the advertisement was "The pint that thinks it's a quart". (A quart is 2 pints.)

    a What was the length ratio of the two glasses used in the advertisement?

    b What was the volume ratio of the two glasses?

    c The smaller glass held a pint. How much would the larger glass have held?

    d Is the advertisement fair?

5 A shape has an area of 15 cm². What is the area of a similar shape whose lengths are three times the corresponding lengths of the first shape?

6 A toy brick has a surface area of 14 cm². What would be the surface area of a similar toy brick whose lengths are?

    a twice the corresponding lengths of the first brick?

    b three times the corresponding lengths of the first brick?

7 A sheepskin rug covers 12 ft² of floor. What area would be covered by rugs with these lengths?

    a twice the corresponding lengths of the first rug

    b half the corresponding lengths of the first rug

8 A brick has a volume of 300 cm³. What would be the volume of a similar brick whose lengths are

    a twice the corresponding lengths of the first brick?

    b three times the corresponding lengths of the first brick?

 9 Thirty cubic centimetres of clay were used to make a model sheep. What volume of clay would be needed to make a similar model sheep with these lengths?

    a five times the corresponding lengths of the first model

    b one half of the corresponding lengths of the first model

 10 A can of paint, 6 cm high, holds a half a litre of paint. How much paint would go into a similar can which is 12 cm high?

 11 It takes 1 litre of paint to fill a can of height 10 cm. How much paint does it take to fill a similar can of height 45 cm?

 12 It takes 1.5 litres of paint to fill a can of height 12 cm.

    a How much paint does it take to fill a similar can whose dimensions are $1\frac{1}{2}$ times the corresponding dimensions of the first can?

    b Which of the information given is not needed to be able to answer part a?

 13 To make a certain dress, it took 2.4 m² of material. How much material would a similar dress need if its lengths were

    a 1.5 times the corresponding lengths of the first dress?

    b three quarters of the corresponding lengths of the first dress?

 14 A model statue is 10 cm high and has a volume of 100 cm³. The real statue is 2.4 m high. What is the volume of the real statue? Give your answer in m³.

 15 A small can of paint costs 75p. What is the cost of a larger similar can whose circumference is twice that of the smaller can? Assume that the cost is based only on the volume of paint in the can.

 16 A triangle has sides of 3, 4 and 5 cm. Its area is 6 cm². How long are the sides of a similar triangle that has an area of 24 cm²?

 17 A ball with a radius of r cm has a volume of 10 cm³. What is the radius of a ball with a volume of 270 cm³?

18 Calculate the area of each of the shaded faces and hence calculate the volume of each of these solids. (They are not drawn to scale.)

a

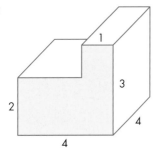

b

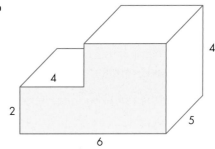

c

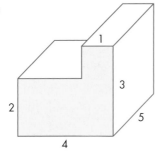

d

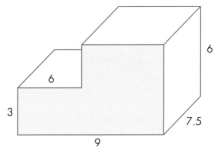

e Which two solids are similar?

Using area and volume ratios

In some problems involving similar shapes, the length ratio is not given, so we have to start with the area ratio or the volume ratio. We usually then need first to find the length ratio in order to proceed with the solution.

EXAMPLE 8

A manufacturer makes a range of clown hats that are all similar in shape. The smallest hat is 8 cm tall and uses 180 cm^2 of card. What will be the height of a hat made from 300 cm^2 of card?

The area ratio is 180 : 300

Therefore, the length ratio is $\sqrt{180} : \sqrt{300}$ (do not calculate these yet)

Let the height of the larger hat be H, then

$$\frac{H}{8} = \frac{\sqrt{300}}{\sqrt{180}} = \sqrt{\frac{300}{180}}$$

$$\Rightarrow H = 8 \times \sqrt{\frac{300}{180}} = 10.3 \text{ cm (1 decimal place)}$$

EXAMPLE 9

A supermarket stocks similar small and large cans of soup. The areas of their labels are 110 cm² and 190 cm² respectively. The weight of a small can is 450 g. What is the weight of a large can?

The area ratio is 110 : 190

Therefore, the length ratio is $\sqrt{110} : \sqrt{190}$ (do not calculate these yet)

So the volume (weight) ratio is $(\sqrt{110})^3 : (\sqrt{190})^3$.

Let the weight of a large can be W, then

$$\frac{W}{450} = \frac{(\sqrt{190})^3}{(\sqrt{110})^3} = \left(\sqrt{\frac{190}{110}}\right)^3$$

$$\Rightarrow \quad W = 450 \times \left(\sqrt{\frac{190}{110}}\right)^3 = 1020 \text{ g} \qquad \text{(3 significant figures)}$$

EXAMPLE 10

Two similar cans hold respectively 1.5 litres and 2.5 litres of paint. The area of the label on the smaller can is 85 cm². What is the area of the label on the larger can?

The volume ratio is 1.5 : 2.5

Therefore, the length ratio is $\sqrt[3]{1.5} : \sqrt[3]{2.5}$ (do not calculate these yet)

So the area ratio is $(\sqrt[3]{1.5})^2 : (\sqrt[3]{2.5})^2$

Let the area of the label on the larger can be A, then

$$\frac{A}{85} = \frac{(\sqrt[3]{2.5})^2}{(\sqrt[3]{1.5})^2} = \left(\sqrt[3]{\frac{2.5}{1.5}}\right)^2$$

$$\Rightarrow \quad A = 85 \times \left(\sqrt[3]{\frac{2.5}{1.5}}\right)^2 = 119 \text{ cm}^2 \qquad \text{(3 significant figures)}$$

EXERCISE 14E

1. A firm produces three sizes of similarly shaped labels for its products. Their areas are 150 cm², 250 cm² and 400 cm². The 250 cm² label just fits around a can of height 8 cm. Find the heights of similar cans around which the other two labels would just fit.

2. A firm makes similar gift boxes in three different sizes: small, medium and large. The areas of their lids are as follows.

    small: 30 cm²,   medium: 50 cm²,   large: 75 cm²

    The medium box is 5.5 cm high. Find the heights of the other two sizes.

3 A cone, height 8 cm, can be made from a piece of card with an area of 140 cm². What is the height of a similar cone made from a similar piece of card with an area of 200 cm²?

4 It takes 5.6 litres of paint to paint a chimney which is 3 m high. What is the tallest similar chimney that can be painted with 8 litres of paint?

5 A man takes 45 minutes to mow a lawn 25 m long. How long would it take him to mow a similar lawn only 15 m long?

6 A piece of card, 1200 cm² in area, will make a tube 13 cm long. What is the length of a similar tube made from a similar piece of card with an area of 500 cm²?

7 All television screens (of the same style) are similar. If a screen of area 220 cm² has a diagonal length of 21 cm, what will be the diagonal length of a screen of area 350 cm²?

8 Two similar statues, made from the same bronze, are placed in a school. One weighs 300 g, the other weighs 2 kg. The height of the smaller statue is 9 cm. What is the height of the larger statue?

9 A supermarket sells similar cans of pasta rings in three different sizes: small, medium and large. The sizes of the labels around the cans are as follows.

   small can: 24 cm²,   medium can: 46 cm²,   large can: 78 cm²

   The medium size can is 6 cm tall with a weight of 380 g. Calculate these quantities.

   a the heights of the other two sizes

   b the weights of the other two sizes

10 Two similar bottles are 20 cm and 14 cm high. The smaller bottle holds 850 ml. Find the capacity of the larger one.

11 A statue weighs 840 kg. A similar statue was made out of the same material but two fifths the height of the first one. What was the weight of the smaller statue?

12 A model stands on a base of area 12 cm². A smaller but similar model, made of the same material, stands on a base of area 7.5 cm². Calculate the weight of the smaller model if the larger one is 3.5 kg.

13 A solid silver statue was melted down to make 100 000 similar miniatures, each 2 cm high. How tall was the original statue?

14 Two similar models have volumes 12 m³ and 30 m³. If the surface area of one of them is 2.4 m², what are the possible surface areas of the other model?

1 Two rectangles have the dimensions shown.

Are the rectangles similar?
Explain your answer clearly.

 2 Triangle ABC is similar to triangle CDE.

Calculate the length of CD.

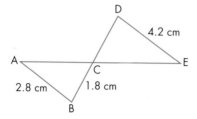

 3 In the triangle PQR, AB is parallel to QR. AB = 10 cm, QR = 16 cm and BR = 12 cm. Find the length PB.

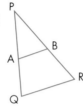

 4 PQR and PXY are similar triangles.

Calculate the length of RY.

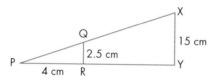

 5 X and Y are two geometrically similar solid shapes.

The total surface area of shape X is 450 cm².
The total surface area of shape Y is 800 cm².

The volume of shape X is 1350 cm³.

Calculate the volume of shape Y.

Edexcel, Question 17, Paper 6 Higher, November 2004

 6

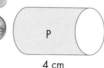

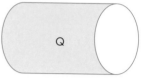

Two cylinders, P and Q, are mathematically similar.
The total surface area of cylinder P is 90π cm².
The total surface area of cylinder Q is 810π cm².
The length of cylinder P is 4 cm.

a Work out the length of cylinder Q.

The volume of cylinder P is 100π cm³.

b Work out the volume of cylinder Q. Give your answer as a multiple of π.

Edexcel, Question 18, Paper 5 Higher, June 2005

 WORKED EXAM QUESTION

A camping gas container is in the shape of a cylinder with a hemispherical top. The dimensions of the container are shown in the diagram.

It is decided to increase the volume of the container by 20%. The new container is mathematically similar to the old one.

Calculate the base diameter of the new container.

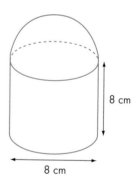

Solution

Old Volume : New volume = 100% : 120% = 1 : 1.2
> First find the volume scale factor.

$\sqrt[3]{1} : \sqrt[3]{1.2}$ = 1 : 1.06265
> Take the cube root to get the linear scale factor.

New diameter = Old diameter × 1.06265 = 8 × 1.06265 = 8.5 cm
> Multiply the old diameter by the linear scale factor to get the new diameter.

Martin works for a light company called "Bright Ideas". He has been asked to calculate accurate measurements for a new table lamp the company are going to produce.

The three main components are the base, the stem and the shade. Below is a sketch of the side view, and an "exploded" diagram which shows the lamp in more detail.

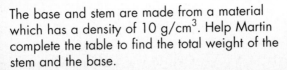

Side view

10cm

15cm

30cm

24cm

3cm

0.5cm

15cm

The base and stem are made from a material which has a density of 10 g/cm³. Help Martin complete the table to find the total weight of the stem and the base.

volume of stem	cm³
weight of stem	g
volume of base	cm³
weight of base	g
total weight	g

The lampshade is the frustum of a cone. It is to be made from a fire-proof material. Martin draws a sketch showing the dimensions he knows.

Help him to calculate the missing dimensions and then the surface area of the shade.

length of x	cm
length of L	cm
length of L	cm
surface area of small cone	cm²
surface area of large cone	cm²
surface area of lampshade	cm²

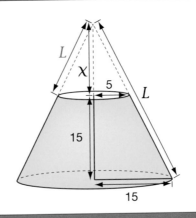

L

x

5

L

15

15

"Exploded" diagram

0.5cm

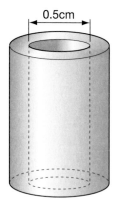

0.5cm

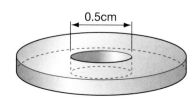

Martin knows a cone is made from the sector of a circle, but he needs to calculate the angle of the sector θ.

He draws this diagram of the large cone to help.

Find the angle θ for Martin.

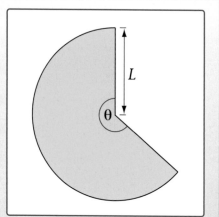

A material trim is to go around the bottom and top circles of the lampshade.

Help Martin use this diagram to calculate the total length of trim needed.

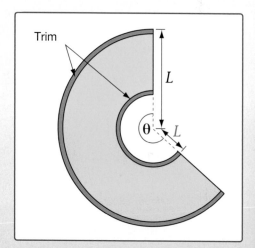

Trim

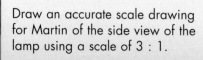

Draw an accurate scale drawing for Martin of the side view of the lamp using a scale of 3 : 1.

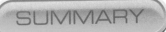

GRADE YOURSELF

C Know why two shapes are similar

C Able to work out unknown sides using scale factors and ratios

B Able to set up equations to find missing sides in similar triangles

A Able to solve problems using area and volume scale factors

A Able to solve practical problems using similar triangles

A* Able to solve related problems involving, for example, capacity, using area and volume scale factors

What you should know now

- How to find the ratios between two similar shapes
- How to work out unknown lengths, areas and volumes of similar 3-D shapes
- How to solve practical problems using similar shapes
- How to solve problems using area and volume ratios

Trigonometry

1 Some 2-D problems

2 Some 3-D problems

3 Trigonometric ratios of angles between 90° and 360°

4 Solving any triangle

5 Sine, cosine and tangent of 30°, 45° and 60°

6 Using sine to find the area of a triangle

This chapter will show you ...

- how to use trigonometric relationships to solve more complex 2-D problems and 3-D problems
- how to use the sine and cosine rules to solve problems involving non right-angled triangles
- how to find the area of a triangle using the rule Area = $\frac{1}{2}ab$ sin C

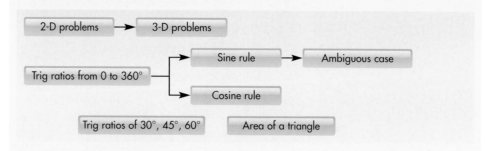

What you should already know

- How to find the sides of right-angled triangles using Pythagoras' theorem
- How to find angles and sides of right-angled triangles using sine, cosine and tangent

Quick check

1 Find the side x in this triangle.

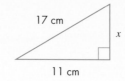

2 Find the angle x in this triangle.

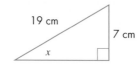

Some 2-D problems

In this section you will learn how to:

- use trigonometric ratios and Pythagoras' theorem to solve more complex two-dimensional problems

Key words

area
length
perpendicular

EXAMPLE 1

In triangle ABC , AB = 6 cm, BC = 9 cm and angle ABC = 52°. Calculate the following.

a the **length** of the **perpendicular** from A to BC

b the **area** of the triangle

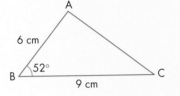

a Drop the perpendicular from A to BC to form the right-angled triangle ADB.

Let h be the length of the perpendicular AD. Then

$h = 6 \sin 52° = 4.73$ (3 significant figures)

b The area of triangle ABC is given by

Area $= \frac{1}{2} \times$ base $\times$ height

$= \frac{1}{2} \times 9 \times h = 21.3$ cm^2 (3 significant figures)

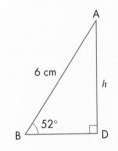

EXAMPLE 2

SR is a diameter of a circle whose radius is 25 cm. PQ is a chord at right angles to SR. X is the midpoint of PQ. The length of XR is 1 cm. Calculate the length of the arc PQ.

To find the length of the arc PQ, you need first to find the angle it subtends at the centre of the circle. (See page 157.)

So join P to the centre of the circle O to obtain the angle POX, which is equal to half the angle subtended by PQ at O.

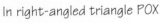

In right-angled triangle POX

OX = OR − XR
OX = 25 − 1 = 24 cm

Therefore,

$\cos x = \dfrac{24}{25}$

$\Rightarrow \quad x = \cos^{-1} 0.96 = 16.26°$

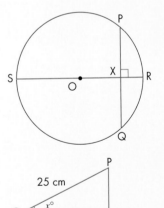

So, the angle subtended at the centre by the arc PQ is 2 × 16.26° = 32.52°, giving the length of the arc PQ as

$\dfrac{32.52}{360} \times 2 \times \pi \times 25 = 14.2$ cm   (3 significant figures)

EXERCISE 15A

1 AC and BC are tangents to a circle of radius 7 cm. Calculate the length of AB.

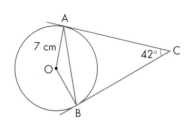

2 CD, length 20 cm, is a diameter of a circle. AB, length 12 cm, is a chord at right angles to DC. Calculate the angle AOB.

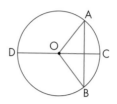

3 Calculate the length of AB.

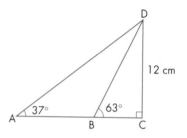

4 A building has a ledge halfway up, as shown in the diagram. Alf measures the length AB as 100 m, the angle CAB as 31° and the angle EAB as 42°. Use this information to calculate the width of the ledge CD.

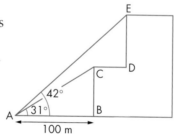

> **HINTS AND TIPS**
>
> Remember, the ledge is halfway, so ED = CB.

5 AB and CD are two equal, perpendicular chords of a circle that intersect at X. The circle is of radius 6 cm and the angle COA is 113°. Calculate these.

a the length AC

b the angle XAO

c the length XB

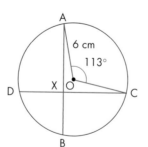

> **HINTS AND TIPS**
>
> AX = XC

6 A vertical flagpole PQ is held by a wooden framework, as shown in the diagram. The framework is in the same vertical plane. Angle SRP = 25°, SQ = 6 m and PR = 4 m. Calculate the size of the angle QRP.

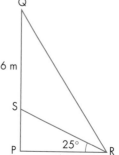

In this section you will learn how to:

- use trigonometric ratios and Pythagoras' theorem to solve more complex three-dimensional problems

Solving a problem set in three dimensions nearly always involves identifying a right-angled triangle that contains the length or angle required. This triangle will have to contain (apart from the right angle) two known measures from which the required calculation can be made.

It is essential to extract the triangle you are going to use from its 3-D situation and redraw it as a separate, plain, right-angled triangle. (It is rarely the case that the required triangle appears as a true right-angled triangle in its 3-D representation. Even if it does, it should still be redrawn as a separate figure.)

The redrawn triangle should be annotated with the known quantities and the unknown quantity to be found.

EXAMPLE 3

A, B and C are three points at ground level. They are in the same horizontal plane. C is 50 km east of B. B is north of A. C is on a bearing of 050° from A.

An aircraft, flying in an easterly direction, passes over B and over C at the same height. When it passes over B, the angle of elevation from A is 12°. Find the angle of elevation of the aircraft from A when it is over C.

First, draw a diagram containing all the known information.

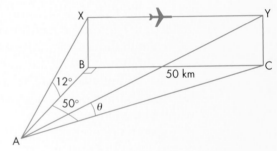

Next, use the right-angled triangle ABC to calculate AB and AC.

$$AB = \frac{50}{\tan 50°} = 41.95 \text{ km} \qquad \text{(4 significant figures)}$$

$$AC = \frac{50}{\sin 50°} = 65.27 \text{ km} \qquad \text{(4 significant figures)}$$

Then use the right-angled triangle ABX to calculate BX, and hence CY.

BX = 41.95 tan 12° = 8.917 km   (4 significant figures)

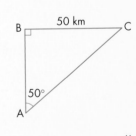

Finally, use the right-angled triangle ACY to calculate the required angle of elevation, θ.

$$\tan \theta = \frac{8.917}{65.27} = 0.1366$$

$$\Rightarrow \theta = \tan^{-1} 0.1366 = 7.8° \qquad \text{(one decimal place)}$$

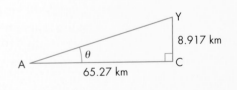

Always write down working values to at least 4 significant figures, to avoid inaccuracy in the final answer.

EXAMPLE 4

The diagram shows a cuboid 22.5 cm by 40 cm by 30 cm.
M is the midpoint of FG.

Calculate these angles.

a ABE

b ECA

c EMH

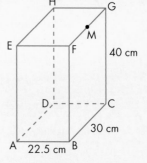

a The right-angled triangle containing the angle required is ABE.

Solving for α gives

$$\tan \alpha = \frac{40}{22.5} = 1.7777$$

$$\Rightarrow \alpha = \tan^{-1} 1.7777 = 60.6° \qquad \text{(3 significant figures)}$$

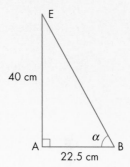

b The right-angled triangle containing the angle required is ACE, but for which only AE is known. Therefore, you need to find AC by applying Pythagoras to the right-angled triangle ABC.

$$x^2 = (22.5)^2 + (30)^2 \text{ cm}^2$$

$$\Rightarrow x = 37.5 \text{ cm}$$

Returning to triangle ACE, you obtain

$$\tan \beta = \frac{40}{37.5} = 1.0666$$

$$\Rightarrow \beta = 46.8° \qquad \text{(3 significant figures)}$$

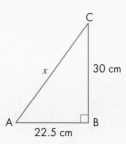

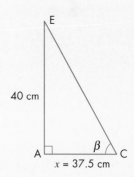

c EMH is an isosceles triangle.

Drop the perpendicular from M to N, the midpoint of HE, to form two right-angled triangles. Angle HMN equals angle EMN, and HN = NE = 15 cm.

Taking triangle MEN, you obtain

$$\tan \theta = \frac{15}{22.5} = 0.66666$$

$$\Rightarrow \theta = \tan^{-1} 0.66666 = 33.7°$$

Therefore, angle HME is 2 × 33.7° = 67.4°   (3 significant figures)

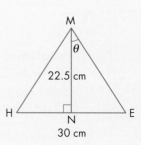

EXERCISE 15B

1 The diagram shows a pyramid. The base is a horizontal rectangle ABCD, 20 cm by 15 cm. The length of each sloping edge is 24 cm. The apex, V, is over the centre of the rectangular base. Calculate these.

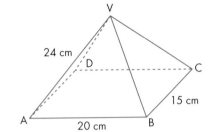

a the size of the angle VAC

b the height of the pyramid

c the volume of the pyramid

d the size of the angle between the face VAD and the base ABCD

2 The diagram shows the roof of a building. The base ABCD is a horizontal rectangle 7 m by 4 m. The triangular ends are equilateral triangles. Each side of the roof is an isosceles trapezium. The length of the top of the roof, EF, is 5 m. Calculate these.

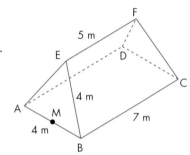

a the length EM, where M is the midpoint of AB

b the size of angle EBC

c the size of the angle between the face EAB and the base ABCD

d the surface area of the roof (excluding the base)

3 ABCD is a vertical rectangular plane. EDC is a horizontal triangular plane. Angle CDE = 90°, AB = 10 cm, BC = 4 cm and ED = 9 cm. Calculate these.

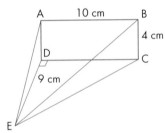

a angle AED   **b** angle DEC

c EC   **d** angle BEC

4 The diagram shows a tetrahedron. The base ABC is a horizontal equilateral triangle of side 8 cm. The vertex D is 5 cm directly above the point B. Calculate these angles.

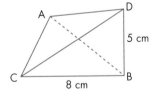

a DCB

b the angle between the face ADC and the face ABC

5 The diagram shows a tetrahedron, each face of which is an equilateral triangle of side 6 m. The lines AN and BM meet the sides CB and AC at a right angle. The lines AN and BM intersect at X, which is directly below the vertex, D. Calculate these.

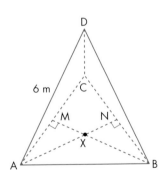

a the distance AX

b the angle between the side DBC and the base ABC

15.3 Trigonometric ratios of angles between 90° and 360°

This section will show you how to:
- find the sine, cosine and tangent of any angle from 0° to 360°

Key words
cosine
sine
tangent

ACTIVITY

a Copy and complete this table using your calculator and rounding off to three decimal places.

x	$\sin x$	x	$\sin x$	x	$\sin x$	x	$\sin x$
0°		180°		180°		360°	
15°		165°		195°		335°	
30°		150°		210°		320°	
45°		135°		225°		315°	
60°		120°		240°		300°	
75°		105°		255°		285°	
90°		90°		270°		270°	

b Comment on what you notice about the **sine** of each acute angle, and the sines of its corresponding non-acute angles.

c Draw a graph of $\sin x$ against x. Take x from 0° to 360° and $\sin x$ from –1 to 1.

d Comment on any symmetries your graph has.

You should have discovered these three facts.

- When $90° < x < 180°$, $\sin x = \sin (180° - x)$
  For example, $\sin 153° = \sin (180° - 153°) = \sin 27° = 0.454$

- When $180° < x < 270°$, $\sin x = -\sin (x - 180°)$
  For example, $\sin 214° = -\sin (214° - 180°) = -\sin 34° = -0.559$

- When $270° < x < 360°$, $\sin x = -\sin (360° - x)$
  For example, $\sin 287° = -\sin (360° - 287°) = -\sin 73° = -0.956$

Note:

- Each and every value of sine between –1 and 1 gives *two* angles between 0° and 360°.

- When the value of sine is positive, both angles are between 0° and 180°.

- When the value of sine is negative, both angles are between 180° and 360°.

- You can use the sine graph from 0° to 360° to check values approximately.

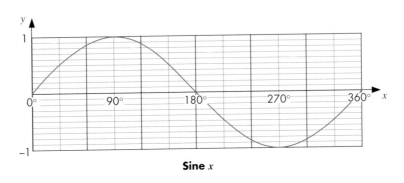

Sine x

EXAMPLE 5

Find the angles with a sine of 0.56.

You know that both angles are between 0° and 180°.

Using your calculator to find $\sin^{-1} 0.56$, you obtain 34.1°.

The other angle is, therefore,

$180° - 34.1° = 145.9°$

So, the angles are 34.1° and 145.9°.

EXAMPLE 6

Find the angles with a sine of –0.197.

You know that both angles are between 180° and 360°.

Using your calculator to find $\sin^{-1} 0.197$, you obtain 11.4°.

So the angles are

$180° + 11.4°$ and $360° - 11.4°$

which give 191.4° and 348.6°.

You can always use your calculator to check your answer to this type of problem by first keying in the angle and the appropriate trigonometric function (which would be sine in the above examples).

EXERCISE 15C

State the two angles between 0° and 360° for each of these sine values.

1 0.6   **2** 0.8   **3** 0.75   **4** −0.7

5 −0.25   **6** −0.32   **7** −0.175   **8** −0.814

9 0.471   **10** −0.097   **11** 0.553   **12** −0.5

ACTIVITY

a Copy and complete this table using your calculator and rounding off to three decimal places.

x	$\cos x$	x	$\cos x$	x	$\cos x$	x	$\cos x$
0°		180°		180°		360°	
15°		165°		195°		335°	
30°		150°		210°		320°	
45°		135°		225°		315°	
60°		120°		240°		300°	
75°		105°		255°		285°	
90°		90°		270°		270°	

b Comment on what you notice about the **cosines** of the angles.

c Draw a graph of cos x against x. Take x from 0° to 360° and cos x from −1 to 1.

d Comment on the symmetry of the graph.

You should have discovered these three facts.

- When 90° < x < 180°, cos x = − cos (180 − x)°
  For example, cos 161° = − cos (180° − 161°) = − cos 19° = − 0.946 (3 significant figures)

- When 180° < x < 270°, cos x = − cos (x − 180°)
  For example, cos 245° = − cos (245° − 180°) = − cos 65° = − 0.423 (3 significant figures)

- When 270° < x < 360°, cos x = cos (360° − x)
  For example, cos 310° = cos (360° − 310°) = cos 50° = 0.643 (3 significant figures)

Note:

- Each and every value of cosine between –1 and 1 gives *two* angles between 0° and 360°.
- When the value of cosine is positive, one angle is between 0° and 90°, and the other is between 270° and 360°.
- When the value of cosine is negative, both angles are between 90° and 270°.
- You can use the cosine graph from 0° to 360° to check values approximately.

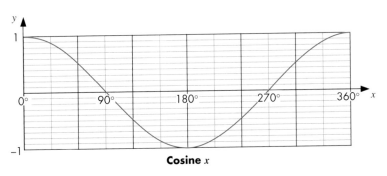

Cosine *x*

EXAMPLE 7

Find the angles with a cosine of 0.75.

One angle is between 0° and 90°, and that the other is between 270° and 360°.

Using your calculator to find $\cos^{-1} 0.75$, you obtain 41.4°.

The other angle is, therefore,

$360° - 41.4° = 318.6°$

So, the angles are 41.4° and 318.6°.

EXAMPLE 8

Find the angles with a cosine of –0.285.

You know that both angles are between 90° and 270°.

Using your calculator to find $\cos^{-1} 0.285$, you obtain 73.4°.

The two angles are, therefore,

$180° - 73.4°$ and $180° + 73.4°$

which give 106.6° and 253.4°.

Here again, you can use your calculator to check your answer, by keying in cosine.

EXERCISE 15D

State the two angles between 0° and 360° for each of these cosine values.

1. 0.6   2. 0.58   3. 0.458   4. 0.575

5. 0.185   6. –0.8   7. –0.25   8. –0.175

9. –0.361   10. –0.974   11. 0.196   12. 0.714

EXERCISE 15E

 1 Write down the sine of each of these angles.

    a 135°   **b** 269°   **c** 305°   **d** 133°

 2 Write down the cosine of each of these angles.

    a 129°   **b** 209°   **c** 95°   **d** 357°

 3 Write down the two possible values of x ($0° < x < 360°$) for each equation. Give your answers to one decimal place.

    a $\sin x = 0.361$ **b** $\sin x = -0.486$

    c $\cos x = 0.641$ **d** $\cos x = -0.866$

    e $\sin x = 0.874$ **f** $\cos x = 0.874$

 4 Find two angles such that the sine of each is 0.5.

 5 $\cos 41° = 0.755$. What is $\cos 139°$?

 6 Write down the value of each of the following, correct to three significant figures.

    a $\sin 50° + \cos 50°$ **b** $\cos 120° - \sin 120°$

    c $\sin 136° + \cos 223°$ **d** $\sin 175° + \cos 257°$

    e $\sin 114° - \sin 210°$ **f** $\cos 123° + \sin 177°$

 7 It is suggested that $(\sin x)^2 + (\cos x)^2 = 1$ is true for all values of x. Test out this suggestion to see if you agree.

 8 Suppose the sine key on your calculator is broken, but not the cosine key. Show how you could calculate these.

    a $\sin 25°$

    b $\sin 130°$

 9 Find a solution to each of these equations.

    a $\sin (x + 20°) = 0.5$

    b $\cos (5x) = 0.45$

 10 By any suitable method, find the solution to the equation $\sin x = (\cos x)^2$.

$$\boxed{\text{ACTIVITY}}$$

a Try to find tan 90°. What do you notice?

Which is the closest angle to 90° for which you can find the **tangent** on your calculator?

What is the largest value for tangent that you can get on your calculator?

b Find values of tan x where 0° < x < 360°. Draw a graph of your results.

State some rules for finding both angles between 0° and 360° that have any given tangent.

EXAMPLE 9

Find the angles between 0° and 360° with a tangent of 0.875.

One angle is between 0° and 90°, and the other is between 180° and 270°.

Using your calculator to find $\tan^{-1} 0.875$, you obtain 41.2°.

The other angle is, therefore,

180° + 41.2° = 221.2°

So, the angles are 41.2° and 221.2°.

EXAMPLE 10

Find the angles between 0° and 360° with a tangent of –1.5.

We know that one angle is between 90° and 180°, and that the other is between 270° and 360°.

Using your calculator to find $\tan^{-1} 1.5$, you obtain 56.3°.

The angles are, therefore,

180° – 56.3° and 360° – 56.3°

which give 123.7° and 303.7°.

EXERCISE 15F

State the angles between 0° and 360° which have each of these tangent values.

1	0.258	2	0.785	3	1.19	4	1.875
5	2.55	6	−0.358	7	−0.634	8	−0.987
9	−1.67	10	−3.68	11	1.397	12	0.907
13	−0.355	14	−1.153	15	4.15	16	−2.05
17	−0.098	18	0.998	19	1.208	20	−2.5

A*

15.4 Solving any triangle

This section will show you how to:
- find the sides and angles of any triangle whether it has a right angle or not

Key words
cosine rule
included
   angle
sine rule

We have already established that any triangle has six elements: three sides and three angles. To solve a triangle (that is, to find any unknown angles or sides), we need to know at least three of the elements. Any combination of three elements – *except that of all three angles* – is enough to work out the rest. In a right-angled triangle, one of the known elements is, of course, the right angle.

When we need to solve a triangle which contains no right angle, we can use one or the other of two rules, depending on what is known about the triangle. These are the **sine rule** and the **cosine rule**.

The sine rule

Take a triangle ABC and draw the perpendicular from A to the opposite side BC.

From right-angled triangle ADB

$$h = c \sin B$$

From right-angled triangle ADC

$$h = b \sin C$$

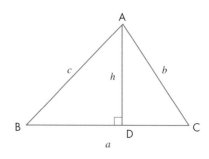

Therefore,

$$c \sin B = b \sin C$$

which can be rearranged to give

$$\frac{c}{\sin C} = \frac{b}{\sin B}$$

By drawing a perpendicular from each of the other two vertices to the opposite side (or by algebraic symmetry), we see that

$$\frac{a}{\sin A} = \frac{c}{\sin C} \quad \text{and that} \quad \frac{a}{\sin A} = \frac{b}{\sin B}$$

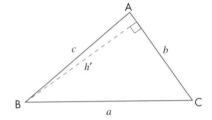

These are usually combined in the form

$$\frac{a}{\sin A} = \frac{b}{\sin B} = \frac{c}{\sin C}$$

which can be inverted to give

$$\frac{\sin A}{a} = \frac{\sin B}{b} = \frac{\sin C}{c}$$

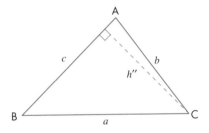

Usually, a triangle is not conveniently labelled as in these diagrams. So, when using the sine rule, it is easier to remember to proceed as follows: take each side in turn, divide it by the sine of the angle opposite, and then equate the resulting quotients.

Note:

• When you are calculating a *side*, use the rule with the *sides on top*.

• When you are calculating an *angle*, use the rule with the *sines on top*.

EXAMPLE 11

In triangle ABC, find the value of *x*.

Use the sine rule with sides on top, which gives

$$\frac{x}{\sin 84°} = \frac{25}{\sin 47°}$$

$$\Rightarrow \quad x = \frac{25 \sin 84°}{\sin 47°} = 34.0 \text{ cm} \quad \text{(3 significant figures)}$$

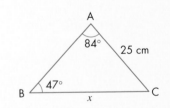

EXAMPLE 12

In the triangle ABC, find the value of the acute angle x.

Use the sine rule with sines on top, which gives

$$\frac{\sin x}{7} = \frac{\sin 40°}{6}$$

$$\Rightarrow \sin x = \frac{7 \sin 40°}{6} = 0.7499$$

$$\Rightarrow \quad x = \sin^{-1} 0.7499 = 48.6° \qquad \text{(3 significant figures)}$$

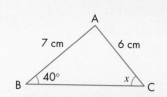

The ambiguous case

EXAMPLE 13

In triangle ABC, AB = 9 cm, AC = 7 cm and angle ABC = 40°. Find the angle ACB.

As you sketch triangle ABC, note that C can have two positions, giving two different configurations.

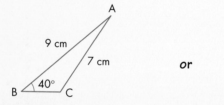 *or*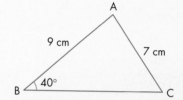

But you still proceed as in the normal sine rule situation, obtaining

$$\frac{\sin C}{9} = \frac{\sin 40°}{7}$$

$$\Rightarrow \sin C = \frac{9 \sin 40°}{7}$$

$$= 0.8264$$

Keying inverse sine on our calculator gives C = 55.7°. But there is another angle with a sine of 0.8264, given by (180° − 55.7°) = 124.3°.

These two values for C give the two different situations shown above.

When an illustration of the triangle is given, it will be clear whether the required angle is acute or obtuse. When an illustration is not given, the more likely answer is an acute angle.

Examiners will not try to catch you out with the ambiguous case. They will indicate clearly, either with the aid of a diagram or by stating it, what is required.

EXERCISE 15G

1 Find the length x in each of these triangles.

a
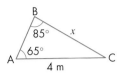

b
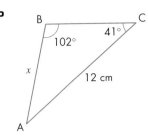

c
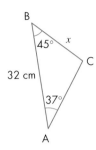

2 Find the angle x in each of these triangles.

a
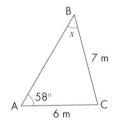

b
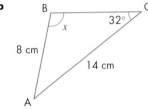

c
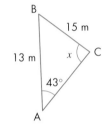

3 In triangle ABC, the angle at A is 38°, the side AB is 10 cm and the side BC is 8 cm. Find the two possible values of the angle at C.

4 In triangle ABC, the angle at A is 42°, the side AB is 16 cm and the side BC is 14 cm. Find the two possible values of the side AC.

5 To find the height of a tower standing on a small hill, Mary made some measurements (see diagram).

From a point B, the angle of elevation of C is 20°, the angle of elevation of A is 50°, and the distance BC is 25 m.

a Calculate these angles.

  i ABC

  ii BAC

b Using the sine rule and triangle ABC, calculate the height h of the tower.

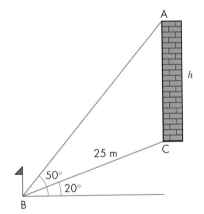

6 Use the information on this sketch to calculate the width, *w*, of the river.

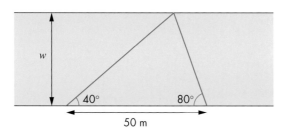

7 An old building is unsafe, so it is protected by a fence. To work out the height of the building, Annie made the measurements shown on the diagram.

    a Use the sine rule to work out the distance AB.

    b Calculate the height of the building, BD.

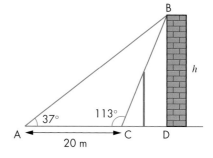

8 A weight is hung from a horizontal beam using two strings. The shorter string is 2.5 m long and makes an angle of 71° with the horizontal. The longer string makes an angle of 43° with the horizontal. What is the length of the longer string?

9 An aircraft is flying over an army base. Suddenly, two searchlights, 3 km apart, are switched on. The two beams of light meet on the aircraft at an angle of 125° vertically above the line joining the searchlights. One of the beams of light makes an angle of 31° with the horizontal. Calculate the height of the aircraft.

10 Two ships leave a port in directions that are 41° from each other. After half an hour, the ships are 11 km apart. If the speed of the slower ship is 7 km/h, what is the speed of the faster ship?

11 For any triangle ABC, prove the sine rule

$$\frac{a}{\sin A} = \frac{b}{\sin B} = \frac{c}{\sin C}$$

The cosine rule

Take the triangle, shown on the right, where D is the foot of the perpendicular to BC from A.

Using Pythagoras on triangle BDA

$$h^2 = c^2 - x^2$$

Using Pythagoras on triangle ADC

$$h^2 = b^2 - (a - x)^2$$

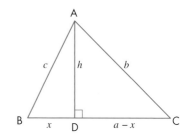

Therefore,

$$c^2 - x^2 = b^2 - (a - x)^2$$

$$c^2 - x^2 = b^2 - a^2 + 2ax - x^2$$

$$\Rightarrow \quad c^2 = b^2 - a^2 + 2ax$$

From triangle BDA, $x = c \cos B$.

Hence

$$c^2 = b^2 - a^2 + 2ac \cos B$$

Rearranging gives

$$b^2 = a^2 + c^2 - 2ac \cos B$$

By algebraic symmetry

$$a^2 = b^2 + c^2 - 2bc \cos A \quad \text{and} \quad c^2 = a^2 + b^2 - 2ab \cos C$$

This is the cosine rule, which can be best remembered by the diagram on the right, where

$$a^2 = b^2 + c^2 - 2bc \cos A$$

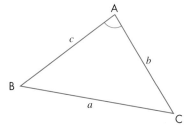

Note the symmetry of the rule and how the rule works using two adjacent sides and the angle between them.

The formula can be rearranged to find any of the three angles

$$\cos A = \frac{b^2 + c^2 - a^2}{2bc}$$

$$\cos B = \frac{a^2 + c^2 - b^2}{2ac}$$

$$\cos C = \frac{a^2 + b^2 - c^2}{2ab}$$

Note that the cosine rule $a^2 = b^2 + c^2 - 2bc \cos A$ is given in the formula sheets in the GCSE examination but the rearranged formula for the angle is not given. You are advised to learn this as trying to rearrange usually ends up with an incorrect formula.

EXAMPLE 14

Find x in this triangle.

By the cosine rule

$$x^2 = 6^2 + 10^2 - 2 \times 6 \times 10 \times \cos 80°$$

$$x^2 = 115.16$$

$$\Rightarrow x = 10.7 \qquad \text{(3 significant figures)}$$

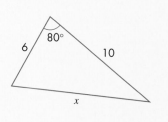

EXAMPLE 15

Find x in this triangle.

By the cosine rule

$$\cos x = \frac{5^2 + 7^2 - 8^2}{2 \times 5 \times 7} = 0.1428$$

$\Rightarrow$ $x = 81.8°$ (3 significant figures)

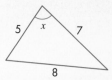

EXAMPLE 16

A ship sails from a port on a bearing of 055° for 40 km. It then changes course to 123° for another 50 km. On what course should the ship be steered to get it straight back to the port?

Previously, you have solved this type of problem using right-angled triangles. This method could be applied here but it would involve at least six separate calculations.

With the aid of the cosine and sine rules, however, you can reduce the solution to two separate calculations, as follows.

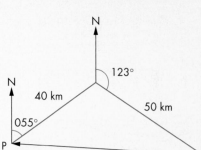

The course diagram gives the triangle PAB (on the right), where angle PAB is found by using alternate angles and angles on a line. 55° + (180° − 123°) = 112°

Let ϕ be the bearing to be steered, then

$$\phi = \theta + 55° + 180°$$

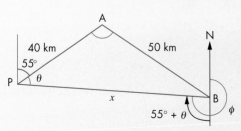

To find θ, you first have to obtain PB(= x), using the cosine rule.

$$x^2 = 40^2 + 50^2 - 2 \times 40 \times 50 \times \cos 112° \text{ km}^2$$

(Remember: the cosine of 112° is negative.)

$\Rightarrow x^2 = 5598.43 \text{ km}^2$

$\Rightarrow$ $x = 74.82 \text{ km}$

You can now find θ from the sine rule.

$$\frac{\sin \theta}{50} = \frac{\sin 112°}{74.82}$$

$$\Rightarrow \sin \theta = \frac{50 \times \sin 112°}{74.82} = 0.6196$$

$\Rightarrow$ $\theta = 38.3°$

So the ship should be steered on a bearing of

$$38.3° + 55° + 180° = 273.3°$$

EXERCISE 15H

1 Find the length x in each of these triangles.

a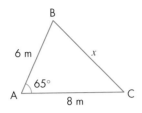

b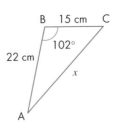

c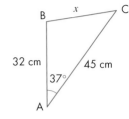

2 Find the angle x in each of these triangles.

a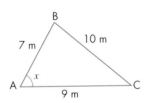

b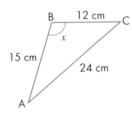

c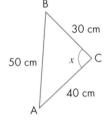

d Explain the significance of the answer to part c.

3 In triangle ABC, AB = 5 cm, BC = 6 cm and angle ABC = 55°. Find AC.

4 A triangle has two sides of length 40 cm and an angle of 110°. Work out the length of the third side of the triangle.

5 The diagram shows a trapezium ABCD. AB = 6.7 cm, AD = 7.2 cm, CB = 9.3 cm and angle DAB = 100°. Calculate these.

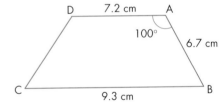

a length DB

b angle DBA

c angle DBC

d length DC

e area of the trapezium

6 A quadrilateral ABCD has AD = 6 cm, DC = 9 cm, AB = 10 cm and BC = 12 cm. Angle ADC = 120°. Calculate angle ABC.

7 A triangle has two sides of length 30 cm and an angle of 50°. Unfortunately, the position of the angle is not known. Sketch the two possible triangles and use them to work out the two possible lengths of the third side of the triangle.

8 A ship sails from a port on a bearing of 050° for 50 km then turns on a bearing of 150° for 40 km. A crewman is taken ill, so the ship drops anchor. What course and distance should a rescue helicopter from the port fly to reach the ship in the shortest possible time?

9 The three sides of a triangle are given as $3a$, $5a$ and $7a$. Calculate the smallest angle in the triangle.

10 ABCD is a trapezium where AB is parallel to CD. AB = 4 cm, BC = 5 cm, CD = 8 cm, DA = 6 cm. A line BX is parallel to AD and cuts DC at X. Calculate these.

    a angle BCD

    b length BD

11 For any triangle ABC prove the cosine rule

$$a^2 = b^2 + c^2 - 2bc \cos A$$

Choosing the correct rule

When solving triangles, there are only four situations that can occur, each of which can be solved completely in three stages.

Two sides and the included angle

1 Use the cosine rule to find the third side.

2 Use the sine rule to find either of the other angles.

3 Use the sum of the angles in a triangle to find the third angle.

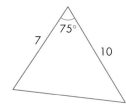

Two angles and a side

1   Use the sum of the angles in a triangle to find the third angle.

2, 3   Use the sine rule to find the other two sides.

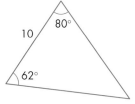

Three sides

1 Use the cosine rule to find one angle.

2 Use the sine rule to find another angle.

3 Use the sum of the angles in a triangle to find the third angle.

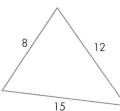

Two sides and a non-included angle

This is the ambiguous case already covered (page 347).

1 Use the sine rule to find the two possible values of the appropriate angle.

2 Use the sum of the angles in a triangle to find the two possible values of the third angle.

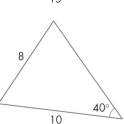

3 Use the sine rule to find the two possible values for the length of the third side.

Note: Apply the sine rule wherever you can – it is always easier to use than the cosine rule. The cosine rule should never need to be used more than once.

EXERCISE 15I

1 Find the length or angle x in each of these triangles.

a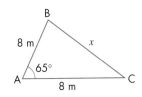

b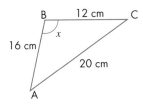

c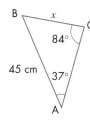

d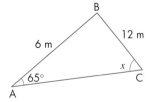

e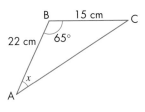

f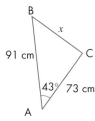

g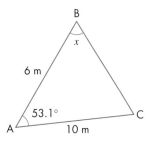

h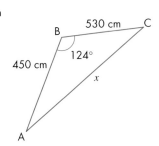

i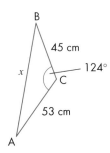

2 The hands of a clock have lengths 3 cm and 5 cm. Find the distance between the tips of the hands at 4 o'clock.

3 A spacecraft is seen hovering at a point which is in the same vertical plane as two towns, X and F. Its distances from X and F are 8.5 km and 12 km respectively. The angle of elevation of the spacecraft when observed from F is 43°. Calculate the distance between the two towns.

4 Two boats, Mary Jo and Suzie, leave port at the same time. Mary Jo sails at 10 knots on a bearing of 065°. Suzie sails on a bearing of 120° and after 1 hour Mary Jo is on a bearing of 330° from Suzie. What is Suzie's speed? (A knot is a nautical mile per hour.)

5 Two ships leave port at the same time, Darling Dave sailing at 12 knots on a bearing of 055°, and Merry Mary at 18 knots on a bearing of 280°.

   a How far apart are the two ships after 1 hour?

   b What is the bearing of Merry Mary from Darling Dave?

Sine, cosine and tangent of 30°, 45° and 60°

In this section you will learn how to:

- work out the trigonometric ratios of 30°, 45° and 60° in surd form

---

EXAMPLE 17

Using an equilateral triangle whose sides are 2 units, write down expressions for the sine, cosine and tangent of 60° and 30°.

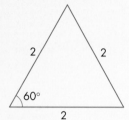 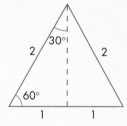 

Divide the equilateral triangle into two equal right-angled triangles. Taking one of them, use Pythagoras and the definition of sine, cosine and tangent to obtain

$$\sin 60° = \frac{\sqrt{3}}{2} \qquad \cos 60° = \frac{1}{2} \qquad \tan 60° = \sqrt{3}$$

and

$$\sin 30° = \frac{1}{2} \qquad \cos 30° = \frac{\sqrt{3}}{2} \qquad \tan 30° = \frac{1}{\sqrt{3}} = \frac{\sqrt{3}}{3}$$

EXAMPLE 18

Using a right-angled isosceles triangle whose equal sides are 1 unit, find the sine, cosine and tangent of 45°.

By Pythagoras, the hypotenuse of the triangle is $\sqrt{2}$ units.

From the definition of sine, cosine and tangent, you obtain

$$\sin 45° = \frac{1}{\sqrt{2}} = \frac{\sqrt{2}}{2} \qquad \cos 45° = \frac{1}{\sqrt{2}} = \frac{\sqrt{2}}{2} \qquad \tan 45° = 1$$

1 The sine of angle x is $\frac{4}{5}$. Work out the cosine of angle x.

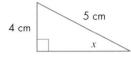

2 The cosine of angle x is $\dfrac{3}{\sqrt{15}}$. Work out the sine of angle x.

3 The two short sides of a right-angled triangle are $\sqrt{6}$ and $\sqrt{13}$. Write down the exact value of the hypotenuse of this triangle, and the exact value of the sine, cosine and tangent of the smallest angle in the triangle.

4 The tangent of angle A is $\frac{6}{11}$. Use this fact to label two sides of the triangle.

    a Calculate the third side of the triangle.

    b Write down the exact values of sin A and cos A.

5 Calculate the exact value of the area of an equilateral triangle of side 6 cm.

6 Work out the exact value of the area of a right-angled isosceles triangle whose hypotenuse is 40 cm.

15.6 Using sine to find the area of a triangle

This section will show you how to:

- work out the area of a triangle if you know two sides and the included angle

Take triangle ABC, whose vertical height is BD and whose base is AC.

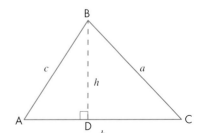

Let BD = h and AC = b, then the area of the triangle is given by

$$\tfrac{1}{2} \times AC \times BD = \tfrac{1}{2}bh$$

However, in triangle BCD

$$h = BC \sin C = a \sin C$$

where BC = a.

Substituting into $\frac{1}{2}bh$ gives

$$\frac{1}{2}b \times (a \sin C) = \frac{1}{2}ab \sin C$$

as the area of the triangle.

By taking the perpendicular from A to its opposite side BC, and the perpendicular from C to its opposite side AB, we can show that the area of the triangle is also given by

$$\frac{1}{2}ac \sin B \quad \text{and} \quad \frac{1}{2}bc \sin A$$

Note the pattern: the area is given by the product of two sides multiplied by the sine of the included angle.

EXAMPLE 19

Find the area of triangle ABC.

Area $= \frac{1}{2}ab \sin C$

Area $= \frac{1}{2} \times 5 \times 7 \times \sin 38° = 10.8 \text{ cm}^2$ (3 significant figures)

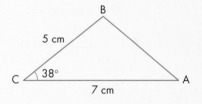

EXAMPLE 20

Find the area of triangle ABC.

You have all three sides but no angle. So first you must find an angle in order to apply the area sine rule.

Find angle C, using the cosine rule.

$$\cos C = \frac{a^2 + b^2 - c^2}{2ab}$$

$$= \frac{13^2 + 19^2 - 8^2}{2 \times 13 \times 19} = 0.9433$$

$$\Rightarrow \quad C = \cos^{-1} 0.9433 = 19.4°$$

(Keep the exact value in your calculator memory.)

Now you apply the area sine rule

$$\frac{1}{2}ab \sin C = \frac{1}{2} \times 13 \times 19 \times \sin 19.4°$$

$$= 41.0 \text{ cm}^2 \quad \text{(3 significant figures)}$$

1 Find the area of each of the following triangles.

   a Triangle ABC where BC = 7 cm, AC = 8 cm and angle ACB = 59°

   b Triangle ABC where angle BAC = 86°, AC = 6.7 cm and AB = 8 cm

   c Triangle PQR where QR = 27 cm, PR = 19 cm and angle QRP = 109°

   d Triangle XYZ where XY = 231 cm, XZ = 191 cm and angle YXZ = 73°

   e Triangle LMN where LN = 63 cm, LM = 39 cm and angle NLM = 85°

2 The area of triangle ABC is 27 cm². If BC = 14 cm and angle BCA = 115°, find AC.

3 The area of triangle LMN is 113 cm², LM = 16 cm and MN = 21 cm. Angle LMN is acute. Calculate these angles.

   a LMN   **b** MNL

4 In a quadrilateral ABCD, DC = 4 cm, BD = 11 cm, angle BAD = 32°, angle ABD = 48° and angle BDC = 61°. Calculate the area of the quadrilateral.

5 A board is in the shape of a triangle with sides 60 cm, 70 cm and 80 cm. Find the area of the board.

6 Two circles, centres P and Q, have radii of 6 cm and 7 cm respectively. The circles intersect at X and Y. Given that PQ = 9 cm, find the area of triangle PXQ.

7 The points A, B and C are on the circumference of a circle, centre O and radius 7 cm. AB = 4 cm and BC = 3.5 cm. Calculate these.

   a angle AOB

   b area of quadrilateral OABC

8 Prove that for any triangle ABC

   Area = $\frac{1}{2}ab \sin C$

9 **a** ABC is a right-angled isosceles triangle with short sides of 1 cm. Write down the value of sin 45°.

   b Calculate the area of triangle PQR.

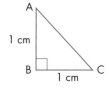

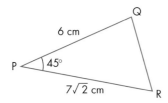

1 The diagram shows triangle ABC.
BC = 8.5 cm.
Angle ABC = 90°.
Angle ACB = 38°.

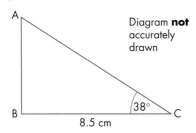

Diagram **not** accurately drawn

Work out the length of AB. Give your answer correct to 3 significant figures.

Edexcel, Question 21, Paper 4 Intermediate, June 2003

 2 ABD and BCD are two right-angled triangles.
AB = 9 cm, CD = 6 cm, ∠BAD = 35°.

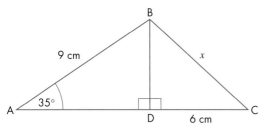

The two triangles are joined together as shown in the diagram. ADC is a straight line. Calculate the length BC, marked *x* on the diagram.

 3 ABC is a right-angled triangle.
AB = 7 cm, ∠CAB = 52°.

Find the length of BC (marked *x* in the diagram). Give your answer to a suitable degree of accuracy.

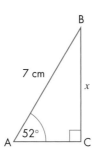

 4 PQR is a triangle.
PQ = 12 cm, PR = 15 cm, QR = 20 cm.

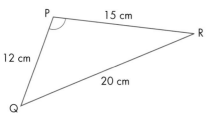

Calculate the angle QPR.

 5 ADC is a right-angled triangle. Point B is such that CBD = 38°. CAB = 21° and AB = 15 cm. Calculate the length of CD.

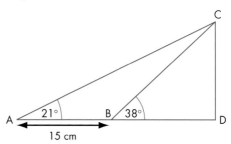

 6 In triangle PQR, PQ = 13 cm, QR = 11 cm and PR = 12 cm.

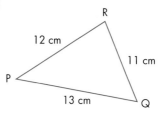

Find the area of triangle PQR.

 7 Two boats, P and Q, leave harbour at 10 am. Boat P sails at a constant speed of 21 km/h on a bearing of 075°. Boat Q sails at a constant speed of 30 km/h on a bearing of 163°.

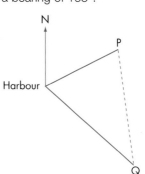

Calculate the distance between the two boats at 11 am.

 8 The diagram represents a prism.
AEFD is a rectangle.
ABCD is a square.
EB and FC are perpendicular to plane ABCD.

AB = 60 cm.
AD = 60 cm.
Angle ABE = 90°
Angle BAE = 30°.

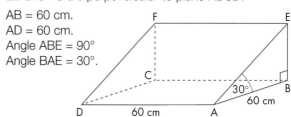

Calculate the size of the angle that the line DE makes with the plane ABCD. Give your answer correct to 1 decimal place.

Edexcel, Question 11, Paper 19 Higher, June 2004

9 In triangle PQR, PR = 6 cm, PQ = 10 cm and angle PRQ = 105°.

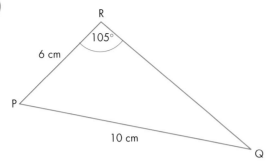

Calculate the area of triangle PQR.

10 VABCD is a right pyramid with a square base.
V is vertically above the centre of the square.
All the slant lengths are 30 cm.
The square base has a side of 20 cm.

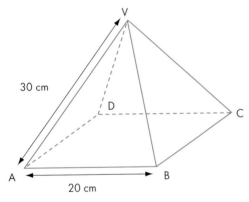

Calculate the angle between the face VAB and the base ABCD.

11 The diagram shows a pyramid. The apex of the pyramid is V. Each of the sloping edges is of length 6 cm.

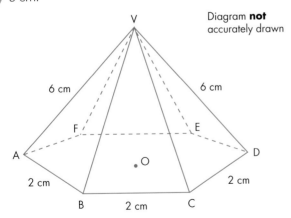

The base of the pyramid is a regular hexagon with sides of length 2 cm. O is the centre of the base.

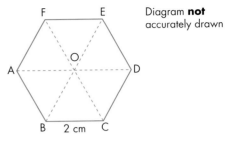

Diagram **not** accurately drawn

a Calculate the height of V above the base of the pyramid. Give your answer correct to 3 significant figures.

b Calculate the size of angle DVA. Give your answer correct to 3 significant figures.

c Calculate the size of angle AVC. Give your answer correct to 3 significant figures.

Edexcel, Question 19, Paper 6 Higher, June 2005

12 A rectangular based pyramid has a base of length 6 cm and width 4 cm.

The vertex of the pyramid is directly over the midpoint of the base.

The volume of the pyramid is 200 cm³.

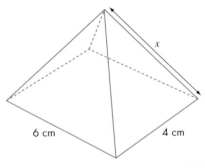

Find the length of the slant edge of the pyramid.

WORKED EXAM QUESTIONS

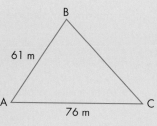

The diagram represents a level triangular piece of land. AB = 61 metres, AC = 76 metres, and the area of the land is 2300 m^2.

Angle BAC is acute.

Calculate the length of BC. Give your answer to an appropriate degree of accuracy.

Solution

$\frac{1}{2} \times 61 \times 76 \times \sin BAC = 2300$

∴ $\sin BAC = 0.9922 \ldots$

∴ Angle BAC = 82.9°

Use Area = $\frac{1}{2}bc$ sin A to set up an equation and solve it to get angle A. You are given that A is acute so there is no problem with any ambiguity.

$BC^2 = 61^2 + 76^2 - 2 \times 61 \times 76 \times \cos 82.9 = 8343.75$

BC = 91.3 m

Use the cosine rule to work out the side BC. If possible keep values in your calculator display but if you have to write down values then use at least 4 significant figures for trig ratios and at least 1 decimal place for angles. This will avoid any inaccuracy in the final answer.

A tetrahedron has one face which is an equilateral triangle of side 6 cm and three faces which are isosceles triangles with sides 6 cm, 9 cm and 9 cm.

Calculate the surface area of the tetrahedron.

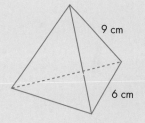

Solution

First work out the area of the base, which has angles of 60°.

Area base = $\frac{1}{2} \times 6 \times 6 \times \sin 60° = 15.59$ cm^2 (4 significant figures)

Next, work out the vertex angle of one side triangle using the cosine rule.

$\cos x = \dfrac{9^2 + 9^2 - 6^2}{2 \times 9 \times 9} = 0.7778$

So $x = 38.9°$ (Keep the exact value in your calculator.)

Work out the area of one side face and then add all faces together.

Area side face = $\frac{1}{2} \times 9 \times 9 \times \sin 38.9° = 25.46$ cm^2 (4 significant figures)

Total area = $3 \times 25.46 + 15.59 = 92.0$ cm^2 (3 significant figures)

GRADE YOURSELF

A Able to solve more complex 2-D problems using Pythagoras' theorem and trigonometry

A Able to use the sine and cosine rules to calculate missing angles or sides in non right-angled triangles

A Able to find the area of a triangle using the formula Area = $\frac{1}{2}ab$ sin C

A* Able to use the sine and cosine rules to solve more complex problems involving non right-angled triangles

A* Able to solve 3-D problems using Pythagoras' theorem and trigonometric ratios

A* Able to find two angles between 0° and 360° for any given value of a trigonometric ratio (positive or negative)

A* Able to solve simple equations where the trigonometric ratio is the subject

What you should know now

- How to use the sine and cosine rules
- How to find the area of a triangle using Area = $\frac{1}{2}ab$ sin C

Really Useful Maths!

Chapter 2
Really Useful Maths!: Sheep Farmer

Date	Number of lambs	Total live weight in kg	Mean live weight in kg	Total weight of meat in kg	Meat as % of live weight	Total price paid for meat	Price paid per kg of meat
1st April	13	468	36	211	45.1% ✓	£812.56	£3.85
15th April	8	290	36	134	46.2% ✓	£451.91	£3.37
22nd April	18	672	37	312	46.4% ✓	£1105.31	£3.54
29th April	11	398	36	179	45.0% ✓	£625.04	£3.49
6th May	18	657	37	291	44.3% ✓	£907.89	£3.12
20th May	8	309	39	130	42.1% ✓	£386.15	£2.97
3rd June	10	416	42	171	41.1% ✗	£480.46	£2.81
17th June	4	174	44	72	41.4% ✗	£196.54	£2.73

The mean weight per lamb has increased from 36 kg to 44 kg. This is an increase of 22%. However the price per kg of lamb has fallen from £3.85 to £2.73, a decrease of 29%.

The only two weeks when the condition of the lambs fell below 42% were 3rd June and 17th June.

Comment: There were only 3 weeks when Mrs Woolman earned less than the average lamb price. The trend of both Mrs Woolman's prices and the average prices were decreasing from April to June.

Chapter 4
Really Useful Maths!: Water recycling

Daily water usage			
	Litres used each: flush/shower/load	Frequency used	Total litres per day
Toilet	13.16	12 times a day	157.92
Shower	91	2 times a day	182
Washing machine	113.75	3 times a week	48.75
Dishwasher	40.95	once every 2 days	20.475
Total:			409.145

They can collect 300 litres from the roof in 1 day.
It will take $4\frac{1}{2}$ days to fill the tank.

Chapter 5
Really Useful Maths!: Riding stables

Horse	Weight in kg	Feed in kg	Worming paste in tubes
Summer	850	6.1	1.5
Sally	400	4.0	0.75
Skip	550	5.4	1
Simon	500	4.0	1
Barney	350	2.8	0.75
Teddy	650	6.2	1.25

Cost per adult: £28.50

Cost per child: £25.50

Chapter 9
Really Useful Maths!: The street

Roof area for one block of 5 bungalows	711 m²
Roof area of whole street	14,227 m²
Number of slates needed	247,552 slates
Total cost of slates	£59,412.48
Total weight of slates	594,124.8 kg

Chapter 10
Really Useful Maths!: Oil

Country	Oil produced, barrels per person per year	Oil consumed, barrels per person per year	Difference produced − consumed	Rank order production	Consumption as a % of production
Algeria	13.5	2.3	11.2	3	17%
Australia	9.8	14.5	−4.7	7	148%
Chile	0.4	5.5	−5.1	8	1297%
Indonesia	1.5	1.8	−0.3	6	122%
Japan	0.05	15.2	−15.15	10	30 525%
Nigeria	6.7	0.8	5.9	4	12%
Saudi Arabia	124.6	21.4	103.2	1	17%
UK	11.8	10.2	1.6	5	86%
USA	9.6	24.3	−14.7	9	252%
Venezuela	37.4	7.2	30.2	2	19%

Year	World population	World oil production, barrels per day	World oil production, barrels per person per day
1984	4.77×10^9	5.45×10^7	4.2
1989	5.19×10^9	5.99×10^7	4.2
1994	5.61×10^9	6.10×10^7	4.0
1999	6.01×10^9	6.58×10^7	4.0
2004	6.38×10^9	7.25×10^7	4.1

Chapter 11
Really Useful Maths!: Dairy farm

3-month moving average for milk production in thousands of litres												
	Jan	Feb	Mar	Apr	May	Jun	Jul	Aug	Sep	Oct	Nov	Dec
2004		53	54.7	58.3	64		68.7	72.3	69.7	67.7	63.3	61.3	69.7
2005	61.7	63	64.7	67	74		78.7	83.3	80.7	78	72.7	70.3

Comments on line graphs: Each year, January has the lowest production. It rises steadily towards July, then decreases again towards the following January. 2005 production is about 10,000 litres more per month than 2004.

Comments on Scatter graphs: Monthly sunshine/milk production: positive correlation. Monthly rainfall/milk production: negative correlation.

Chapter 12
Really Useful Maths!: Garden design

Perimeter of patio	56.55 m	Area of patio	254.47 m²
Perimeter of play area	45.13 m	Area of play area	130.27 m²
Perimeter of one flower bed	13.83 m	Area of one flower bed	7.5 m²
Dimensions of top pond	length = 4 m width = 2 m	Area of top pond	8 m²
Dimensions of second pond	length = 5 m width = 3 m	Area of second pond	15 m²
Dimensions of third pond	length = 6 m width = 4 m	Area of third pond	24 m²
Dimensions of bottom pond	length = 7 m width = 5 m	Area of bottom pond	35 m²
		Area of lawn	703.26 m²

Chapter 14
Really Useful Maths!: Bright ideas

Volume of stem	164.9 cm³	Length of x	7.5 cm
Weight of stem	1649 g	Length of L	9 cm
Volume of base	88.3 cm³	Length of L	27 cm
Weight of base	883 g	Surface area of small cone	141 cm²
Total weight	2532 g	Surface area of large cone	1272 cm²
		Surface area of lampshade	1131 cm²

$\theta = 200°$.
Total length of trim = 125.66 cm.

Quick check

1 a 3841　**b** 41　**c** 625

2 a any multiple of 7, e.g. 7, 14, 21, ..., 70...
b 11, 13, 17 or 19
c 1, 4, 9 ,16, 25 ,36 ,49 or 64
d 1, 3, 9

3 a 17　**b** 25　**c** 5

Exercise 1A

1 a 6000
b 5 cans cost £1.95, so 6 cans cost £1.95.
32 = 5 × 6 + 2. cost is £10.53.
2 a 288　**b** 16
3 a 38
b coach price for adults = £8, coach price for juniors = £4,
money for coaches raised by tickets = £12 400, cost of
coaches = £12 160, profit = £240
4 £68.70
5 (18.81...) Kirsty can buy 18 models.
6 (7.58...) Eunice must work for 8 weeks.
7 £8.40
8 £450

Exercise 1B

1 a 18　**b** 140　**c** 1.4　**d** 12　**e** 21.3
f 6.9　**g** 2790　**h** 12.1　**i** 18.9
2 a 280　**b** 12　**c** 0.18　**d** 450　**e** 0.62
f 380　**g** 0.26　**h** 240　**i** 12
3 750
4 300

Exercise 1C

1 a 50 000　**b** 60 000　**c** 30 000　**d** 90 000
e 90 000　**f** 0.5　**g** 0.3　**h** 0.006
i 0.05　**j** 0.0009　**k** 10　**l** 90
m 90　**n** 200　**o** 1000
2 a 56 000　**b** 27 000　**c** 80 000　**d** 31 000
e 14 000　**f** 1.7　**g** 4.1　**h** 2.7
i 8.0　**j** 42　**k** 0.80　**l** 0.46
m 0.066　**n** 1.0　**o** 0.0098
3 a 60 000　**b** 5300　**c** 89.7　**d** 110
e 9　**f** 1.1　**g** 0.3　**h** 0.7
i 0.4　**j** 0.8　**k** 0.2　**l** 0.7
4 a 65, 74　**b** 95, 149　**c** 950, 1499
5 Elsecar 750, 849, Hoyland 1150, 1249,
Barnsley 164 500, 165 400

Exercise 1D

1 a 60 000　**b** 120 000　**c** 10 000　**d** 15　**e** 140
f 100　**g** 200　**h** 0.028
i 0.09　**j** 400　**k** 8000　**l** 0.16
m 45　**n** 0.08　**o** 0.25
p 4 000 000　**q** 360 000

2 a 5　**b** 50　**c** 25　**d** 600　**e** 3000
f 5000　**g** 2000　**h** 2000　**i** 400　**j** 8000
k 4 000 000　**l** 3 200 000

Exercise 1E

The answers will depend on the approximations made. Your
answers should be to the same order as these.
1 a 35 000　**b** 15 000　**c** 960　**d** 5
e 1200　**f** 500
2 a 39 700　**b** 17 000　**c** 933　**d** 4.44
e 1130　**f** 550
3 a 4000　**b** 10　**c** 1　**d** 19　**e** 3　**f** 18
4 a 4190　**b** 8.79　**c** 1.01　**d** 20.7　**e** 3.07　**f** 18.5
5 a £3000　**b** £2000　**c** £1500　**d** £700
6 a £15 000　**b** £18 000　**c** £17 500
7 £20 000
8 8p
9 a 40 miles per hour　**b** 10 gallons　**c** £70
10 a 80 000　**b** 2000　**c** 1000　**d** 30 000
e 5000　**f** 200 000　**g** 75　**h** 140
i 100　**j** 3000
11 a 86 900　**b** 1760　**c** 1030　**d** 29 100
e 3930　**f** 237 000　**g** 84.8　**h** 163
i 96.9　**j** 2440
12 approx. 500
13 a i 27.57142857　**ii** 27.6
b i 16.89651639　**ii** 16.9
c i 704.4198895　**ii** 704

Exercise 1F

You may not have the same approximations. Can you justify
your answers?
1 a 1.74 m　**b** 5 minutes　**c** 240 g　**d** 82°C
e 35 000 people　**f** 15 miles　**g** 14 m^2
2 82°F, $5\frac{1}{2}$ km, 110 min, 43 000 people, 6.2 seconds, 67th,
1788, 15 practice walks, 5 seconds
The answers will depend on the approximations made.
Your answers should be to the same order as these.
3 40
4 40 minutes
5 60 stamps
6 70 mph
7 270 fans
8 80 000 kg (80 tonnes)

Exercise 1G

1 a 12　**b** 9　**c** 6　**d** 13　**e** 15　**f** 14
g 16　**h** 10　**i** 18　**j** 17　**k** 8 (or 16)　**l** 21
2 4 packs of sausages and 5 packs of buns (or multiples of
these)
3 24 seconds
4 30 seconds
5 1 + 3 + 5 + 7 + 9 = 25, 1 + 3 + 5 + 7 + 9 + 11 = 36, 1 +
3 + 5 + 7 + 9 + 11 + 13 = 49,
1 + 3 + 5 + 7 + 9 + 11 + 13 + 15 = 64

6 a −2   **b** −5   **c** −7   **d** −1   **e** −9
   f −11   **g** −12   **h** −20   **i** −30   **j** −13

7 a 1   **b** 3   **c** 4   **d** 2   **e** 10
   f −2   **g** −1   **h** 20   **i** 40   **j** −4

8 a 1, 3, 6, 10, 15, 21, 28, 36, 45, 55, 66, 78, 91, 105
   b Adding consecutive pairs gives you square numbers.

9 a 1, 64, 729, 4096, 15 625
   b 1, 8, 27, 64, 125
   c $\sqrt{a^3} = a \times \sqrt{a}$
   d square numbers

10 a 0.2   **b** 0.5   **c** 0.6   **d** 0.9   **e** 1.2
   f 0.8   **g** 1.1   **h** 1.5

11 The answers will depend on the approximations made. Your answers should be to the same order as these.
   a 60   **b** 1500   **c** 180

Exercise 1H

1 a $84 = 2 \times 2 \times 3 \times 7$ **b** $100 = 2 \times 2 \times 5 \times 5$
   c $180 = 2 \times 2 \times 3 \times 3 \times 5$
   d $220 = 2 \times 2 \times 5 \times 11$
   e $280 = 2 \times 2 \times 2 \times 5 \times 7$
   f $128 = 2 \times 2 \times 2 \times 2 \times 2 \times 2 \times 2$
   g $50 = 2 \times 5 \times 5$

2 a $84 = 2^2 \times 3 \times 7$ **b** $100 = 2^2 \times 5^2$
   c $180 = 2^2 \times 3^2 \times 5$ **d** $220 = 2^2 \times 5 \times 11$
   e $280 = 2^3 \times 5 \times 7$ **f** $128 = 2^7$
   g $50 = 2 \times 5^2$ **h** $1000 = 2^3 \times 5^3$
   i $576 = 2^6 \times 3^2$ **j** $650 = 2 \times 5^2 \times 13$

3 1, 2, 3, 2^2, 5, 2×3, 7, 2^3, 3^2, 2×5, 11, $2^2 \times 3$, 13, 2×7, 3×5, 2^4, 17, 2×3^2, 19, $2^2 \times 5$, 3×7, 2×11, 23, $2^3 \times 3$, 5^2, 2×13, 3^3, $2^2 \times 7$, 29, $2 \times 3 \times 5$, 31, 2^5, 3×11, 2×17, 5×7, $2^2 \times 3^2$, 37, 2×19, 3×13, $2^3 \times 5$, 41, $2 \times 3 \times 7$, 43, $2^2 \times 11$, $3^3 \times 5$, 2×23, 47, $2^4 \times 3$, 7^2, 2×5^2

4 a Double each time
   b 64, 128
   c 81, 243
   d 256, 1024, 4096
   e 3, 3^2, 3^3, 3^4, 3^5, 3^6, 4, 4^2, 4^3, 4^4, 4^5

Exercise 1I

1 a 20   **b** 56   **c** 6   **d** 28   **e** 10   **f** 15
   g 24   **h** 30

2 They are the two numbers multiplied together.

3 a 8   **b** 18   **c** 12   **d** 30

4 No. The numbers have a common factor. Multiplying them together would mean using this factor twice, thus increasing the size of the common multiple. It would not be the lowest common multiple.

5 a 168   **b** 105   **c** 84   **d** 168   **e** 48
   f 54   **g** 75   **h** 144

6 a 8   **b** 7   **c** 4   **d** 14   **e** 12   **f** 9
   g 5   **h** 4   **i** 3   **j** 16   **k** 5   **l** 18

7 a ii and iii   **b** iii

Exercise 1J

1 a −15   **b** −14   **c** −24   **d** 6   **e** 14
   f 2   **g** −2   **h** −8   **i** −4   **j** 3
   k −24   **l** −10   **m** −18   **n** 16   **o** 36

2 a −9   **b** 16   **c** −3   **d** −32   **e** 18
   f 18   **g** 6   **h** −4   **i** 20   **j** 16
   k 8   **l** −48   **m** 13   **n** −13   **o** −8

3 a −2   **b** 30   **c** 15   **d** −27   **e** −7

4 a −9   **b** 3   **c** 1

5 a 16   **b** −2   **c** −12

6 Any appropriate divisions.

Exercise 1K

1 a −4   **b** −6   **c** 4   **d** 45   **e** 6   **f** 6

2 a 38   **b** 24   **c** −3   **d** −6   **e** −1   **f** 2
   g −25   **h** 25   **i** 0   **j** −20   **k** 4   **l** 0

3 a $(3 \times -4) + 1 = -11$ **b** $-6 \div (-2 + 1) = 6$
   c $(-6 \div -2) + 1 = 4$ **d** $4 + (-4 \div 4) = 3$
   e $(4 + -4) \div 4 = 0$ **f** $(16 - -4) \div 2 = 10$

4 a 49   **b** −1   **c** −5   **d** −12

ANSWERS TO CHAPTER 2

Quick check

1 a $\frac{2}{5}$ **b** $\frac{3}{8}$ **c** $\frac{3}{7}$

2

Fraction	Percentage	Decimal
$\frac{3}{4}$	75%	0.75
$\frac{2}{5}$	40%	0.4
$\frac{11}{20}$	55%	0.55

3 a £23   **b** £4.60   **c** 23p

Exercise 2A

1 a $\frac{1}{3}$ **b** $\frac{1}{5}$ **c** $\frac{2}{5}$ **d** $\frac{5}{24}$ **e** $\frac{2}{5}$ **f** $\frac{1}{6}$ **g** $\frac{2}{7}$ **h** $\frac{1}{3}$

2 $\frac{3}{5}$ **3** $\frac{12}{31}$ **4** $\frac{7}{12}$

5 $\frac{1}{8}$ **6** $\frac{5}{12}$ **7** $\frac{1}{5}$

8 $\frac{3}{20}$

Exercise 2B

1 a $\frac{8}{15}$ **b** $\frac{7}{12}$ **c** $\frac{3}{10}$ **d** $\frac{11}{12}$ **e** $\frac{1}{10}$ **f** $\frac{1}{8}$
   g $\frac{1}{12}$ **h** $\frac{1}{3}$

2 a $\frac{7}{9}$ **b** $\frac{5}{8}$ **c** $\frac{3}{8}$ **d** $\frac{1}{15}$ **e** $3\frac{31}{45}$ **f** $4\frac{47}{60}$
   g $\frac{41}{72}$ **h** $\frac{29}{48}$ **i** $1\frac{43}{48}$ **j** $1\frac{109}{120}$ **k** $1\frac{23}{30}$ **l** $1\frac{31}{84}$

3 $\frac{1}{20}$ **4** $\frac{1}{6}$

5 $\frac{1}{3}$ **6** 260

7 three-quarters of 68   **8** £51

9 10 minutes

Exercise 2C

1 a $\frac{1}{6}$ **b** $\frac{1}{10}$ **c** $\frac{3}{8}$ **d** $\frac{3}{14}$ **e** $\frac{7}{20}$ **f** $\frac{16}{45}$
   g $\frac{3}{5}$ **h** $\frac{5}{8}$

2 a $\frac{5}{12}$ **b** $2\frac{1}{12}$ **c** $6\frac{1}{4}$ **d** $2\frac{11}{12}$ **e** $3\frac{9}{10}$
   f $3\frac{1}{3}$ **g** $12\frac{1}{2}$ **h** 30

3 21 tonnes   **4** $\frac{3}{8}$

5 $\frac{3}{8}$ **6** $\frac{2}{5}$ of $6\frac{1}{2}$

7 £5   **8** £10.40

Exercise 2D

1 a $\frac{3}{4}$ **b** $1\frac{2}{5}$ **c** $1\frac{1}{15}$ **d** $1\frac{1}{14}$ **e** 4   **f** 4
   g 5   **h** $1\frac{5}{7}$ **i** $\frac{4}{9}$ **j** $1\frac{3}{5}$

2 40

3 15

4 16

5 a $2\frac{2}{15}$ **b** 38   **c** $1\frac{7}{8}$ **d** $\frac{9}{32}$ **e** $\frac{1}{16}$ **f** $\frac{256}{625}$

Exercise 2E

1 a 1.1   **b** 1.03   **c** 1.2   **d** 1.07   **e** 1.12

2 a £62.40   **b** 12.96 kg   **c** 472.5 g
   d 599.5 m   **e** £38.08   **f** £90
   g 391 kg   **h** 824.1 cm   **i** 253.5 g
   j £143.50   **k** 736 m   **l** £30.24

3 1 690 200

4 Bob £17 325, Jean £20 475, Anne £18 165, Brian £26 565

5 575 g

6 60 girls

7 £287.88, £84.60, £135.13, £34.66

8 £540.96

9 Calculate the VAT on certain amounts, and $\frac{1}{6}$ of that amount. Show the error grows as the amount increases. After £600 the error is greater than £5, so the method works to within £5 with prices up to £600.

Exercise 2F

1 a 0.92   **b** 0.85   **c** 0.75   **d** 0.91   **e** 0.88

2 a £9.40   **b** 23 kg   **c** 212.4 g   **d** 339.5 m
   e £4.90   **f** 39.6 m   **g** 731 m   **h** 83.52 g
   i 360 cm

3 £5525   **4** 448 people

Quick check

1 a $\frac{3}{5}$ **b** $\frac{1}{5}$ **c** $\frac{1}{3}$ **d** $\frac{16}{25}$ **e** $\frac{2}{5}$ **f** $\frac{3}{4}$ **g** $\frac{1}{3}$

2 a £12   **b** £33   **c** 175 litres   **d** 15 kg
   e 40 m   **f** £35   **g** 135 g   **h** 1.05 litres

5 705 pupils   **6** £18 975

7 a 66.5 mph   **b** 73.5 mph

8 £39.60   **9** 524.8 units

10 £765   **11** $1.10 \times 0.9 = 0.99$ (99%)

Exercise 2G

1 a 25%   **b** 60.6%   **c** 46.3%   **d** 12.5%
   e 41.7%   **f** 60%   **g** 20.8%   **h** 10%
   i 1.9%   **j** 8.3%   **k** 45.5%   **l** 10.5%

2 32%   **3** 6.49%   **4** 33.7%

5 a 49.2%   **b** 64.5%   **c** 10.6%

6 17.9%   **7** 7.4%   **8** 90.5%

9 a Commonwealth 20.9%, USA 26.5%, France 10.3%, Other 42.3%
   b 100%, because this is all imports.

Exercise 2H

1 a i 10.5 kg   **ii** 11.03 kg   **iii** 12.16 kg   **iv** 14.07 kg
   b 9 days

2 12 years   **3 a** £14272.27   **b** 20 years

4 a i 2550   **ii** 2168   **iii** 1331   **b** 7 years

5 a £6800   **b** £5440   **c** £3481.60

6 a i 1.9 million litres   **ii** 1.6 million litres
    iii 1.2 million litres
   b 10th August

7 a i 51 980   **ii** 84 752   **iii** 138 186
   b 2010

8 a 21 years   **b** 21 years

9 3 years   **10** 30 years

11 $1.1 \times 1.1 = 1.21$ (21% increase)

Exercise 2I

1 a 800 g   **b** 250 m   **c** 60 cm   **d** £3075
   e £200   **f** £400

2 80

3 T shirt £8.40, Tights £1.20, Shorts £5.20, Sweater £10.74, Trainers £24.80, Boots £32.40

4 £833.33

5 £300

6 240

7 £350

8 4750 blue bottles

9 £22

10 less by $\frac{1}{4}$%

11 Calculate the pre-VAT price for certain amounts, and $\frac{5}{6}$ of that amount. Show the error grows as the amount increases. Up to £280 the error is less than £5.

ANSWERS TO CHAPTER 3

Exercise 3A

1 $\frac{7}{10}$ **2** $\frac{2}{5}$

3 a $\frac{2}{5}$ **b** $\frac{3}{5}$ **4 a** $\frac{7}{10}$ **b** $\frac{3}{10}$

5 a $\frac{2}{9}$ **b** $\frac{1}{3}$ **c** $\frac{2}{9}$

6 sugar $\frac{5}{22}$, flour $\frac{3}{11}$, margarine $\frac{2}{11}$, fruit $\frac{7}{22}$

Exercise 3B

1 a 160 g : 240 g   **b** 80 kg : 200 kg
  c 150 : 350   **d** 950 m : 50 m
  e 175 min : 125 min   **f** £20 : £30 : £50
  g £36 : £60 : £144   **h** 50 g : 250 g : 300 g
2 a 160   **b** 37.5%
3 a 28.6%   **b** 250 kg
4 a 21 horses   **b** 94% (2 sf)
5 a 1 : 400 000   **b** 1 : 125 000   **c** 1 : 250 000
  d 1 : 25 000   **e** 1 : 20 000   **f** 1 : 40 000
6 a 1 : 1 000 000   **b** 47 km   **c** 0.8 cm
7 a 1 : 250 000   **b** 2 km   **c** 4.8 cm
8 a 1 : 1.6   **b** 1 : 3.25   **c** 1 : 1.125
  d 1 : 1.44   **e** 1 : 5.4   **f** 1 : 1.5
  g 1 : 4.8   **h** 1 : 42   **i** 1 : 1.25

Exercise 3C

1 a 3 : 2   **b** 32   **c** 80
2 a 100   **b** 160
3 1000 g Assam tea   **4** 10 125 people
5 5.5 l of tea   **6 a** 11 pages   **b** 32%
7 Kevin £2040, John £2720
8 20 l lemonade, 0.5 l ginger
9 a 14% (2sf)   **b** 75 good apples

Exercise 3D

1 18 mph   **2** 52.5 mph   **3** 11:50 am

4

	Distance	Time	Av speed
a	150 miles	2 hr	75 mph
b	260 miles	6 hr 30 min	40 mph
c	175 miles	5 hr	35 mph
d	240 km	3 hr	80 km/h
e	544 km	8 hr 30 min	64 km/h
f	325 km	3 hr 15 min	100 km/h
g	215 km	4 hr 18 min	50 km/h

5 a 120 km   **b** 48 km/h
6 a 30 min   **b** 6 mph
7 a 2.25 h   **b** 99 miles
8 a 1.25 h   **b** 1 h 15 min
9 a 48 mph   **b** 6 h 40 min

10 a 10 m/s   **b** $3\frac{1}{3}$ m/s   **c** $16\frac{2}{3}$ m/s
   d $41\frac{2}{3}$ m/s   **e** $20\frac{5}{6}$ m/s
11 a 90 km/h   **b** 43.2 km/h   **c** 14.4 km/h
   d 108 km/h   **e** 1.8 km/h
12 a 64.8 km/h   **b** 27.8 sec (1dp)
   c 8:07 (nearest minute)

Exercise 3E

1 60 g
2 £5.22
3 45 trees
4 a £312.50   **b** 8 textbooks
5 a 56 l   **b** 350 miles
6 a 300 kg   **b** 9 weeks
7 40 sec

Exercise 3F

1 a large jar as more g per £
  b 600 g tin as more g per p
  c 5 kg bag as more kg per £
  d 75 ml tube as more ml per £
  e large box as more g per £
  f large box as more g per £
  g 400 ml bottle as more ml per £
2 large tin (small £5.11/l, medium £4.80/l, large £4.47/l)
3 a 95p   **b** Family size
4 Bashir's
5 Mary
6 Kelly

Exercise 3G

1 a 0.75 g/cm^3
2 $8\frac{1}{3}$ g/cm^3
3 32 g
4 120 cm^3
5 156.8 g
6 3200 cm^3
7 2.72 g/cm^3
8 36 800 kg
9 1.79 g/cm^3 (3 sf)
10 1.6 g/cm^3

ANSWERS TO CHAPTER 4

Quick check

1 a 90 mm^2 **b** 40 cm^2 **c** 21 m^2

2 120 cm^3

Exercise 4A

1 a 8 cm, 25.1 cm, 50.3 cm^2 **b** 5.2 m, 16.3 m, 21.2 m^2
  c 6 cm, 37.7 cm, 113 cm^2 **d** 1.6 m, 10.1 m, 8.04 m^2
2 a 5π cm   **b** 8π cm   **c** 18π m   **d** 12π cm
3 a 25π cm^2 **b** 36π cm^2 **c** 100π cm^2 **d** 0.25π m^2
4 8.80 m

5 a 440 cm   **b** 4
6 1p : 3.1 cm^2, 2p : 5.3 cm^2, 5p : 2.3 cm^2, 10p : 4.5 cm^2
7 7.96 cm
8 38.6 cm
9 (14π + 14) cm
10 a 18π cm^2 **b** 4π cm^2 **c** 48π cm^2
11 a 16π m^2 **b** 21π cm^2 **c** 9π cm^2
12 a Sue 62.8 cm, Julie 69.1 cm, Dave 75.4 cm, Brian 81.7 cm
  b the difference between the distances round the waists of two people is 2π times the difference between their radii
  c 6.28 m

Exercise 4B

1 a 30 cm² **b** 77 cm² **c** 24 cm² **d** 42 cm²
 e 40 m² **f** 6 cm **g** 3 cm **h** 10 cm
2 a 27.5 cm, 36.25 cm² **b** 33.4 cm, 61.2 cm²
 c 38.5 m, 90 m²
3 a 57 m² **b** 702.5 cm² **c** 84 m²
4 a 47 m² **b** 51 m² **c** 86 m²
5 Any five pairs of lengths that add up to 10 cm.
 For example: 1 cm, 9 cm; 2 cm, 8 cm; 3 cm, 7 cm; 4
 cm, 6 cm; 4.5 cm, 5.5 cm
6 80.2% **7** 1 100 000 km²
8

The 2 trapezia form a parallelogram.

 area of parallelogram = perpendicular height × base
  = h × (a + b)
 area of trapezium = ½ area of parallelogram
  = ½ h × (a + b)

Exercise 4C

1 a i 5.59 cm **ii** 22.3 cm²
 b i 8.29 cm **ii** 20.7 cm²
 c i 16.3 cm **ii** 98.0 cm²
 d i 15.9 cm **ii** 55.6 cm²
2 2π cm, 6π cm²
3 a 73.8 cm **b** 20.3 cm
4 a 107 cm² **b** 173 cm² **c** 18.8 cm² **d** 34.9 cm²
5 (36π − 72) cm² **6** 36.5 cm² **7** 6π cm
8 i 13.9 cm **ii** 7.07 cm²

Exercise 4D

1 i a **b** **c**

 ii a 21 cm² **b** 48 cm² **c** 36 m²
 iii a 63 cm³ **b** 432 cm³ **c** 324 m³
2 a 432 m³ **b** 225 m³ **c** 1332 m³
3 525 000 litres **4** 7650 litres
5 a 21 cm³, 210 cm³ **b** 54 cm², 270 cm²
6 146 cm³ **7** 19 600 m³

8 327 litres **9** 1.02 tonnes
Exercise 4E

1 a i 226 cm³ **ii** 207 cm²
 b i 14.9 cm³ **ii** 61.3 cm²
 c i 346 cm³ **ii** 275 cm²
 d i 1060 cm³ **ii** 636 cm²
2 a i 72π cm³ **ii** 48π cm²
 b i 112π cm³ **ii** 56π cm²
 c i 180π cm³ **ii** 60π cm²
 d i 600π m³ **ii** 120π m²
3 £80 **4** 1.23 tonnes
5 5 cm **6** 10 cm
7 3 cm **8** 332 litres
9 1.71 g/cm³ **10** 7.78 g/cm³
11 905 g

Exercise 4F

1 a 56 cm³ **b** 168 cm³ **c** 1040 cm³
 d 84 cm³ **e** 160 cm³
2 270 cm³
3 a 73.3 m³ **b** 45 m³ **c** 3250 cm³
4 208 g
5 1.5 g/cm³
6 a 202 g **b** 441 g **c** 47.25 g
7 a 9 cm **b** 6 cm
8 260 cm³

Exercise 4G

1 a i 3560 cm³ **ii** 1430 cm²
 b i 314 cm³ **ii** 283 cm²
 c i 1020 cm³ **ii** 679 cm²
2 935 g
3 24π cm²
4 283 cm²
5 a 816π cm³ **b** 720π mm³
6 140 g
7 2.81 cm

Exercise 4H

1 a 36π cm³ **b** 288π cm³ **c** 1330π cm³
2 a 36π cm² **b** 100π cm² **c** 196π cm²
3 65 400 cm³, 7850 cm²
4 i 1960 cm² **ii** 8180 cm³
5 125 cm
6 6231
7 a 3.5 cm **b** 3.3 cm

ANSWERS TO CHAPTER 5

Quick check

1 a 2x + 12 **b** 4x − 12 **c** 12x − 6
2 a 5y **b** 4x − 3 **c** −x − 4
3 a 6x **b** 8y² **c** 2c³
4 a x = 1 **b** x = 3 **c** x = 9
 d x = 8 **e** x = 24 **f** x = 15

Exercise 5A

1 a 13 **b** −3 **c** 5
2 a 2 **b** 8 **c** −10
3 a 6 **b** 3 **c** −2
4 a −7 **b** −10 **c** 6.5
5 a −4.8 **b** 48 **c** 32
6 a 1.4 **b** 1.4 **c** −0.4
7 a 13 **b** 74 **c** 17
8 a 75 **b** 22.5 **c** −135
9 a 2.5 **b** −20 **c** 2.5

Exercise 5B

1 $6 + 2m$ **2** $10 + 5l$ **3** $12 - 3y$
4 $20 + 8k$ **5** $6 - 12f$ **6** $10 - 6w$
7 $10k + 15m$ **8** $12d - 8n$ **9** $t^2 + 3t$
10 $k^2 - 3k$ **11** $4t^2 - 4t$ **12** $8k - 2k^2$
13 $8g^2 + 20g$ **14** $15h^2 - 10h$ **15** $y^3 + 5y$
16 $h^4 + 7h$ **17** $k^3 - 5k$ **18** $3t^3 + 12t$
19 $15d^3 - 3d^4$ **20** $6w^3 + 3wt$ **21** $15a^3 - 10ab$
22 $12p^4 - 15mp$ **23** $12h^3 + 8h^2g$ **24** $8m^3 + 2m^4$

Exercise 5C

1 a $7t$ **b** $9d$ **c** $3e$ **d** $2t$ **e** $5t^2$
f $4y^2$ **g** $5ab$ **h** $3a^2d$
2 a $22 + 5t$ **b** $21 + 19k$
c $22 + 2f$ **d** $14 + 3g$
3 a $2 + 2h$ **b** $9g + 5$
c $17k + 16$ **d** $6e + 20$
4 a $4m + 3p + 2mp$ **b** $3k + 4h + 5hk$
c $12r + 24p + 13pr$ **d** $19km + 20k - 6m$
5 a $9t^2 + 13t$ **b** $13y^2 + 5y$
c $10e^2 - 6e$ **d** $14k^2 - 3kp$
6 a $17ab + 12ac + 6bc$ **b** $18yw + 6yt - 8wt$
c $14mn - 15mp - 6np$ **d** $8r^3 - 6r^2$

Exercise 5D

1 $6(m + 2t)$ **2** $3(3t + p)$ **3** $4(2m + 3k)$
4 $4(r + 2t)$ **5** $m(n + 3)$ **6** $g(5g + 3)$
7 $2(2w - 3t)$ **8** $y(3y + 2)$ **9** $t(4t - 3)$
10 $3m(m - p)$ **11** $3p(2p + 3t)$ **12** $2p(4t + 3m)$
13 $4b(2a - c)$ **14** $5bc(b - 2)$ **15** $2b(4ac + 3ed)$
16 $2(2a^2 + 3a + 4)$ **17** $3b(2a + 3c + d)$
18 $t(5t + 4 + a)$ **19** $3mt(2t - 1 + 3m)$
20 $2ab(4b + 1 - 2a)$ **21** $5pt(2t + 3 + p)$
22 a, d, f and **h** do not factorise **b** $m(5 + 2p)$
c $t(t - 7)$ **e** $2m(2m - 3p)$ **g** $a(4a - 5b)$ **i** $b(5a - 3bc)$

Exercise 5E

1 30 **2** 21 **3** 72 **4** 12 **5** 6
6 $10\frac{1}{2}$ **7** -10 **8** 7 **9** 11 **10** -4
11 7 **12** $2\frac{4}{5}$ **13** 1 **14** $11\frac{1}{2}$ **15** $\frac{1}{5}$

Exercise 5F

1 3 **2** 7 **3** 5 **4** 3 **5** 4
6 6 **7** 8 **8** 1 **9** $1\frac{1}{2}$ **10** $2\frac{1}{2}$
11 $\frac{1}{2}$ **12** $1\frac{1}{5}$ **13** 2 **14** -2 **15** -1
16 -2 **17** -2 **18** -1

Exercise 5G

1 $x = 2$ **2** $y = 1$ **3** $a = 7$ **4** $t = 4$
5 $p = 2$ **6** $k = -1$ **7** $m = 3$ **8** $s = -2$
9 $d = 6$ **10** $x = 11$ **11** $y = 1$ **12** $h = 4$
13 $b = 9$ **14** $c = 6$

Exercise 5H

1 55p **2 a** $1\frac{1}{2}$ **b** 2 **3 a** $1\frac{1}{2}$ cm **b** 6.75 cm^2
4 17 sweets **5** 3 years old **6** 9 years old
7 3 cm **8** 5

Exercise 5I

1 a 4 and 5 **b** 4 and 5 **c** 2 and 3
2 3.5 **3** 3.7 **4** 2.5 **5** 1.5 (or -2)
6 a 2.4 **b** 2.8 **c** 3.2
7 b 7.8 cm by 12.8 cm **8** 5 (or -6)

Exercise 5J

1 $x = 4, y = 1$ **2** $x = 1, y = 4$ **3** $x = 3, y = 1$
4 $x = 5, y = -2$ **5** $x = 7, y = 1$ **6** $x = 5, y = \frac{1}{2}$
7 $x = 4\frac{1}{2}, y = 1\frac{1}{2}$ **8** $x = -2, y = 4$ **9** $x = 2\frac{1}{2}, y = -1\frac{1}{2}$
10 $x = 2\frac{1}{4}, y = 6\frac{1}{2}$ **11** $x = 4, y = 3$ **12** $x = 5, y = 3$

Exercise 5K

1 $x = 2, y = -3$ **2** $x = 7, y = 3$ **3** $x = 4, y = 1$
4 $x = 2, y = 5$ **5** $x = 4, y = -3$ **6** $x = 1, y = 7$
7 $x = 2\frac{1}{2}, y = 1\frac{1}{2}$ **8** $x = -1, y = 2\frac{1}{2}$ **9** $x = 6, y = 3$
10 $x = \frac{1}{2}, y = -\frac{3}{4}$ **11** $x = -1, y = 5$ **12** $x = 1\frac{1}{2}, y = \frac{3}{4}$

Exercise 5L

1 $x = 5, y = 1$ **2** $x = 3, y = 8$ **3** $x = 9, y = 1$
4 $x = 7, y = 3$ **5** $x = 4, y = 2$ **6** $x = 6, y = 5$
7 $x = 3, y = -2$ **8** $x = 2, y = \frac{1}{2}$ **9** $x = -2, y = -3$
10 $x = -1, y = 2\frac{1}{2}$ **11** $x = 2\frac{1}{2}, y = -\frac{1}{2}$ **12** $x = -1\frac{1}{2}, y = 4\frac{1}{2}$
13 $x = -\frac{1}{2}, y = -6\frac{1}{2}$ **14** $x = 3\frac{1}{2}, y = 1\frac{1}{2}$ **15** $x = -2\frac{1}{2}, y = -3\frac{1}{2}$

Exercise 5M

1 Amul £7.20, Kim £3.50
2 a $10x + 5y = 3.45, 8x + 10y = 4.38$ **b** £1.71
3 a $6x + 3y = 4.35, 11x + 7y = 8.80$ **b** £5.55
4 84p **5** 10.3 kg **6** £4.40
7 £62 **8** £195 **9** 2 hr 10 min

Exercise 5N

1 $k = \dfrac{T}{3}$ **2** $y = X + 1$ **3** $p = 3Q$

4 $r = \dfrac{A - 9}{4}$ **5** $n = \dfrac{W + 1}{3}$

6 a $m = p - t$ **b** $t = p - m$ **7** $m = gv$

8 $m = \sqrt{t}$ **9** $r = \dfrac{C}{2\pi}$ **10** $b = \dfrac{A}{h}$

11 $l = \dfrac{P - 2w}{2}$ **12** $p = \sqrt{m - 2}$

13 a $a = \dfrac{v - u}{t}$ **b** $t = \dfrac{v - u}{a}$ **14** $d = \sqrt{\dfrac{4A}{\pi}}$

15 a $n = \dfrac{W - t}{3}$ **b** $t = W - 3n$

16 a $y = \dfrac{x + w}{5}$ **b** $w = 5y - x$ **17** $p = \sqrt{\dfrac{k}{2}}$

18 a $t = u^2 - v$ **b** $u = \sqrt{v + t}$

19 a $m = k - n^2$ **b** $n = \sqrt{k - m}$ **20** $r = \sqrt{\dfrac{T}{5}}$

21 a $w = K - 5n^2$ **b** $n = \sqrt{\dfrac{K - w}{5}}$

Quick check

1 5.3   **2** 246.5

3 0.6   **4** 2.8

5 16.1   **6** 0.7

Exercise 6A

1 10.3 cm   **2** 5.9 cm

3 8.5 cm   **4** 20.6 cm

5 18.6 cm   **6** 17.5 cm

7 5 cm   **8** 13 cm

9 10 cm

Exercise 6B

1 a 15 cm   **b** 14.7 cm   **c** 6.3 cm   **d** 18.3 cm

2 a 20.8 m   **b** 15.5 cm   **c** 15.5 m   **d** 12.4 cm

3 a 5 m   **b** 6 m   **c** 3 m   **d** 50 cm

Exercise 6C

1 6.63 m   **2** 2.06 m

3 11.3 m   **4** 19.2 km

5 a 127 m   **b** 99.6 m   **c** 27.4 m

6 4.58 m

7 a 3.87 m   **b** 1.74 m

8 3.16 m   **9** 13 units

10 a 4.74 m   **b** 4.54 m

11 16.5 cm^2 **12** 12.1 m

13 $25^2 = 24^2 + 7^2$: therefore, right-angled

14 7.21 units

Exercise 6D

1 a 32.2 cm^2 **b** 2.83 cm^2 **c** 50.0 cm^2

2 22.2 cm^2

3 15.6 cm^2

4 a

b The areas are 12 cm^2 and 13.6 cm^2 respectively, so triangle with 6 cm, 6 cm, 5 cm sides has the greater area

5 a   **b** 166.3 cm^2

6 259.8 cm^2

7 a 10 cm   **b** 26 cm   **c** 9.6 cm

Exercise 6E

1 a i 14.4 cm   **ii** 13 cm   **iii** 9.4 cm   **b** 15.2 cm

2 No, 6.6 m is longest length

3 a 24 cm and 20.6 cm   **b** 15.0 cm

4 21.3 cm

---

5 a 8.49 m   **b** 9 m

6 a 11.3 cm   **b** 7 cm   **c** 8.06 cm

7 a 50.0 cm   **b** 54.8 cm   **c** 48.3 cm   **d** 27.0 cm

Exercise 6F

1 a 0.682   **b** 0.829   **c** 0.922   **d** 1   **e** 0.707

   f 0.342   **g** 0.375   **h** 0

2 a 0.731   **b** 0.559   **c** 0.388   **d** 0   **e** 0.707

   f 0.940   **g** 0.927   **h** 1

3 45°

4 a i 0.574   **ii** 0.574   **b i** 0.208   **ii** 0.208

   c i 0.391   **ii** 0.391   **d** Same

   e i sin 15° is the same as cos 75°

     ii cos 82° is the same as sin 8°

     iii sin x is the same as cos $(90° - x)$

5 a 0.933   **b** 1.48   **c** 2.38   **d** Infinite   **e** 1

   f 0.364   **g** 0.404   **h** 0

6 a 0.956   **b** 0.899   **c** 2.16   **d** 0.999

   e 0.819   **f** 0.577   **g** 0.469   **h** 0.996

7 Has values > 1

8 a 4.53   **b** 4.46   **c** 6   **d** 0

9 a 10.7   **b** 5.40   **c** Infinite   **d** 0

10 a 3.56   **b** 8.96   **c** 28.4   **d** 8.91

11 a 5.61   **b** 7.08   **c** 6   **d** 10

12 a 1.46   **b** 7.77   **c** 0.087   **d** 7.15

13 a 7.73   **b** 48.6   **c** 2.28   **d** 15.2

14 a 29.9   **b** 44.8   **c** 20.3   **d** 2.38

15 a $\frac{4}{5}, \frac{3}{5}, \frac{4}{3}$ **b** $\frac{5}{13}, \frac{12}{13}, \frac{5}{12}$ **c** $\frac{7}{25}, \frac{24}{25}, \frac{7}{24}$

Exercise 6G

1 a 30°   **b** 51.7°   **c** 39.8°   **d** 61.3°

   e 87.4°   **f** 45.0°

2 a 60°   **b** 50.2°   **c** 2.6°   **d** 45.0

   e 78.5°   **f** 45.6°

3 a 31.0°   **b** 20.8°   **c** 41.8°   **d** 46.4°

   e 69.5°   **f** 77.1°

4 a 53.1°   **b** 41.8°   **c** 44.4°   **d** 56.4°

   e 2.4°   **f** 22.6°

5 a 36.9°   **b** 48.2°   **c** 45.6°   **d** 33.6°

   e 87.6°   **f** 67.4°

6 a 31.0°   **b** 37.9°   **c** 15.9°   **d** 60.9°

   e 57.5°   **f** 50.2°

7 Error message, largest value 1, smallest value –1

8 a i 17.5°   **ii** 72.5°   **iii** 90°   **b** Yes

Exercise 6H

1 a 17.5°   **b** 22.0°   **c** 32.2°

2 a 5.29 cm   **b** 5.75 cm   **c** 13.2 cm

3 a 4.57 cm   **b** 6.86 cm   **c** 100 cm

4 a 5.12 cm   **b** 9.77 cm   **c** 11.7 cm   **d** 15.5 cm

5 a 47.2°   **b** 5.42 cm   **c** 13.7 cm   **d** 38.0°

6 a 6   **b** 15   **c** 30

Exercise 6I

1 a 51.3°   **b** 75.5°   **c** 51.3°

2 a 6.47 cm   **b** 32.6 cm   **c** 137 cm

3 a 7.32 cm   **b** 39.1 cm   **c** 135 cm

4 a 5.35 cm   **b** 14.8 cm   **c** 12.0 cm   **d** 8.62 cm
5 a 5.59 cm   **b** 46.6°   **c** 9.91 cm   **d** 40.1°
6 a 10   **b** 39   **c** 2.5

Exercise 6J
1 a 33.7°   **b** 36.9°   **c** 52.1°
2 a 5.09 cm   **b** 30.4 cm   **c** 1120 cm
3 a 8.24 cm   **b** 62.0 cm   **c** 72.8 cm
4 a 9.02 cm   **b** 7.51 cm   **c** 7.14 cm   **d** 8.90 cm
5 a 13.7 cm   **b** 48.4°   **c** 7.03 cm   **d** 41.2°
6 12, 12, 2

Exercise 6K
1 a 12.6   **b** 59.6   **c** 74.7   **d** 16.0   **e** 67.9   **f** 20.1
2 a 44.4°   **b** 39.8°   **c** 44.4°   **d** 49.5°
    e 58.7°   **f** 38.7°
3 a 67.4°   **b** 11.3   **c** 134   **d** 28.1°   **e** 39.7
    f 263   **g** 50.2°   **h** 51.3°   **i** 138   **j** 22.8
4 b $\sin \theta \div \cos \theta = \frac{b}{c} \div \frac{a}{c} = \frac{b}{a} = \tan \theta$

Exercise 6L
 1 a 65°   **2** 2.05–3.00 m
 3 44°   **4** 6.82 m

5 31°   **6 a** 25°   **b** 2.10 m
7 a 20°   **b** 4.78 m   **8** 42.4 m
9 21.1 m   **10 a** 4 **b** $\frac{4}{5}$, $\frac{3}{4}$ **c i** 1.5 **ii** 20 **iii** 30

Exercise 6M
1 10.1 km   **2** 22°
3 429 m   **4** 156 m
5 a 222 m   **b** 42°   **6 a** 21.5 m   **b** 17.8 m
7 13.4 m   **8** 19°

Exercise 6N
1 a 73.4 km   **b** 15.6 km
2 a 14.7 miles   **b** 8.5 miles
3 120°   **4 a** 59.4 km   **b** 8.4 km
5 a 15.9 km   **b** 24.1 km   **c** 31.2 km   **d** 052°
6 2.28 km
7 a 66.2 km   **b** 11.7 km   **c** 13.1 km   **d** 170°
8 48.4 km, 100°

Exercise 6P
1 5.79 cm **2** 48.2° **3** 7.42 cm **4** 81.6 cm **5** 9.86 m
6 a 36.4 cm² **b** 115 cm² **c** 90.6 cm² **d** 160 cm²

ANSWERS TO CHAPTER 7

Quick check

1 $a = 50°$

2 $b = 140°$

3 $c = d = 65°$

Exercise 7A
1 $a = b = 70°$, $c = 50°$, $d = 80°$, $e = 55°$, $f = 70°$,
    $g = h = 57.5°$
2

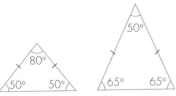

3 a $a = 110°$, $b = 55°$ **b** $c = e = 105°$, $d = 75°$
    c $f = 135°$, $g = 25°$ **d** $e = f = 94°$
    e $f = l = 105°$, $k = 75°$ **f** $m = o = 49°$, $n = 131°$
4 40°, 40°, 100°
5 $a = b = 65°$, $c = d = 115°$, $e = f = 65°$, $g = 80°$,
    $h = 60°$, $i = 60°$, $j = 60°$, $k = 20°$
6 a $x = 25°$, $y = 15°$ **b** $x = 7°$, $y = 31°$
    c $x = 60°$, $y = 30°$
7 a $x = 50°$: 60°, 70°, 120°, 110° – possibly trapezium
    b $x = 60°$: 50°, 130°, 50°, 130° – parallelogram or
        isosceles trapezium
    c $x = 30°$: 20°, 60°, 140°, 140° – possibly kite
    d $x = 20°$: 90°, 90°, 90°, 90° – square or rectangle

Exercise 7B
1 a 1440°   **b** 2340°   **c** 17 640°   **d** 7740°
2 a 150°   **b** 162°   **c** 140°   **d** 174°
3 a 9   **b** 15   **c** 102   **d** 50
4 a 15   **b** 36   **c** 24   **d** 72
5 a 12   **b** 9   **c** 20   **d** 40
6 a 130°   **b** 95°   **c** 130°
7 a 50°   **b** 40°   **c** 59°
8 Hexagon
9 a Octagon   **b** 89°
10 a i 71°   **ii** 109°   **iii** Equal
    b If S = sum of the two opposite interior angles,
        then $S + I = 180$ (angles in a triangle), and we know E
        $+ I = 180$ (angles on a straight line),
        so $S + I = E + I$, therefore $S = E$

Exercise 7C
1 a 56°   **b** 62°   **c** 105°   **d** 55°   **e** 45°
    f 30°   **g** 60°   **h** 145°
2 a 55°   **b** 52°   **c** 50°   **d** 24°   **e** 39°
    f 80°   **g** 34°   **h** 30°
3 a 41°   **b** 49°   **c** 41°
4 a 72°   **b** 37°   **c** 72°
5 a $x = y = 40°$ **b** $x = 131°$, $y = 111°$
    c $x = 134°$, $y = 23°$ **d** $x = 32°$, $y = 19°$
    e $x = 59°$, $y = 121°$ **f** $x = 155°$, $y = 12.5°$
6 68°
7 a x **b** $2x$
    c $\angle ABC = (x + y)$ and $\angle AOC = 2(x + y)$

Exercise 7D

1 a $a = 50°$, $b = 95°$ **b** $c = 92°$, $x = 90°$
   c $d = 110°$, $e = 110°$, $f = 70°$
   d $g = 105°$, $h = 99°$ **e** $j = 89°$, $k = 89°$, $l = 91°$
   f $m = 120°$, $n = 40°$ **g** $p = 44°$, $q = 68°$
   h $x = 40°$, $y = 34°$
2 a $x = 26°$, $y = 128°$ **b** $x = 48°$, $y = 78°$
   c $x = 133°$, $y = 47°$ **d** $x = 36°$, $y = 72°$
   e $x = 55°$, $y = 125°$ **f** $x = 35°$
   g $x = 48°$, $y = 45°$ **h** $x = 66°$, $y = 52°$
3 a $x = 49°$, $y = 49°$ **b** $x = 70°$, $y = 20°$
   c $x = 80°$, $y = 100°$ **d** $x = 100°$, $y = 75°$
4 a $x = 50°$, $y = 62°$ **b** $x = 92°$, $y = 88°$
   c $x = 93°$, $y = 42°$ **d** $x = 55°$, $y = 75°$
5 a $x = 95°$, $y = 138°$ **b** $x = 14°$, $y = 62°$
   c $x = 32°$, $y = 48°$ **d** $52°$
6 a $71°$ **b** $125.5°$ **c** $54.5°$
7 a x **b** $360° - 2x$
   c $\angle ADC = \frac{1}{2}$ reflex $\angle AOC = 180° - x$,
    so $\angle ADC + \angle ABC = 180°$

Exercise 7E

1 a $38°$ **b** $110°$ **c** $15°$ **d** $45°$

2 a 6 cm   **b** 10.8 cm   **c** 3.21 cm   **d** 8 cm
3 a $x = 12°$, $y = 156°$ **b** $x = 100°$, $y = 50°$
   c $x = 62°$, $y = 28°$ **d** $x = 30°$, $y = 60°$
4 a $62°$ **b** $66°$ **c** $19°$ **d** $20°$
5 19.5 cm
6 a $\angle AOB = \cos^{-1}\dfrac{OA}{OB} = \cos^{-1}\dfrac{OC}{OB} = \angle COB$

   b As $\angle AOB = \angle COB$, so $\angle ABO = \angle CBO$, so OB bisects $\angle ABC$

Exercise 7F

1 a $a = 65°$, $b = 75°$, $c = 40°$
   b $d = 79°$, $e = 58°$, $f = 43°$
   c $g = 41°$, $h = 76°$, $i = 76°$
   d $k = 80°$, $m = 52°$, $n = 80°$
2 a $a = 75°$, $b = 75°$, $c = 75°$, $d = 30°$
   b $a = 47°$, $b = 86°$, $c = 86°$, $d = 47°$
   c $a = 53°$, $b = 53°$ **d** $a = 55°$
3 a $36°$ **b** $70°$
4 a $x = 25°$ **b** $x = 46°$, $y = 69°$, $z = 65°$
   c $x = 38°$, $y = 70°$, $z = 20°$ **d** $x = 48°$, $y = 42°$
5 a $2x$ **b** $90° - x$ **c** $\angle OPT = 90°$, so $\angle APT = x$

ANSWERS TO CHAPTER 8

Quick check

Trace shape **a** and check whether it fits exactly on top of the others. You should find that shape **b** is not congruent to the others.

Exercise 8A

1 a Yes, SAS   **b** Yes, SSS   **c** No   **d** No
   e Yes, ASA   **f** Yes, RHS   **g** Yes, SSS
   h Yes, ASA
2 a Yes, SSS. A to R, B to P, C to Q   **b** No
   c Yes, SAS. A to R, B to Q, C to P   **d** No
3 i $60°$ **ii** $80°$ **iii** $40°$ **iv** 5 cm
4 i $110°$ **ii** $55°$ **iii** $85°$ **iv** $110°$ **v** 4 cm
5 SSS or RHS
6 SSS or SAS or RHS

Exercise 8B

1 a i $\begin{pmatrix}1\\3\end{pmatrix}$ **ii** $\begin{pmatrix}4\\2\end{pmatrix}$ **iii** $\begin{pmatrix}2\\-1\end{pmatrix}$ **iv** $\begin{pmatrix}5\\1\end{pmatrix}$
   v $\begin{pmatrix}-1\\6\end{pmatrix}$ **vi** $\begin{pmatrix}4\\6\end{pmatrix}$
  b i $\begin{pmatrix}-1\\-3\end{pmatrix}$ **ii** $\begin{pmatrix}3\\-1\end{pmatrix}$ **iii** $\begin{pmatrix}1\\-4\end{pmatrix}$ **iv** $\begin{pmatrix}4\\-2\end{pmatrix}$
   v $\begin{pmatrix}-2\\3\end{pmatrix}$ **vi** $\begin{pmatrix}3\\3\end{pmatrix}$
  c i $\begin{pmatrix}-4\\-2\end{pmatrix}$ **ii** $\begin{pmatrix}-3\\1\end{pmatrix}$ **iii** $\begin{pmatrix}-2\\-3\end{pmatrix}$ **iv** $\begin{pmatrix}1\\-1\end{pmatrix}$
   v $\begin{pmatrix}-5\\4\end{pmatrix}$ **vi** $\begin{pmatrix}0\\4\end{pmatrix}$

  d i $\begin{pmatrix}3\\2\end{pmatrix}$ **ii** $\begin{pmatrix}-4\\2\end{pmatrix}$ **iii** $\begin{pmatrix}5\\-4\end{pmatrix}$ **iv** $\begin{pmatrix}-2\\-7\end{pmatrix}$
   v $\begin{pmatrix}5\\0\end{pmatrix}$ **vi** $\begin{pmatrix}1\\-5\end{pmatrix}$

2

3 a $\begin{pmatrix}-3\\-1\end{pmatrix}$ **b** $\begin{pmatrix}4\\-4\end{pmatrix}$ **c** $\begin{pmatrix}-5\\-2\end{pmatrix}$ **d** $\begin{pmatrix}4\\7\end{pmatrix}$ **e** $\begin{pmatrix}-1\\5\end{pmatrix}$
  f $\begin{pmatrix}1\\6\end{pmatrix}$ **g** $\begin{pmatrix}-4\\4\end{pmatrix}$ **h** $\begin{pmatrix}-4\\-7\end{pmatrix}$

4 $10 \times 10 = 100$ (including $\begin{pmatrix}0\\0\end{pmatrix}$)

Exercise 8C

1

2 a–e

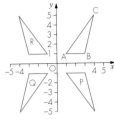

f Reflection in the *y*-axis

3 b A′(2, −1), B′(5, 0), C′(−3, −3), D′(3, 2)
c *y*-value changes sign **d** (*a*, −*b*)

4 b A′(−2, 1), B′(0, 5), C′(−3, −2), D′(4, −3)
c *x*-value changes sign **d** (−*a*, *b*)

5

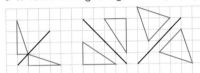

6 a–i

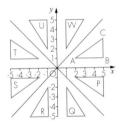 **7**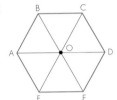

j A reflection in *y* = *x*

8 c A′(1, 2), B′(0, 5), C′(2, −3), D′(−4, −2)
d Coordinates are reversed: *x* becomes *y* and
y becomes *x* **e** (*b*, *a*)

9 c A′(−1, −2), B′(−5, 0), C′(2, −3) D′(3, 4)
d Coordinates are reversed and change sign,
x becomes −*y* and *y* becomes −*x* **e** (−*b*, −*a*)

Exercise 8D

1 a

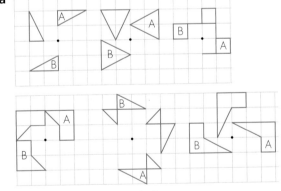

b i Rotation 90° anticlockwise
ii Rotation 180°

2

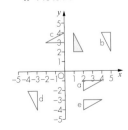

3 a 90° anticlockwise
b 270° anticlockwise
c 300° clockwise
d 260° clockwise

4 c ii A′(2, −1), B′(4, −2), C′(1, −4)
c iii Original coordinates (*x*, *y*) become (*y*, −*x*) **iv** Yes

5 ii A′(−1, −2), B′(−2, −4), C′(−4, −1)
iii Original coordinates (*x*, *y*) become (−*x*, −*y*) **iv** Yes

6 ii A′(−2, 1), B′(−4, 2), C′(−1, 4)
iii Original coordinates (*x*, *y*) become (−*y*, *x*) **iv** Yes

7 Show by drawing a shape or use the fact that (*a*, *b*)
becomes (*a*, −*b*) after reflection in the *x*-axis, and
(*a*, −*b*) becomes (−*a*, −*b*) after reflection in the *y*-axis,
which is equivalent to a single rotation of 180°

8 Show by drawing a shape or use the fact that (*a*, *b*)
becomes (*b*, *a*) after reflection in the line *y* = *x*, and (*b*, *a*)
becomes (−*a*, −*b*) after reflection in the line
y = −*x*, which is equivalent to a single rotation of 180°

9 a

b i Rotation 60° clockwise about O
ii Rotation 120° clockwise about O
iii Rotation 180° about O
iv Rotation 240° clockwise about O
c i Rotation 60° clockwise about O
ii Rotation 180° about O

Exercise 8E

1

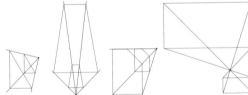

2 d All shapes are the same.

3

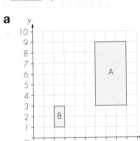

4 a

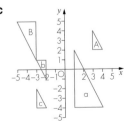

b 3:1
c 3:1
d 9:1

5 a–c

d Scale factor $-\frac{1}{2}$, centre (1, 3)

e Scale factor –2, centre (1, 3)

f Scale factor –1, centre (–2.5, –1.5)

g Scale factor –1, centre (–2.5, –1.5)

h Same centres, and the scale factor are reciprocals of each other

Exercise 8F

1 A translation $\begin{pmatrix} 1 \\ -2 \end{pmatrix}$, B reflection in y-axis,

C rotation 90° clockwise about (0, 0),

D reflection in $x = 3$, E reflection in $y = 4$,

F enlargement by scale factor 2, centre (0, 1)

2 **a** T_1 to T_2: rotation 90° clockwise about (0, 0)

b T_1 to T_6: rotation 90° anticlockwise about (0, 0)

c T_2 to T_3: translation $\begin{pmatrix} 2 \\ 2 \end{pmatrix}$

d T_6 to T_2: rotation 180° about (0, 0)

e T_6 to T_5: reflection in y-axis

f T_5 to T_4: translation $\begin{pmatrix} 4 \\ 0 \end{pmatrix}$

3 a–d

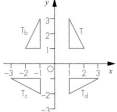

e T_d to T: rotation 90° anticlockwise about (0,0)

4 (–4, –3)

5 **a** (–5, 2)   **b** Reflection in y-axis

6 (3, 1)

7 Reflection in x-axis, translation $\begin{pmatrix} 0 \\ -5 \end{pmatrix}$, rotation 90° clockwise about (0, 0)

8 Translation $\begin{pmatrix} 0 \\ -8 \end{pmatrix}$, reflection in x-axis, rotation 90° clockwise about (0, 0)

9 Rotation 180° clockwise or anticlockwise about (0, 0)

ANSWERS TO CHAPTER 9

Exercise 9B

4 **a** **i** Construct 60° angle and bisect it

  ii Bisect 30° angle

  iii Construct 90° angle and bisect it to get 45°, then bisect 45° angle

  iv Construct 45° angle on upper arm of 30° angle

8 **b** AC = 5.1 cm, BC = 6.3 cm

9 **b** PR = 5.9 cm, RQ = 4.1 cm

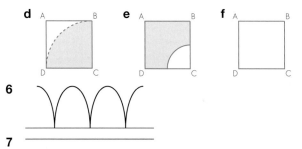

6

7

Exercise 9C

1 **a** Circle with radius 2 cm

  b Circle with radius 4 cm

  c Circle with radius 5 cm

2 **a**   **b**

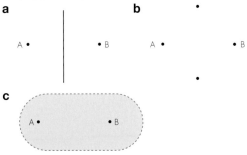

  c

3 Circle with radius 4 m

4

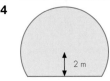

5 **a**   **b**   **c**

Exercise 9D

1

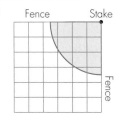

2

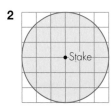

3

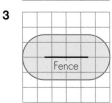

4

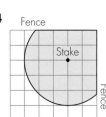

5

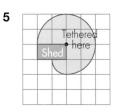

6

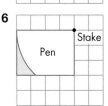

7

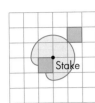

Stake

8 a Sketch should show a circle of radius 6 cm around London and one of radius 4cm around Glasgow.
  b No
  c Yes

9 a Yes
  b Sketch should show a circle of radius 4 cm around Leeds and one of radius 4cm around Exeter. The area where they overlap should be shaded.
10 a This is the perpendicular bisector of the line from York to Birmingham. It should pass just below Manchester and just through the top of Norwich.
  b Sketch should show a circle of radius 7cm around Glasgow and one of radius 5 cm around London.
  c The transmitter can be built anywhere on line constructed in part **a** that is within the area shown in part **b**.
11 Sketch should show two circles around Birmingham, one of radius 3 cm and one of radius 5cm. The area of good reception is the area between the two circles.
12 Sketch should show a circle of radius 6 cm around Glasgow, 2 circles around York, one of radius 4 cm and one of radius 6 cm and a circle around London of radius 8 cm. The small area in the Irish sea that is between the 2 circles around York and inside both the circle around Glasgow and the circle around London is where the boat can be.

13 Sketch should show 2 circles around Newcastle upon Tyne, one of radius 4 cm and one of radius 6 cm, and two circles around Bristol, one of radius 3 cm and one of radius 5 cm. The area that is between both pairs of circles is the area that should be shaded.
14 Sketch should show the perpendicular bisector of the line running from Newcastle upon Tyne to Manchester and that of the line running from Sheffield to Norwich. Where the lines cross is where the oil rig is located.
15 Sketch should show the perpendicular bisector of the line running from Glasgow to Norwich and that of the line running from Norwich to Exeter. Where the lines cross is where Fred's house is.
16 Sketch should show the bisectors of the angles made by the piers and the sea wall at points A and B. These are the paths of each boat.
17 a If $x = 3$, and $y = 4$, then $x^2 + y^2 = 3^2 + 4^2 = 9 + 16 = 25$. Therefore the point (3, 4) lies on the circle. If $x = -4$, and $y = 3$, then $x^2 + y^2 = (-4)^2 + 3^2 = 16 + 9 = 25$. Therefore the point (−4, 3) lies on the circle.
  b

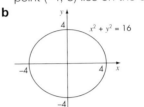

$x^2 + y^2 = 16$

ANSWERS TO CHAPTER 10

Quick check

1 a 0.6 **b** 0.44 **c** 0.375
2 a $\frac{17}{100}$ **b** $\frac{16}{25}$ **c** $\frac{429}{500}$
3 a $\frac{13}{15}$ **b** $\frac{9}{40}$
4 a 5 **b** 4

Exercise 10A
1 a 2^4 **b** 3^5 **c** 7^2 **d** 5^3 **e** 10^7 **f** 6^4
  g 4^1 **h** 1^7 **i** 0.5^4 **j** 100^3
2 a $3 \times 3 \times 3 \times 3$ **b** $9 \times 9 \times 9$ **c** 6×6
  d $10 \times 10 \times 10 \times 10 \times 10$
  e $2 \times 2 \times 2 \times 2 \times 2 \times 2 \times 2 \times 2 \times 2 \times 2$
  f 8 **g** $0.1 \times 0.1 \times 0.1$ **h** 2.5×2.5
  i $0.7 \times 0.7 \times 0.7$ **j** 1000×1000
3 a 16 **b** 243 **c** 49 **d** 125 **e** 10 000 000
  f 1296 **g** 4 **h** 1 **i** 0.0625 **j** 1 000 000
4 a 81 **b** 729 **c** 36 **d** 100 000 **e** 1024
  f 8 **g** 0.001 **h** 6.25 **i** 0.343 **j** 1 000 000
5 a 1 **b** 4 **c** 1 **d** 1 **e** 1
6 Any power of 1 is equal to 1.
7 10^6
8 10^6
9 a 1 **b** −1 **c** 1 **d** 1 **e** −1
10 a 1 **b** −1 **c** −1 **d** 1 **e** 1

Exercise 10B
1 a $\frac{1}{5^3}$ **b** $\frac{1}{6}$ **c** $\frac{1}{10^5}$ **d** $\frac{1}{3^2}$ **e** $\frac{1}{8^2}$

  f $\frac{1}{9}$ **g** $\frac{1}{w^2}$ **h** $\frac{1}{t}$ **i** $\frac{1}{x^m}$ **j** $\frac{4}{m^3}$
2 a 3^{-2} **b** 5^{-1} **c** 10^{-3} **d** m^{-1} **e** t^{-n}
3 a i 2^4 **ii** 2^{-1} **iii** 2^{-4} **iv** -2^3
  b i 10^3 **ii** 10^{-1} **iii** 10^{-2} **iv** 10^6
  c i 5^3 **ii** 5^{-1} **iii** 5^{-2} **iv** 5^{-4}
  d i 3^2 **ii** 3^{-3} **iii** 3^{-4} **iv** -3^5
4 a $\frac{5}{x^3}$ **b** $\frac{6}{t}$ **c** $\frac{7}{m^2}$ **d** $\frac{4}{q^4}$ **e** $\frac{10}{y^5}$
  f $\frac{1}{2x^3}$ **g** $\frac{1}{2m}$ **h** $\frac{3}{4t^4}$ **i** $\frac{4}{5y^3}$ **j** $\frac{7}{8x^5}$
5 a $7x^{-3}$ **b** $10p^{-1}$ **c** $5t^{-2}$ **d** $8m^{-5}$ **e** $3y^{-1}$
6 a i 25 **ii** $\frac{1}{125}$ **iii** $\frac{4}{5}$ **b i** 64 **ii** $\frac{1}{16}$ **iii** $\frac{5}{256}$
  c i 8 **ii** $\frac{1}{32}$ **iii** $4\frac{1}{2}$ **d** 1 000 000 **ii** $\frac{1}{1000}$ **iii** $\frac{1}{4}$

Exercise 10C
1 a 5^4 **b** 5^3 **c** 5^2 **d** 5^3 **e** 5^{-5}
2 a 6^3 **b** 6^0 **c** 6^6 **d** 6^{-7} **e** 6^2
3 a a^3 **b** a^5 **c** a^7 **d** a^4 **e** a^2 **f** a^1
4 a 4^6 **b** 4^{15} **c** 4^6 **d** 4^{-6} **e** 4^6 **f** 4^0
5 a $6a^5$ **b** $9a^2$ **c** $8a^6$ **d** $-6a^4$ **e** $8a^8$
  f $-10a^{-3}$
6 a $3a$ **b** $4a^3$ **c** $3a^4$ **d** $6a^{-1}$ **e** $4a^7$ **f** $5a^{-4}$
7 a $8a^5b^4$ **b** $10a^3b$ **c** $30a^{-2}b^{-2}$ **d** $2ab^3$
  e $8a^{-5}b^7$
8 a $3a^3b^2$ **b** $3a^2c^4$ **c** $8a^2b^2c^3$
9 $1 = \dfrac{a^x}{a^x} = a^x \div a^x = a^{x-x} = a^0$

Exercise 10D

1 5	**2** 10	**3** 8	**4** 9	**5** 25	**6** 3
7 4	**8** 10	**9** 5	**10** 8	**11** 12	**12** 20
13 5	**14** 3	**15** 10	**16** 3	**17** 2	**18** 2
19 6	**20** 6	**21** $\frac{1}{4}$	**22** $\frac{1}{2}$	**23** $\frac{1}{3}$	**24** $\frac{1}{5}$
25 $\frac{1}{10}$	**26** $\frac{5}{6}$	**27** $1\frac{2}{3}$	**28** $\frac{8}{9}$	**29** $1\frac{4}{5}$	**30** $\frac{5}{8}$
31 $\frac{3}{5}$	**32** $\frac{1}{4}$	**33** $2\frac{1}{2}$	**34** $\frac{4}{5}$	**35** $1\frac{1}{7}$	

36 $(x^{\frac{1}{n}})^n = x^{\frac{1}{n} \times n} = x^1 = x$, but

$(\sqrt[n]{x})^n = \sqrt[n]{x} \times \sqrt[n]{x} \dots n$ times $= x$, so $x^{\frac{1}{n}} = \sqrt[n]{x}$

Exercise 10E

1 a 16   **b** 25   **c** 216   **d** 81

2 a $t^{\frac{2}{3}}$ **b** $m^{\frac{3}{4}}$ **c** $k^{\frac{2}{5}}$ **d** $x^{\frac{3}{2}}$

3 a 4   **b** 9   **c** 64   **d** 3125

4 a $\frac{1}{5}$ **b** $\frac{1}{6}$ **c** $\frac{1}{2}$ **d** $\frac{1}{3}$ **e** $\frac{1}{4}$ **f** $\frac{1}{2}$ **g** $\frac{1}{2}$

   h $\frac{1}{3}$

5 a $\frac{1}{125}$ **b** $\frac{1}{216}$ **c** $\frac{1}{8}$ **d** $\frac{1}{27}$ **e** $\frac{1}{64}$ **f** $\frac{1}{4}$

   g $\frac{1}{256}$ **h** $\frac{1}{9}$

6 a $\frac{1}{100\,000}$ **b** $\frac{1}{12}$ **c** $\frac{1}{25}$ **d** $\frac{1}{27}$ **e** $\frac{1}{32}$ **f** $\frac{1}{32}$

   g $\frac{1}{81}$ **h** $\frac{1}{13}$

Exercise 10F

1 a 31   **b** 310   **c** 3100   **d** 31 000

2 a 65   **b** 650   **c** 6500   **d** 65 000

3 a 0.31   **b** 0.031   **c** 0.0031   **d** 0.000 31

4 a 0.65   **b** 0.065   **c** 0.0065   **d** 0.000 65

5 a 250   **b** 34.5   **c** 4670   **d** 346

   e 207.89   **f** 56 780   **g** 246   **h** 0.76

   i 999 000   **j** 23 456   **k** 98 765.4   **l** 43 230 000

   m 345.78   **n** 6000   **o** 56.7   **p** 560 045

6 a 0.025   **b** 0.345   **c** 0.004 67

   d 3.46   **e** 0.207 89   **f** 0.056 78

   g 0.0246   **h** 0.0076   **i** 0.000 000 999

   j 2.3456   **k** 0.098 765 4   **l** 0.000 043 23

   m 0.000 000 034 578   **n** 0.000 000 000 06

   o 0.000 000 567   **p** 0.005 600 45

7 a 230   **b** 578 900   **c** 4790   **d** 57 000 000

   e 216   **f** 10 500   **g** 0.000 32   **h** 9870

8 a, b and **c**

Exercise 10G

1 a 0.31   **b** 0.031   **c** 0.0031   **d** 0.000 31

2 a 0.65   **b** 0.065   **c** 0.0065   **d** 0.000 65

3 a $9\,999\,999\,999 \times 10^{99}$

   b $0.000\,000\,001 \times 10^{-99}$ (depending on number of digits displayed)

4 a 31   **b** 310   **c** 3100   **d** 31 000

5 a 65   **b** 650   **c** 6500   **d** 65 000

6 a 250   **b** 34.5   **c** 0.004 67

   d 34.6   **e** 0.020 789   **f** 5678

   g 246   **h** 7600   **i** 89 700

   j 0.008 65   **k** 60 000 000   **l** 0.000 567

7 a 2.5×10^2 **b** 3.45×10^{-1} **c** 4.67×10^4

   d 3.4×10^9 **e** 2.078×10^{10} **f** 5.678×10^{-4}

   g 2.46×10^3 **h** 7.6×10^{-2} **i** 7.6×10^{-4}

   j 9.99×10^{-1} **k** 2.3456×10^2

   l $9.876\,54 \times 10^1$ **m** 6×10^{-4}

   n 5.67×10^{-3} **o** $5.600\,45 \times 10^1$

8 2.7797×10^4

9 $3.036\,21 \times 10^5$, 3×10^1, $4.002\,136 \times 10^6$

10 1.298×10^7, 2.997×10^9, 9.3×10^4

Exercise 10H

1 a 5.67×10^3 **b** 6×10^2 **c** 3.46×10^{-1}

   d 7×10^{-4} **e** 5.6×10^2 **f** 6×10^5

   g 7×10^3 **h** 1.6   **i** 2.3×10^7

   j 3×10^{-6} **k** 2.56×10^6 **l** 4.8×10^2

   m 1.12×10^2 **n** 6×10^5 **o** 2.8×10^6

2 a 1.08×10^8 **b** 4.8×10^6 **c** 1.2×10^9

   d 1.08   **e** 6.4×10^2 **f** 1.2×10^1

   g 2.88   **h** 2.5×10^7 **i** 8×10^{-6}

3 a 1.1×10^8 **b** 6.1×10^6 **c** 1.6×10^9

   d 3.9×10^{-2} **e** 9.6×10^8 **f** 4.6×10^{-7}

   g 2.1×10^3 **h** 3.6×10^7 **i** 1.5×10^2

   j 3.5×10^9 **k** 1.6×10^4

4 a 2.7×10^7 **b** 1.6×10^6 **c** 2×10^7

   d 4×10^{-2} **e** 2×10^1 **f** 6×10^{-2}

   g 2×10^{-1} **h** 5×10^8 **i** 2×10^5

5 a 5.4×10^5 **b** 2.9×10^9 **c** 1.1×10^{-2}

   d 6.3×10^{-4} **e** 2.8×10^2 **f** 5.5×10^{-2}

   g 4.9×10^8 **h** 8.6×10^2

6 2×10^{13}, 1×10^{-10}, mass $= 2 \times 10^3$ g (2 kg)

7 a (2^{63}) 9.2×10^{18} grains

   b $(1 + 9.2 \times 10^{18}) \times 32 = 3 \times 10^{20}$ grains

8 a 6×10^7 sq miles   **b** 30%

9 1.5×10^7 sq miles   **10** 5×10^4

11 2.3×10^5 **12** 3.2×10^8 kg

13 250   **14** 9.41×10^4

Exercise 10I

1 a 0.5 **b** $0.\dot{3}$ **c** 0.25 **d** 0.2 **e** $0.1\dot{6}$

   f $0.\dot{1}42\,85\dot{7}$ **g** 0.125 **h** $0.\dot{1}$ **i** 0.1

   j $0.\dot{0}7692\dot{3}$

2 b They all contain the same pattern of digits, starting at a different point in the pattern.

3 $0.\dot{1}$, $0.\dot{2}$, $0.\dot{3}$, etc. Digit in decimal fraction same as numerator.

4 $0.\dot{0}\dot{9}$, $0.\dot{1}\dot{8}$, $0.\dot{2}\dot{7}$, etc. Sum of digits in recurring pattern = 9. First digit is one less than numerator.

5 0.444 ..., 0.454 ..., 0.428 ..., 0.409 ..., 0.432 ...,

   0.461 ..., $\frac{9}{22}, \frac{3}{7}, \frac{16}{37}, \frac{4}{9}, \frac{5}{11}, \frac{6}{13}$

6 $\frac{38}{120}, \frac{35}{120}, \frac{36}{120}, \frac{48}{120}, \frac{50}{120}, \frac{7}{24}, \frac{3}{10}, \frac{19}{60}, \frac{2}{5}, \frac{5}{12}$

7 a $\frac{1}{8}$ **b** $\frac{17}{50}$ **c** $\frac{29}{40}$ **d** $\frac{5}{16}$ **e** $\frac{89}{100}$ **f** $\frac{1}{20}$

   g $\frac{27}{20}$ **h** $\frac{7}{32}$

8 a $0.08\dot{3}$ **b** 0.0625   **c** 0.05   **d** 0.04   **e** 0.02

9 a $\frac{4}{3}$ **b** $\frac{6}{5}$ **c** $\frac{5}{2}$ **d** $\frac{10}{7}$ **e** $\frac{20}{11}$ **f** $\frac{15}{4}$

10 a 0.75, $1.\dot{3}$; $0.8\dot{3}$, 1.2; 0.4, 2.5; 0.7, $1.\dot{4}28\,5\dot{7}$;

   0.55, $1.8\dot{1}$; $0.2\dot{6}$, 3.75

   b no

11 1

12 a $24.242\,42\dots$ **b** 24   **c** $\frac{24}{99}$

13 a $\frac{8}{9}$ **b** $\frac{34}{99}$ **c** $\frac{5}{11}$ **d** $\frac{21}{37}$ **e** $\frac{4}{9}$ **f** $\frac{2}{45}$

   g $\frac{13}{90}$ **h** $\frac{1}{22}$ **i** $2\frac{7}{9}$ **j** $7\frac{7}{11}$ **k** $3\frac{1}{3}$ **l** $2\frac{2}{33}$

14 a true   **b** true   **c** recurring

15 a $\frac{9}{9}$ **b** $\frac{45}{90} = \frac{1}{2} = 0.5$

Exercise 10J

1 a $\sqrt{6}$ **b** $\sqrt{15}$ **c** 2 **d** 4 **e** $2\sqrt{10}$ **f** 3 **g** $2\sqrt{3}$
h $\sqrt{21}$ **i** $\sqrt{14}$ **j** 6 **k** 6 **l** $\sqrt{30}$

2 a 2 **b** $\sqrt{5}$ **c** $\sqrt{6}$ **d** $\sqrt{3}$ **e** $\sqrt{5}$ **f** 1 **g** $\sqrt{3}$ **h** $\sqrt{7}$
i 2 **j** $\sqrt{6}$ **k** 1 **l** 3

3 a $2\sqrt{3}$ **b** 15 **c** $4\sqrt{2}$ **d** $4\sqrt{3}$ **e** $8\sqrt{5}$
f $3\sqrt{3}$ **g** 24 **h** $3\sqrt{7}$ **i** $2\sqrt{7}$ **j** $6\sqrt{5}$
k $6\sqrt{3}$ **l** 30

4 a $\sqrt{3}$ **b** 1 **c** $2\sqrt{2}$ **d** $\sqrt{2}$ **e** $\sqrt{5}$
f $\sqrt{3}$ **g** $\sqrt{2}$ **h** $\sqrt{7}$ **i** $\sqrt{7}$ **j** $2\sqrt{3}$
k $2\sqrt{3}$ **l** 1

5 a a **b** 1 **c** $\sqrt{a}$

6 a $3\sqrt{2}$ **b** $2\sqrt{6}$ **c** $2\sqrt{3}$ **d** $5\sqrt{2}$ **e** $2\sqrt{2}$
f $3\sqrt{3}$ **g** $4\sqrt{3}$ **h** $5\sqrt{3}$ **i** $3\sqrt{5}$ **j** $3\sqrt{7}$
k $4\sqrt{2}$ **l** $10\sqrt{2}$ **m** $10\sqrt{10}$ **n** $5\sqrt{10}$ **o** $7\sqrt{2}$
p $9\sqrt{3}$

7 a 36 **b** $16\sqrt{30}$ **c** 54 **d** 32 **e** $48\sqrt{6}$
f $48\sqrt{6}$ **g** $18\sqrt{15}$ **h** 84 **i** 64 **j** 100
k 50 **l** 56

8 a $20\sqrt{6}$ **b** $6\sqrt{15}$ **c** 24 **d** 16 **e** $12\sqrt{10}$
f 18 **g** $20\sqrt{3}$ **h** $10\sqrt{21}$ **i** $6\sqrt{14}$ **j** 36
k 24 **l** $12\sqrt{30}$

9 a 6 **b** $3\sqrt{5}$ **c** $6\sqrt{6}$ **d** $2\sqrt{3}$ **e** $4\sqrt{5}$
f 5 **g** $7\sqrt{3}$ **h** $2\sqrt{7}$ **i** 6 **j** $2\sqrt{7}$
k 5 **l** 24

10 a $2\sqrt{3}$ **b** 4 **c** $6\sqrt{2}$ **d** $4\sqrt{2}$ **e** $6\sqrt{5}$
f $24\sqrt{3}$ **g** $3\sqrt{2}$ **h** $\sqrt{7}$ **i** $10\sqrt{7}$ **j** $8\sqrt{3}$
k $10\sqrt{3}$ **l** 6

11 a abc **b** $\frac{a}{c}$ **c** $c\sqrt{b}$
12 a 20 **b** 24 **c** 10 **d** 24 **e** 3 **f** 6
13 a $\frac{3}{4}$ **b** $8\frac{1}{3}$ **c** $\frac{5}{16}$ **d** 12 **e** 2

Exercise 10K

1 $11 + 6\sqrt{2}$

2 a $2\sqrt{3} - 3$ **b** $3\sqrt{2} - 8$ **c** $10 + 4\sqrt{5}$
d $12\sqrt{7} - 42$ **e** $15\sqrt{2} - 24$ **f** $9 - \sqrt{3}$

3 a $2\sqrt{3}$ **b** $1 + \sqrt{5}$ **c** $-1 - \sqrt{2}$ **d** $\sqrt{7} - 30$ **e** -41
f $7 + 3\sqrt{6}$ **g** $9 + 4\sqrt{5}$ **h** $3 - 2\sqrt{2}$
i $11 + 6\sqrt{2}$

4 a $3\sqrt{2}$ cm **b** $2\sqrt{3}$ cm **c** $2\sqrt{10}$ cm

5 a $\sqrt{3} - 1$ cm² **b** $2\sqrt{5} + 5\sqrt{2}$ cm²
c $2\sqrt{3} + 18$ cm²

6 a $\dfrac{\sqrt{3}}{3}$ **b** $\dfrac{\sqrt{2}}{2}$ **c** $\dfrac{\sqrt{5}}{5}$ **d** $\dfrac{\sqrt{3}}{6}$
e $\sqrt{3}$ **f** $\dfrac{5\sqrt{2}}{2}$ **g** $\dfrac{3}{2}$ **h** $\dfrac{5\sqrt{2}}{2}$
i $\dfrac{\sqrt{21}}{3}$ **j** $\dfrac{\sqrt{2}+2}{2}$ **k** $\dfrac{2\sqrt{3}-3}{3}$ **l** $\dfrac{5\sqrt{3}+6}{3}$

7 a i 1 **ii** -4 **iii** 2 **iv** 17 **v** -44
b They become whole numbers. Difference of two squares makes the 'middle terms' (and surds) disappear.
c i $\dfrac{5+5\sqrt{5}}{-4}$ **ii** $\dfrac{5+3\sqrt{3}}{2}$

ANSWERS TO CHAPTER 11

Quick check

1 a 7 **b** 6 **c** 8 **d** 6

Exercise 11A

1 Mode

2 Three possible answers: 12, 14, 14, 16, 18, 20, 24; or 12, 14, 14, 16, 18, 22, 24; or 12, 14, 14, 16, 20, 22, 24

3 53

4 a median (mean could be unduly influenced by results of very able and/or very poor candidates)
b median (mean could be unduly influenced by pocket money of students with very rich or generous parents)
c mode (numerical value of shoe sizes irrelevant, just want most common size)
d median (mean could be distorted by one or two extremely short or tall performers)
e mode (the only way to get an "average" of non-numerical values)
f median (mean could be unduly influenced by very low weights of premature babies)

5 The mean is 31.5 which rounds up to 32, so the statement is correct (though the mode and median are 31)

6 a i £18 000 **ii** £24 000 **iii** £23 778
b A 6% rise would increase the mean salary to £25 204, a £1500 pay increase would produce a mean of £25 278

7 a Median **b** Mode **c** Mean
8 11.6 **9** 42.7 kg **10** 24

Exercise 11B

1 a i 7 **ii** 6 **iii** 6.4 **b i** 8 **ii** 8.5 **iii** 8.2
2 a 668 **b** 1.9 **c** 0 **d** 328
3 a 2.2, 1.7, 1.3 **b** Better dental care
4 a 50 **b** 2 **c** 2.8
5 a Roger 5, Brian 4 **b** Roger 3, Brian 8
c Roger 5, Brian 4 **d** Roger 5.4, Brian 4.5
e Roger, smaller range **f** Brian, better mean
6 a 40 **b** 7 **c** 3 **d** 2 **e** 2.5 **f** 2.5
g 2.4
7 a 34 **b** $x + 80 + 3y + 104 = 266$, so $x + 3y = 266 - 184 = 82$
c $x = 10, y = 24$ **d** 2.5

Exercise 11C

1 a i $30 < x \leq 40$ **ii** 29.5 **b i** $0 < y \leq 100$ **ii** 158.3
c i $5 < z \leq 10$ **ii** 9.43 **d i** 7–9 **ii** 8.41
2 a 100 g $< w \leq$ 120 g **b** 10.86 kg **c** 108.6 g
3 a $175 < h \leq 200$ **b** 31% **c** 193.3 hours **d** No
4 a Yes, average distance is 11.7 miles per day
b Because shorter runs will be done faster which will affect the average.
c Yes because the shortest could be 1 mile, the longest 25 miles
5 24
6 Soundbuy; average increases are Soundbuy 17.7p, Springfields 18.7p, Setco 18.2p

Exercise 11D

1 b 1.7

2 b 2.8

3 a i 17, 13, 6, 3, 1   **ii** £1.45

  b ii £5.35

  c Much higher mean. Early morning, people just want a paper or a few sweets, later they are buying food for the day.

4 c 140.4 cm

5 b Monday 28.4 min, Tuesday 20.9 min, Wednesday 21.3 min

  c There are more patients on a Monday, and so longer waiting times, because the surgery is closed at the weekend

Exercise 11E

1 The respective frequency densities on which each histogram should be based are

  a 2.5, 6.5, 6, 2, 1, 1.5   **b** 4, 27, 15, 3   **c** 17, 18, 12, 6.67   **d** 0.4, 1.2, 2.8, 1   **e** 9, 21, 13.5, 9

2 a 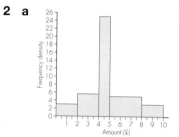   **b**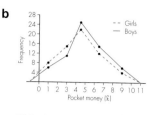

  c Girls £4.36, boys £4.81

3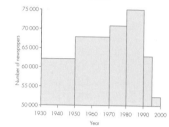

4 a 775   **b** 400

5 a i

Age, y (years)					
Frequency					

  ii 10–12   **iii** 13   **iv** 11, 16, 5   **v** 13.4

  b i

Temperature, t (°C)				
Frequency				

  ii 12–14°C   **iii** 14.5°C   **iv** 12°C, 17°C, 5°C   **v** 14.8°C

  c i

Weight, w (kg)				
Frequency				

  ii 70–90 kg and 120–170 kg   **iii** 93.33 kg   **iv** 74 kg, 120 kg, 46 kg   **v** 99.0 kg

6 a 7.33 hours   **b** 8.44 hours   **c** 7 hours

7 b 14.3 kg   **c** 14.7 kg   **d** 33 plants

8 a

Speed, v (mph)					
Frequency					

  b 360   **c** 64.5 mph   **d** 59.2 mph

Exercise 11F

1 Moving averages are: 9.3, 9.1, 9.0, 9.1, 8.7, 8.6, 9.1, 9.0, 9.4, 9.7, 9.7, 9.9, 10.1, 9.7, 9.9, 9.4, 9.9, 10.0, 10.0, 9.9, 10.1, 10.7

2 a Moving averages are: 44.5, 42.3, 41.0, 41.3, 42.3, 44.5, 45.8

  b Amounts raised dip in the middle of the collection period

3 a Moving averages are: 108.10, 107.24, 108.39, 105.89, 109.54, 111.40, 112.55, 118.70, 118.50, 119.80, 120.30, 123.18, 124.33

  b Gradually rises

  c Trend suggests next moving average about £125.50, so estimated first quarter 2006 bill is £137.29

4 b Moving averages are: 80, 81, 82, 83, 82, 85, 87, 90, 94, 92, 91, 89, 86

  c Recent fall may be due to moving to cheaper provider or using e-mail rather than making calls

  d Trend suggests next moving average about 83.5, so first quarter 2006 bill is £78

5 a Moving averages are: 12.3, 13.0, 13.0, 10.0, 10.3, 10.0, 13.7, 13.0, 13.7, 13.0, 13.0, 13.0, 13.3, 13.0, 13.7, 13.3, 13.3, 13.7, 14.3, 15.0, 14.7

  b Apart from a blip in June 2004, sales showing slight improvement

  c Trend suggests next moving average about 14.6, so January 2006 sales estimate is 15

6 b Moving averages are: (videos) 3.7, 3.6, 3.3, 2.8, 2.5; (DVDs) 0.6, 1.1, 1.4, 2.1, 2.8

  c Sales of DVD players increasingly strongly, video recorder sales falling

  d Trend suggests next moving averages about 2.3 (videos) and 3.5 (DVDs), so 2006 sales estimates are 2.1 (videos) and 4.0 (DVDs)

Exercise 11H

1 a It is a leading question, and there is no option to disagree with the statement

  b Unbiased, and the responses do not overlap

2 a Responses overlap

  b Give as options: up to £2, more than £2 and up to £5, more than £5 and up to £10, more than £10

Exercise 11I

1 Price 78p, 80.3p, 84.2p, 85p, 87.4p, 93.6p

2 a £1 = $1.80   **b** Greatest drop was from June to July

c There is no trend in the data

3 a 9.7 million   **b** 4.5 years   **c** 12 million   **d** 10 million

4 £74.73

5 a Holiday month   **b i** 138–144 thousand

                          ii 200–210 thousand

Quick check

1 a $-3x$ **b** $2x$ **c** $-3x$ **d** $6m^2$
e $-6x^2$ **f** $-12p^2$

2 a -6 **b** $-\frac{1}{2}$ **c** $\frac{2}{3}$

Exercise 12A
1 $x^2 + 5x + 6$ **2** $t^2 + 7t + 12$ **3** $w^2 + 4w + 3$
4 $m^2 + 6m + 5$ **5** $k^2 + 8k + 15$ **6** $a^2 + 5a + 4$
7 $x^2 + 2x - 8$ **8** $t^2 + 2t - 15$ **9** $w^2 + 2w - 3$
10 $f^2 - f - 6$ **11** $g^2 - 3g - 4$ **12** $y^2 + y - 12$
13 $x^2 + x - 12$ **14** $p^2 - p - 2$ **15** $k^2 - 2k - 8$
16 $y^2 + 3y - 10$ **17** $a^2 + 2a - 3$ **18** $t^2 + t - 12$
19 $x^2 - 9$ **20** $t^2 - 25$ **21** $m^2 - 16$
22 $t^2 - 4$ **23** $y^2 - 64$ **24** $p^2 - 1$
25 $25 - x^2$ **26** $49 - g^2$ **27** $x^2 - 36$

Exercise 12B
1 $6x^2 + 11x + 3$ **2** $12y^2 + 17y + 6$ **3** $6t^2 + 17t + 5$
4 $8t^2 + 2t - 3$ **5** $10m^2 - 11m - 6$ **6** $12k^2 - 11k - 15$
7 $6p^2 + 11p - 10$ **8** $10w^2 + 19w + 6$ **9** $6a^2 - 7a - 3$
10 $8r^2 - 10r + 3$ **11** $15g^2 - 16g + 4$ **12** $12d^2 + 5d - 2$
13 $8p^2 + 26p + 15$ **14** $6t^2 + 7t + 2$ **15** $6p^2 + 11p + 4$
16 $6 - 7t - 10t^2$ **17** $12 + n - 6n^2$ **18** $6f^2 - 5f - 6$
19 $12 + 7q - 10q^2$ **20** $3 - 7p - 6p^2$ **21** $4 + 10t - 6t^2$

Exercise 12C
1 $4x^2 - 1$ **2** $9t^2 - 4$ **3** $25y^2 - 9$
4 $16m^2 - 9$ **5** $4k^2 - 9$ **6** $16h^2 - 1$
7 $4 - 9x^2$ **8** $25 - 4t^2$ **9** $36 - 25y^2$
10 $a^2 - b^2$ **11** $9t^2 - k^2$ **12** $4m^2 - 9p^2$
13 $25k^2 - g^2$ **14** $a^2b^2 - c^2d^2$ **15** $a^4 - b^4$

Exercise 12D
1 $x^2 + 10x + 25$ **2** $m^2 + 8m + 16$ **3** $t^2 + 12t + 36$
4 $p^2 + 6p + 9$ **5** $m^2 - 6m + 9$ **6** $t^2 - 10t + 25$
7 $m^2 - 8m + 16$ **8** $k^2 - 14k + 49$ **9** $9x^2 + 6x + 1$
10 $16t^2 + 24t + 9$ **11** $25y^2 + 20y + 4$ **12** $4m^2 + 12m + 9$
13 $16t^2 - 24t + 9$ **14** $9x^2 - 12x + 4$ **15** $25t^2 - 20t + 4$
16 $25r^2 - 60r + 36$ **17** $x^2 + 2xy + y^2$ **18** $m^2 - 2mn + n^2$
19 $4t^2 + 4ty + y^2$ **20** $m^2 - 6mn + 9n^2$ **21** $x^2 + 4x$
22 $x^2 - 10x$ **23** $x^2 + 12x$ **24** $x^2 - 4x$

Exercise 12E
1 $(x + 2)(x + 3)$ **2** $(t + 1)(t + 4)$ **3** $(m + 2)(m + 5)$
4 $(k + 4)(k + 6)$ **5** $(p + 2)(p + 12)$ **6** $(r + 3)(r + 6)$
7 $(w + 2)(w + 9)$ **8** $(x + 3)(x + 4)$ **9** $(a + 2)(a + 6)$
10 $(k + 3)(k + 7)$ **11** $(f + 1)(f + 21)$ **12** $(b + 8)(b + 12)$
13 $(t - 2)(t - 3)$ **14** $(d - 4)(d - 1)$ **15** $(g - 2)(g - 5)$
16 $(x - 3)(x - 12)$ **17** $(c - 2)(c - 16)$ **18** $(t - 4)(t - 9)$
19 $(y - 4)(y - 12)$ **20** $(j - 6)(j - 8)$ **21** $(p - 3)(p - 5)$
22 $(y + 6)(y - 1)$ **23** $(t + 4)(t - 2)$ **24** $(x + 5)(x - 2)$
25 $(m + 2)(m - 6)$ **26** $(r + 1)(r - 7)$ **27** $(n + 3)(n - 6)$
28 $(m + 4)(m - 11)$ **29** $(w + 4)(w - 6)$ **30** $(t + 9)(t - 10)$
31 $(h + 8)(h - 9)$ **32** $(t + 7)(t - 9)$ **33** $(d + 1)^2$
34 $(y + 10)^2$ **35** $(t - 4)^2$ **36** $(m - 9)^2$
37 $(x - 12)^2$ **38** $(d + 3)(d - 4)$ **39** $(t + 4)(t - 5)$
40 $(q + 7)(q - 8)$

Exercise 12F
1 $(x + 3)(x - 3)$ **2** $(t + 5)(t - 5)$ **3** $(m + 4)(m - 4)$
4 $(3 + x)(3 - x)$ **5** $(7 + t)(7 - t)$ **6** $(k + 10)(k - 10)$
7 $(2 + y)(2 - y)$ **8** $(x + 8)(x - 8)$ **9** $(t + 9)(t - 9)$
10 $(x + y)(x - y)$ **11** $(x + 2y)(x - 2y)$ **12** $(x + 3y)(x - 3y)$
13 $(3x + 1)(3x - 1)$ **14** $(4x + 3)(4x - 3)$ **15** $(5x + 8)(5x - 8)$
16 $(2x + 3y)(2x - 3y)$ **17** $(3t + 2w)(3t - 2w)$ **18** $(4y + 5x)(4y - 5x)$

Exercise 12G
1 $(2x + 1)(x + 2)$ **2** $(7x + 1)(x + 1)$ **3** $(4x + 7)(x - 1)$
4 $(3t + 2)(8t + 1)$ **5** $(3t + 1)(5t - 1)$ **6** $(4x - 1)^2$
7 $3(y + 7)(2y - 3)$ **8** $4(y + 6)(y - 4)$ **9** $(2x + 3)(4x - 1)$
10 $(2t + 1)(3t + 5)$ **11** $(x - 6)(3x + 2)$ **12** $(x - 5)(7x - 2)$

Exercise 12H
1 $-2, -5$ **2** $-3, -1$ **3** $-6, -4$ **4** $-3, 2$
5 $-1, 3$ **6** $-4, 5$ **7** $1, -2$ **8** $2, -5$
9 $7, -4$ **10** $3, 2$ **11** $1, 5$ **12** $4, 3$
13 $-4, -1$ **14** $-9, -2$ **15** $2, 4$ **16** $3, 5$
17 $-2, 5$ **18** $-3, 5$ **19** $-6, 2$ **20** $-6, 3$
21 $-1, 2$ **22** -2 **23** -5 **24** 4
25 $-2, -6$ **26** $5, -3$ **27** 7 **28** $-6, -4$
29 $2, 16$ **30** $-6, 4$ **31** $-9, 6$ **32** $-10, 3$
33 $-4, 11$ **34** $-8, 9$ **35** $8, 9$ **36** 1

Exercise 12I
1 a $\frac{1}{3}, -3$ **b** $1\frac{1}{3}, -\frac{1}{2}$ **c** $-\frac{1}{5}, 2$ **d** $-2\frac{1}{2}, 3\frac{1}{2}$
e $-\frac{1}{6}, -\frac{1}{3}$ **f** $\frac{2}{3}, 4$ **g** $\frac{1}{2}, -3$ **h** $\frac{5}{2}, -\frac{7}{6}$
i $-1\frac{2}{3}, 1\frac{2}{5}$ **j** $1\frac{3}{4}, 1\frac{2}{7}$ **k** $\frac{2}{3}, \frac{1}{8}$ **l** $\pm\frac{1}{4}$
m $-2\frac{1}{4}, 0$ **n** $\pm1\frac{2}{5}$ **p** $-\frac{1}{3}, 3$

2 a $7, -6$ **b** $-2\frac{1}{2}, 1\frac{1}{2}$ **c** $7, -6$ **d** $-1, 1\frac{11}{13}$
e $3, -2$ **f** $-\frac{2}{5}, \frac{1}{2}$ **g** $-\frac{1}{3}, -\frac{1}{4}$ **h** $\frac{1}{5}, -2$
i 4 **j** $-2, \frac{1}{8}$ **k** $-\frac{1}{3}, 0$ **l** ±5
m $-1\frac{2}{3}$ **n** $\pm3\frac{1}{2}$ **p** $-2\frac{1}{2}, 3$

Exercise 12J
1 $1.77, -2.27$ **2** $-0.23, -1.43$ **3** $3.70, -2.70$
4 $0.29, -0.69$ **5** $-0.19, -1.53$ **6** $-1.23, -2.43$
7 $-0.41, -1.84$ **8** $-1.39, -2.27$ **9** $1.37, -4.37$
10 $2.18, 0.15$ **11** $-0.39, -5.11$ **12** $0.44, -1.69$
13 $1.64, 0.61$ **14** $0.36, -0.79$ **15** $1.89, 0.11$

Exercise 12K
1 a $(x + 2)^2 - 4$ **b** $(x + 7)^2 - 49$ **c** $(x - 3)^2 - 9$
d $(x + 3)^2 - 9$ **e** $(x - 2)^2 - 4$ **f** $(x + 1.5)^2 - 2.25$
g $(x - 2.5)^2 - 6.25$ **h** $(x + 0.5)^2 - 0.25$ **i** $(x + 5)^2 - 25$
j $(x + 3.5)^2 - 12.25$ **k** $(x - 1)^2 - 1$ **l** $(x + 1)^2 - 1$
2 a $(x + 2)^2 - 5$ **b** $(x + 7)^2 - 54$ **c** $(x - 3)^2 - 6$
d $(x + 3)^2 - 2$ **e** $(x - 2)^2 - 5$ **f** $(x + 1.5)^2 + 0.75$
g $(x - 2.5)^2 - 11.25$ **h** $(x + 0.5)^2 - 1.25$ **i** $(x + 5)^2 - 25$
j $(x + 1)^2 - 2$ **k** $(x - 1)^2 - 8$ **l** $(x + 1)^2 - 10$
3 a $-2 \pm \sqrt{5}$ **b** $-7 \pm 3\sqrt{6}$ **c** $3 \pm \sqrt{6}$ **d** $-3 \pm \sqrt{2}$
e $2 \pm \sqrt{5}$ **f** $-1.5 \pm \sqrt{0.75}$ **g** $2.5 \pm \sqrt{11.25}$
h $-0.5 \pm \sqrt{1.25}$ **i** $-4 \pm \sqrt{22}$
j $-1 \pm \sqrt{2}$ **k** $1 \pm 2\sqrt{2}$ **l** $-1 \pm \sqrt{10}$
4 a $1.45, -3.45$ **b** $5.32, -1.32$ **c** $-4.16, 2.16$

Exercise 12L
1 $52, 2$ **2** $65, 2$ **3** $24, 2$ **4** $85, 2$
5 $145, 2$ **6** $68, 2$ **7** $-35, 0$ **8** $-23, 0$
9 $41, 2$ **10** $40, 2$ **11** $-135, 0$ **12** $37, 2$

Exercise 12M

1 a $1 \pm \sqrt{5}$ **b** $-1 \pm 2\sqrt{2}$ **c** $-2 \pm 4\sqrt{3}$
d $-1 \pm \sqrt{7}$ **e** $4 \pm \sqrt{14}$ **f** $2 \pm \sqrt{2}$

2 a $-1 \pm \dfrac{\sqrt{14}}{2}$ **b** $-1 \pm \dfrac{3\sqrt{2}}{2}$ **c** $\dfrac{-3 \pm \sqrt{19}}{2}$
d $\dfrac{5 \pm \sqrt{89}}{4}$ **e** $\dfrac{-1 \pm \sqrt{61}}{10}$ **f** $\dfrac{-3 \pm \sqrt{33}}{4}$

Exercise 12N

1 6, 8, 10 **2** 15 m, 20 m **3** 29 **4** 6.54, 0.46
5 5, 0.5 **6** 16 m by 14 m **7** 48 km/h **8** 45, 47
9 2.54 m, 3.54 m **10** 6 cm **11** 30 km/h **12** 10p
13 1.25, 0.8 **14** 10 **15** 5 h **16** 0.75 m

ANSWERS TO CHAPTER 13

Quick check

1 A (3, 0), B ((1, 4), C (4, 5)

2 a 18 **b** 145

Exercise 13A

1 a i 9 am **ii** 10 am **iii** 12 noon
b i 40 km/h **ii** 120 km/h **iii** 40 km/h
2 a i 125 km **ii** 125 km/h
b i between 2 pm and 3 pm **ii** about $12\frac{1}{2}$ km/h
3 a i 263 m/min (3 sf) **ii** 15.8 km/h (3 sf)
b i 500 m/min **ii** Paul by 1 minute
4 a Patrick ran quickly at first, then had a slow middle section but he won the race with a final sprint. Araf ran steadily all the way and came second. Sean set off the slowest, speeded up towards the end but still came in third.
b i 1.67 m/s **ii** 6 km/h

Exercise 13B

1 a $\frac{15}{2}$ **b** $\frac{25}{8}$ **c** $\frac{15}{16}$ **d** $\frac{2}{25}$ **e** $\frac{6}{35}$ **f** $\frac{1}{2}$ **g** $-\frac{4}{5}$
2 a $2\frac{1}{2}$ km/h **b** 3.75 m/s **c** $2\frac{1}{2}$ km/h
3 a AB: 30 km/h, BC: 6 km/h, CD: 0 km/h, DE: 36 km/h (in opposite direction)
b FG: 4 m/s, GH: 16 m/s, HI: 2 m/s (in opposite direction), IJ: 16 m/s (in opposite direction)

Exercise 13C

1 a 20 m/s^2 **b** 7.1 m/s
2 a 3.5 m/s^2 **b** 3.5 m/s^2
3 a between 2 and 4 hours, and between 8 and 10 hours
b 10 km/h^2, 0 km/h^2, 5 km/h^2, 0 km/h^2, -6.25 km/h^2, -3.75 km/h^2

4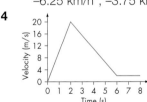

5 a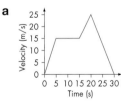
b 3 m/s^2

Exercise 13D

1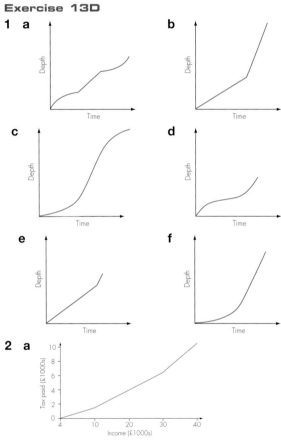

2 a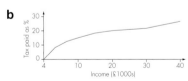
b

3 a

End of year	Amount owing (£)	End of year	Amount owing (£)	End of year	Amount owing (£)
1	52 500	6	34 356	11	17 324
2	50 085	7	31 273	12	13 391
3	42 749	8	28 037	13	9260
4	40 087	9	24 639	14	4923
5	37 291	10	21 071	15	369

b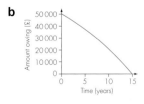

Quick check

1 Triangles a, c and d are congruent to the triangle in the question

2 a 28   **b** 14

Exercise 14A

1 2, 3
2 a Yes, 4
   b No, corresponding sides have different ratios
3 a PQR is an enlargement of ABC   **b** 1 : 3
   c Angle R   **d** BA
4 a Sides in same ratio   **b** Angle P   **c** PR
5 a Same angles   **b** Angle Q   **c** AR
6 a 8 cm   **b** 7.5 cm   **c** $x = 6.67$ cm, $y = 13.5$ cm
   d $x = 24$ cm, $y = 13$ cm   **e** AB = 10 cm, PQ = 6 cm
   f 4.2 cm
7 a Sides in same ratio   **b** 1 : 3   **c** 13 cm   **d** 39 cm
8 4.8 m

Exercise 14B

1 a 9 cm   **b** 12 cm
2 a 5 cm   **b** 5 cm   **c** $x = 60$ cm, $y = 75$ cm
   d $x = 45$ cm, $y = 60$ cm   **e** DC = 10 cm, EB = 8 cm
3 82 m   **4** 220 feet   **5** 15 m
6 3.09 m   **7** 6 m

Exercise 14C

1 5 cm
2 6 cm
3 10 cm
4 $x = 6$ cm, $y = 7.5$ cm
5 $x = 15$ cm, $y = 21$ cm
6 $x = 3$ cm, $y = 2.4$ cm

Exercise 14D

1 a 4 : 25   **b** 8 : 125
2 a 16 : 49   **b** 64 : 343
3 Linear scale factor 2, 3, $\frac{1}{4}$, 5, $\frac{1}{10}$, 7, $\frac{1}{5}$, $\frac{1}{2}$;
   linear ratio 1 : 2, 1 : 3, 4 : 1, 1: 5, 10 : 1, 1 : 7, 5 : 1, 2 : 1;
   linear fraction $\frac{2}{1}$, $\frac{3}{1}$, $\frac{1}{4}$, $\frac{5}{1}$, $\frac{1}{10}$, $\frac{7}{1}$, $\frac{1}{5}$, $\frac{1}{2}$; area scale factor 4, 9, $\frac{1}{16}$,
   25, $\frac{1}{100}$, 49, $\frac{1}{25}$, $\frac{1}{4}$; volume scale factor 8, 27, $\frac{1}{64}$, 125, $\frac{1}{1000}$,
   343, $\frac{1}{125}$, $\frac{1}{8}$
4 a 1 : 2   **b** 1 : 8   **c** 8 pints   **d** No
5 135 cm^2
6 a 56 cm^2 **b** 126 cm^2
7 a 48 ft^2 **b** 3 ft^2
8 a 2400 cm^3 **b** 8100 cm^3
9 a 3750 cm^3 **b** 3.75 cm^3
10 4 litres
11 91.125 litres
12 a 5.0625 litres   **b** The height of the can
13 a 5.4 m^2 **b** 1.35 m^2
14 1.38 m^3
15 £6
16 6 cm, 8 cm, 10 cm
17 $3r$ cm
18 a 9, 36   **b** 16, 80   **c** 9, 45   **d** 36, 270   **e** Solids b and d

Exercise 14E

1 6.2 cm, 10.1 cm   **2** 4.26 cm, 6.74 cm
3 9.56 cm   **4** 3.38 m
5 35 mins   **6** 8.39 cm
7 26.5 cm   **8** 16.9 cm
9 a 4.33 cm, 7.81 cm   **10** 2478 ml
   b 143 g, 839 g
11 53.8 kg   **12** 1.73 kg
13 92.8 cm   **14** 1.30 m^2, 4.42 m^2

Quick check

1 12.96 cm

2 21.6°

Exercise 15A

1 13.1 cm
2 73.7°
3 9.81 cm
4 33.5 m
5 a 10.0 cm   **b** 11.5°   **c** 4.69 cm
6 63.0°

Exercise 15B

1 a 58.6°   **b** 20.5 cm   **c** 2049 cm^3 **d** 64.0°
2 a 3.46 m   **b** 75.5°   **c** 73.2°   **d** 60.3 m^2
3 a 24.0°   **b** 48.0°   **c** 13.5 cm   **d** 16.6°
4 a 32.0°   **b** 35.8°
5 a 3.46 m   **b** 70.5°

Exercise 15C

1 36.9°, 143.1°   **2** 53.1°, 126.9°
3 48.6°, 131.4°   **4** 224.4°, 315.6°
5 194.5°, 345.5°   **6** 198.7°, 341.3°
7 190.1°, 349.9°   **8** 234.5°, 305.5°
9 28.1°, 151.9°   **10** 185.6°, 354.4°
11 33.6°, 146.4°   **12** 210°, 330°

Exercise 15D

1 53.1°, 306.9°   **2** 54.5°, 305.5°
3 62.7°, 297.3°   **4** 54.9°, 305.1°
5 79.3°, 280.7°   **6** 143.1°, 216.9°
7 104.5°, 255.5°   **8** 100.1°, 259.9°
9 111.2°, 248.8°   **10** 166.9°, 193.1°
11 78.7°, 281.3°   **12** 44.4°, 315.6°

Exercise 15E

1 a 0.707   **b** −1 (−0.9998)   **c** −0.819   **d** 0.731
2 a −0.629   **b** −0.875   **c** −0.087   **d** 0.999

3 a 21.2°, 158.8° **b** 209.1°, 330.9°
  c 50.1°, 309.9° **d** 150.0°, 210.0°
  e 60.9°, 119.1° **f** 29.1°, 330.9°
4 30°, 150°
5 −0.755
6 a 1.41 **b** −1.37 **c** −0.0367 **d** −0.138
  e 1.41 **f** −0.492
7 True
8 a cos 65° **b** cos 40°
9 a 10°, 130° **b** 12.7°, 59.3°
10 38.2°, 141.8°

Exercise 15F
1 14.5°, 194.5°   **2** 38.1°, 218.1°
3 50.0°, 230.0°   **4** 61.9°, 241.9°
5 68.6°, 248.6°   **6** 160.3°, 340.3°
7 147.6°, 327.6°   **8** 135.4°, 315.4°
9 120.9°, 300.9°   **10** 105.2°, 285.2°
11 54.4°, 234.4°   **12** 42.2°, 222.2°
13 160.5°, 340.5°   **14** 130.9°, 310.9°
15 76.5°, 256.5°   **16** 116.0°, 296.0°
17 174.4°, 354.4°   **18** 44.9°, 224.9°
19 50.4°, 230.4°   **20** 111.8°, 291.8°

Exercise 15G
1 a 3.64 m **b** 8.05 cm **c** 19.4 cm
2 a 46.6° **b** 112.0° **c** 36.2°
3 50.3°, 129.7°
4 2.88 cm, 20.9 cm
5 a i 30° **ii** 40° **b** 19.4 m
6 36.5 m
7 a 36.8 m **b** 22.2 m
8 3.47 m
9 767 m
10 26.8 km/h

Exercise 15H
1 a 7.71 m **b** 29.1 cm **c** 27.4 cm
2 a 76.2° **b** 125.1° **c** 90° **d** Right-angled triangle
3 5.16 cm
4 65.5 cm

5 a 10.7 cm **b** 41.7° **c** 38.3° **d** 6.69 cm
  e 54.4 cm^2
6 72.3°
7 25.4 cm, 38.6 cm
8 58.4 km at 092.5°
9 21.8°
10 a 82.8° **b** 8.89 cm

Exercise 15I
1 a 8.60 m **b** 90° **c** 27.2 cm **d** 26.9°
  e 41.0° **f** 62.4 cm **g** 90.0° **h** 866 cm
  i 86.6 cm
2 7 cm
3 11.1 km
4 19.9 knots
5 a 27.8 miles **b** 262°

Exercise 15J
1 $\dfrac{3}{5}$ **2** $\sqrt{\dfrac{2}{5}}$

3 $\sqrt{19}$, $\sin x = \dfrac{\sqrt{6}}{\sqrt{19}}$, $\cos x = \dfrac{\sqrt{13}}{\sqrt{19}}$, $\tan x = \dfrac{\sqrt{6}}{\sqrt{13}}$

4 a $\sqrt{157}$ **b** $\sin A = \dfrac{6}{\sqrt{157}}$, $\cos A = \dfrac{11}{\sqrt{157}}$

5 $9\sqrt{3}$ cm^2
6 400 cm^2

Exercise 15K
1 a 24.0 cm^2 **b** 26.7 cm^2 **c** 243 cm^2
  d 21 097 cm^2 **e** 1224 cm^2
2 4.26 cm
3 a 42.3° **b** 49.6°
4 103 cm^2
5 2033 cm^2
6 21.0 cm^2
7 a 33.2° **b** 25.3 cm^2
9 a $\dfrac{1}{\sqrt{2}}$ **b** 21 cm^2

Index